Number Recognition

Name ____________________

Color: 1's—red
2's—blue
3's—yellow
4's—green
5's—orange

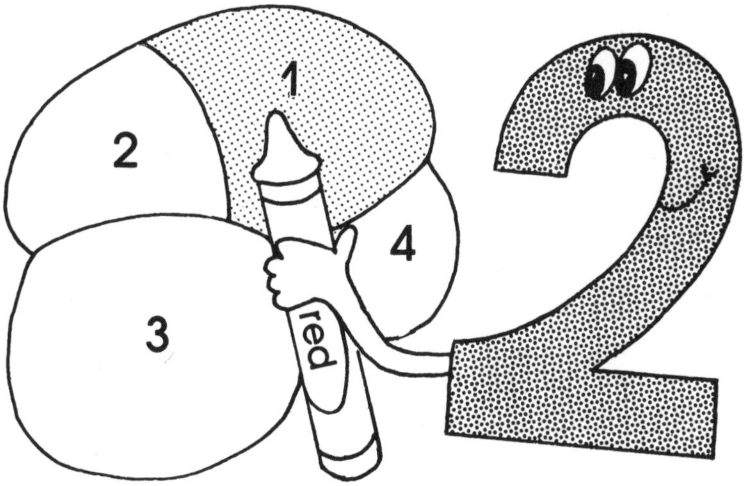

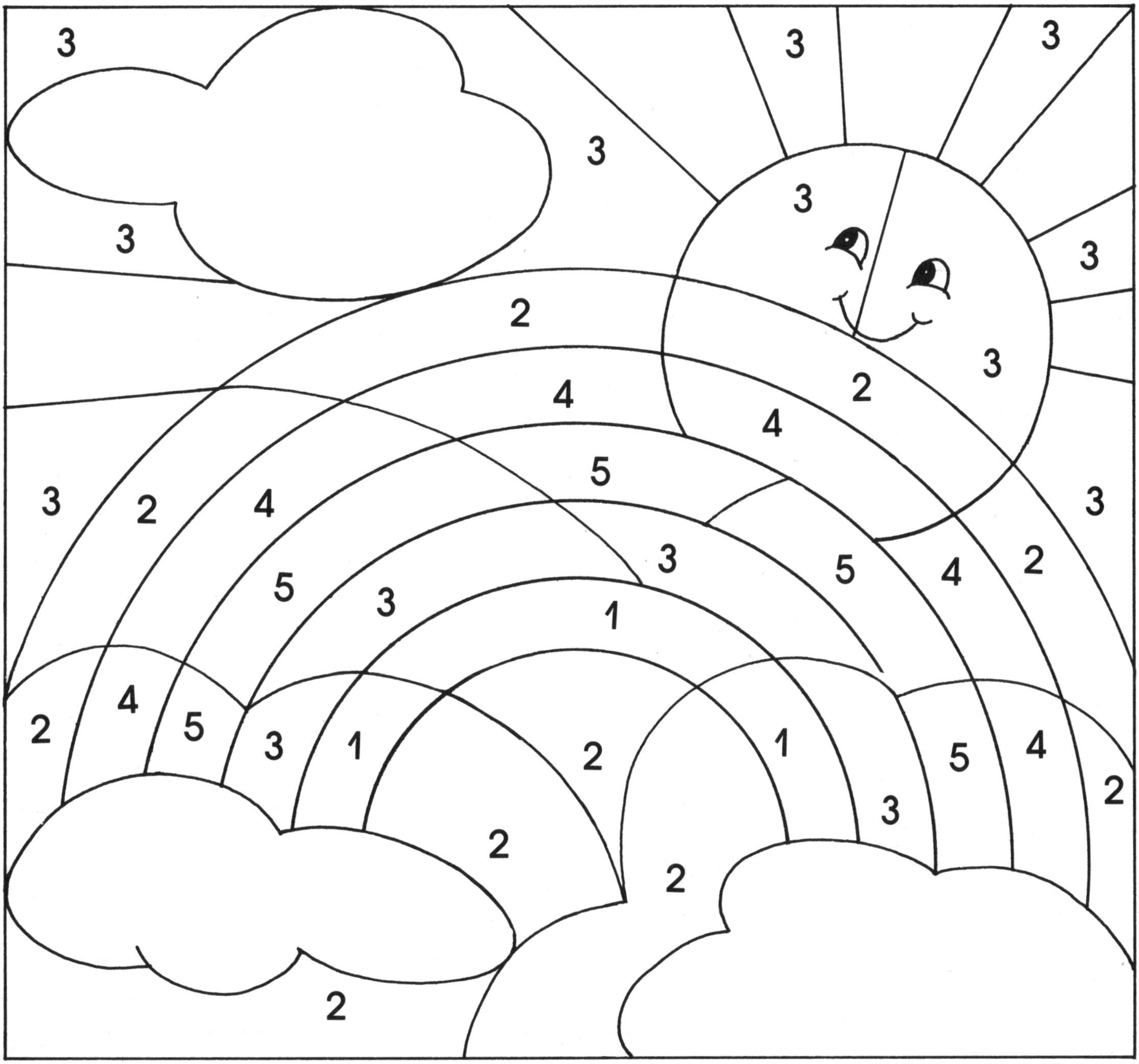

Number Recognition

Name ____________________

Color: 6's—purple
7's—yellow
8's—black
9's—orange
10's—brown

Sequencing Numbers

Name ____________________

Count the number of balloons.
Write the number in the blank.

Sequencing Numbers

Name ____________________

Write the missing numbers.

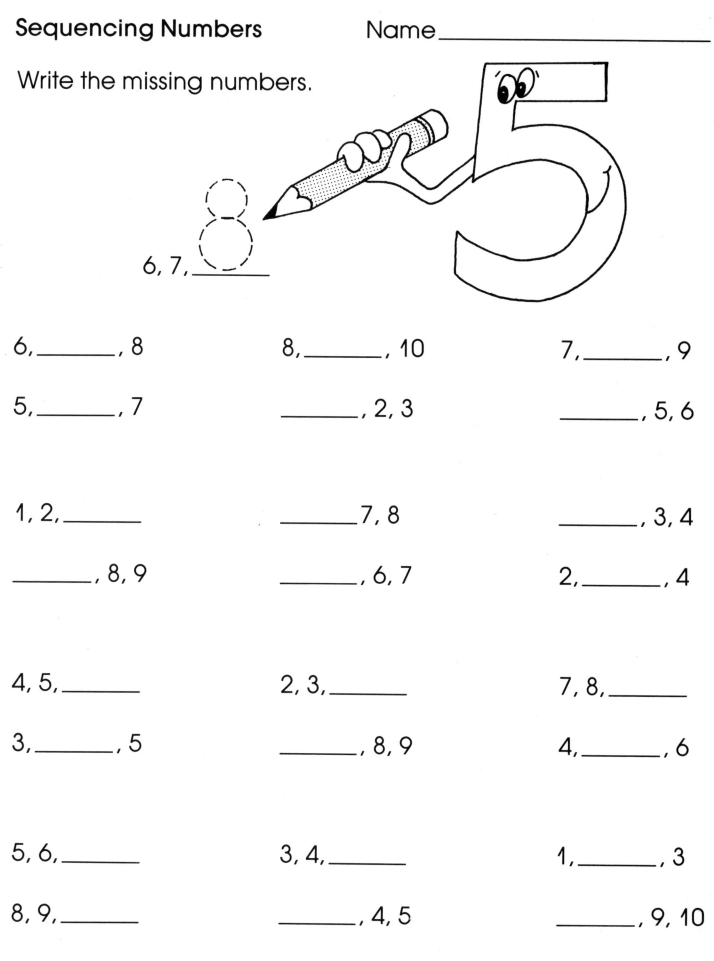

6, 7, ____

6, ____, 8

8, ____, 10

7, ____, 9

5, ____, 7

____, 2, 3

____, 5, 6

1, 2, ____

____ 7, 8

____, 3, 4

____, 8, 9

____, 6, 7

2, ____, 4

4, 5, ____

2, 3, ____

7, 8, ____

3, ____, 5

____, 8, 9

4, ____, 6

5, 6, ____

3, 4, ____

1, ____, 3

8, 9, ____

____, 4, 5

____, 9, 10

Counting to Nine

Name ____________________

How many?

Counting to Nine

Name ______________________

Count. Use code to color answers.

1—blue	4—red	7—purple
2—yellow	5—orange	8—gray
3—green	6—brown	9—black

Counting to Twenty

Name ____________________

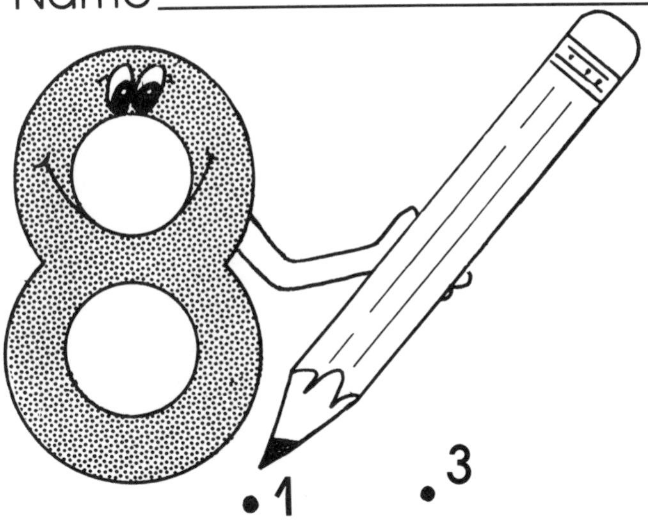

Join the dots in order.
Color the surprise.

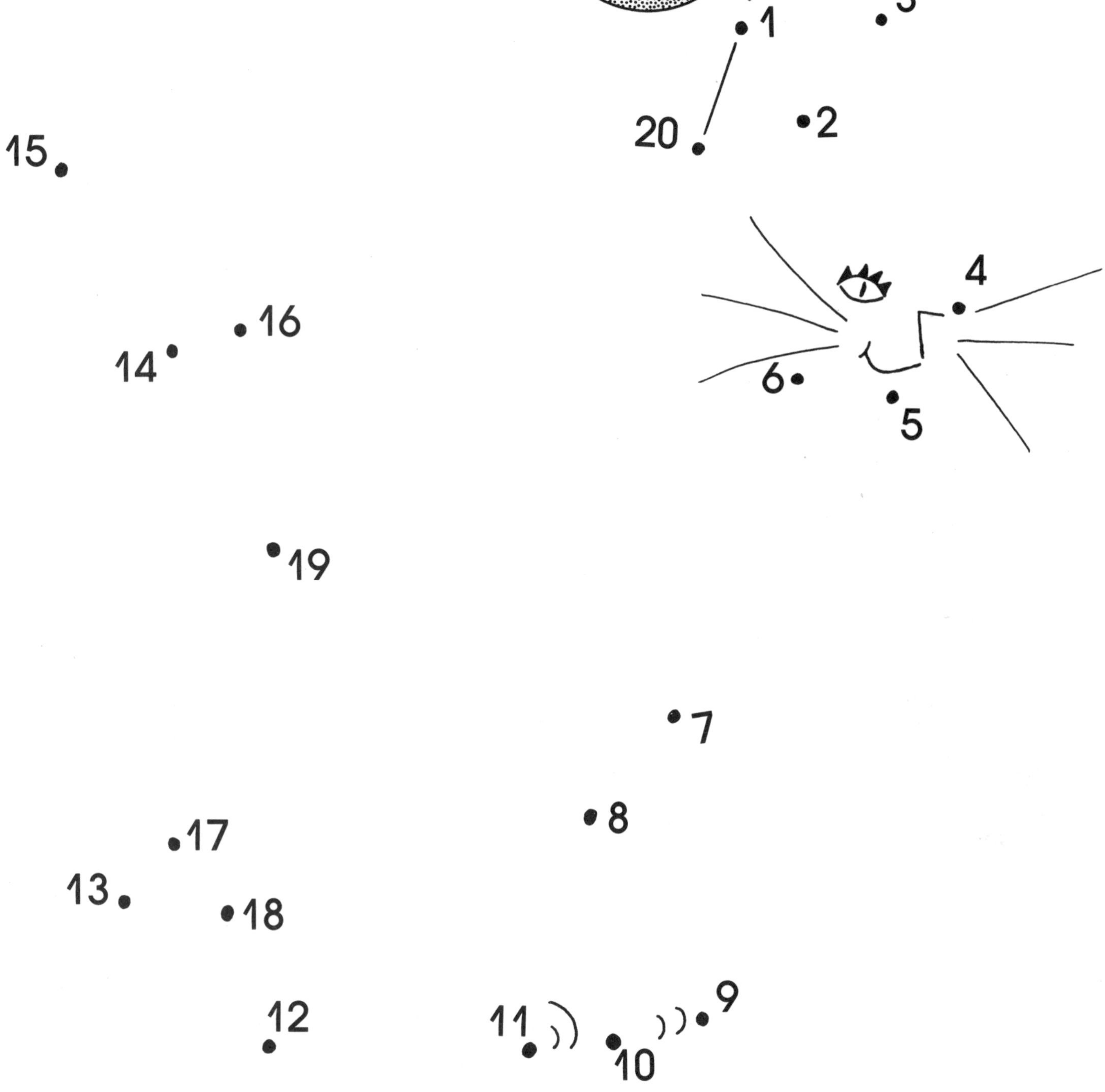

Number Word Recognition

Name ______________________

Number the train.

Draw a line from the word to the number.

seven	1
two	8
five	3
nine	4
six	7
four	5
one	6
three	2
eight	9

Color train cars. one-**red** three-**green** five-**orange**

two-**blue** four-**yellow** six-**brown**

 Name ____________________

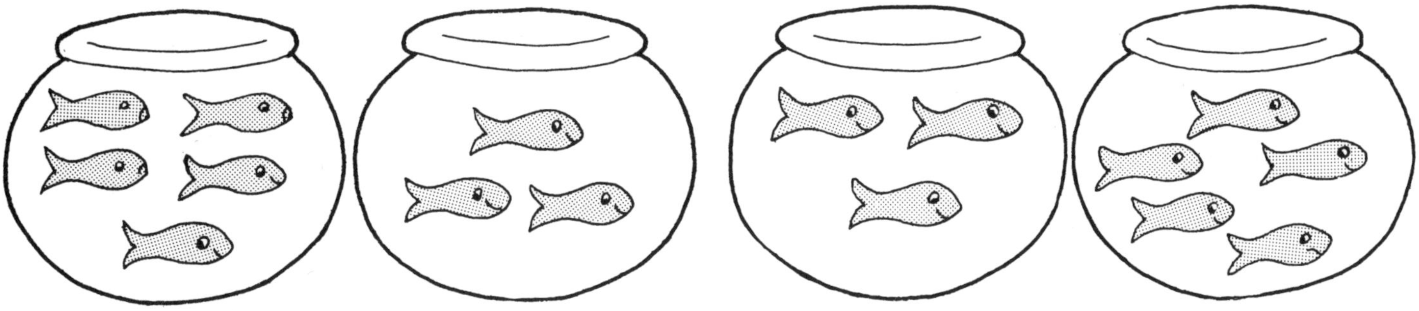

5 > 3

5 is **greater than** 3.

3 < 5

3 is **less than** 5.

Fill in number line.

1	2				6				

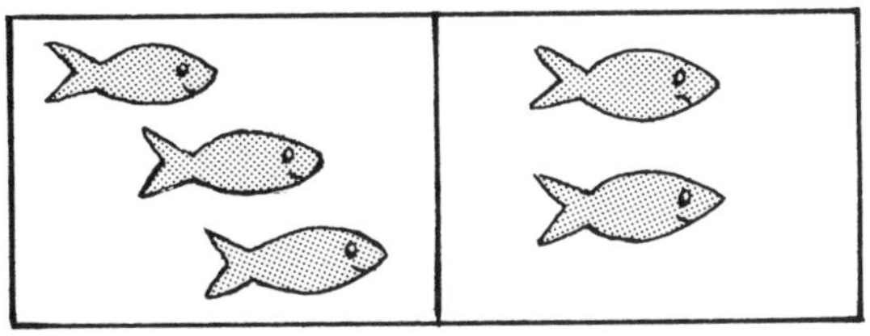

3 > 2

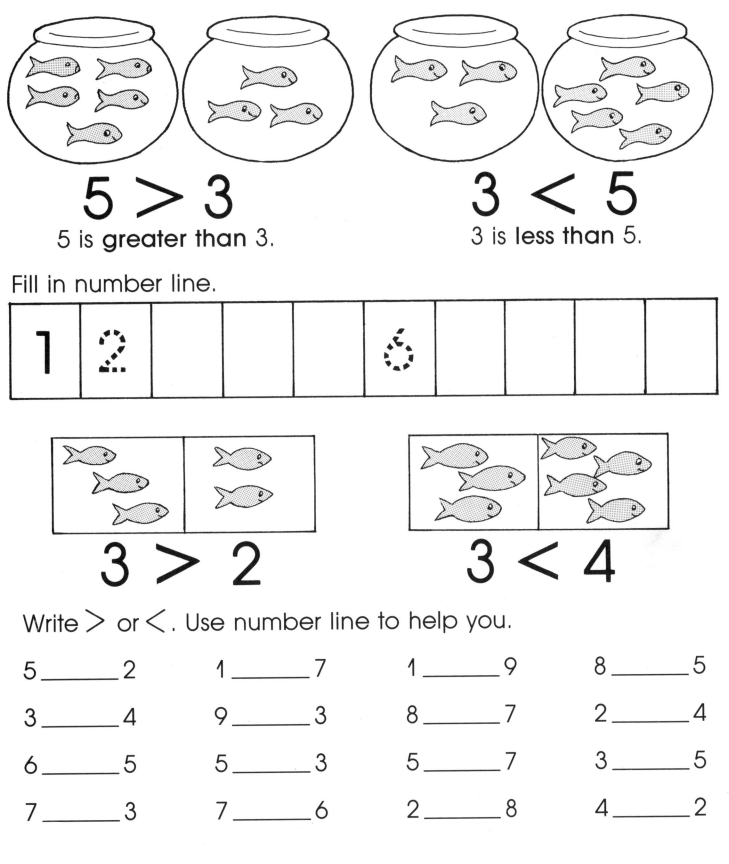

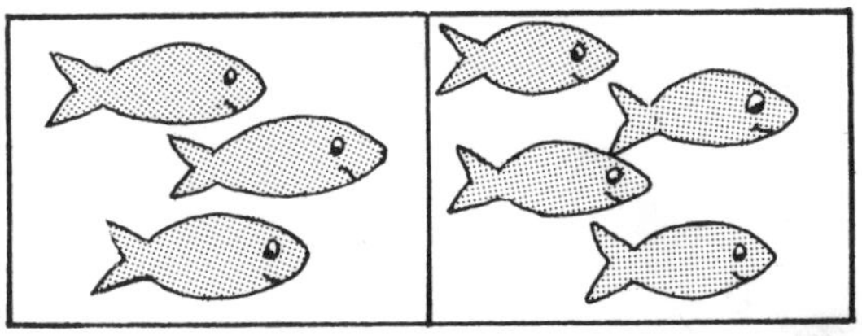

3 < 4

Write > or <. Use number line to help you.

5 ______ 2 1 ______ 7 1 ______ 9 8 ______ 5

3 ______ 4 9 ______ 3 8 ______ 7 2 ______ 4

6 ______ 5 5 ______ 3 5 ______ 7 3 ______ 5

7 ______ 3 7 ______ 6 2 ______ 8 4 ______ 2

Addition (1-5) Name______________________

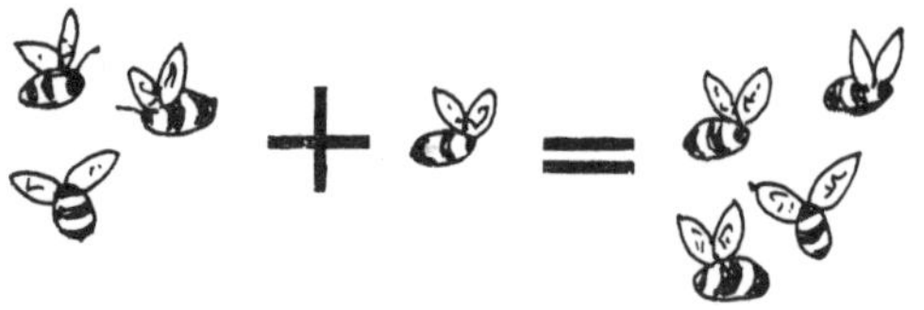

3 + 1 = 

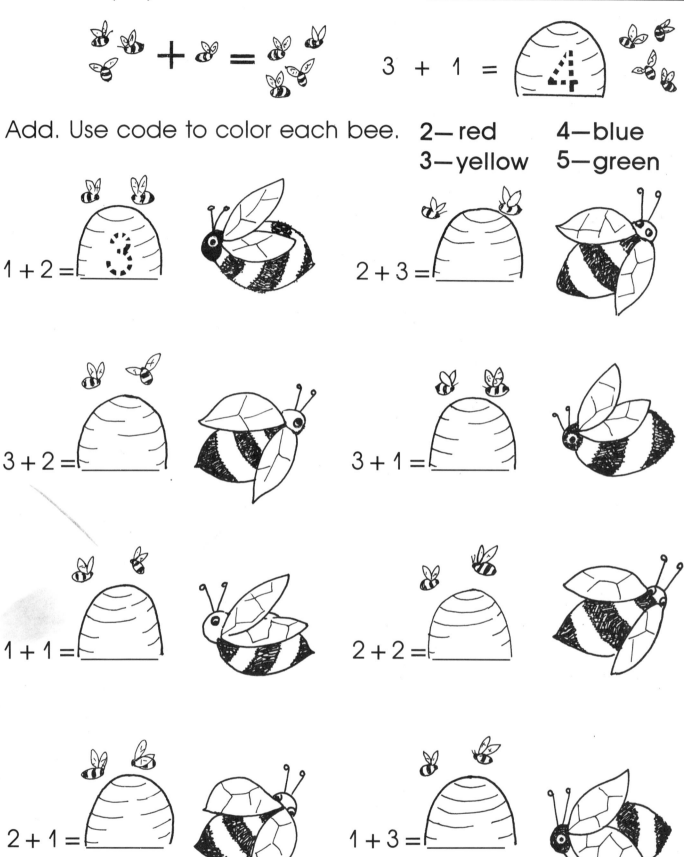

Add. Use code to color each bee.

2—red **4—blue**
3—yellow **5—green**

1 + 2 = 

2 + 3 = 

3 + 2 = 

3 + 1 = 

1 + 1 = 

2 + 2 = 

2 + 1 = 

1 + 3 = 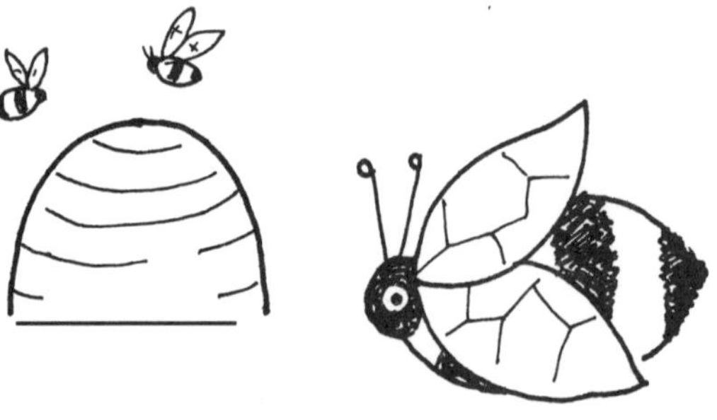

Name ____________________

5 + 1 = 6

4 + 6 = 10

1 + 9 = ____

7 + 1 = ____

7 + 3 = ____

5 + 2 = ____

6 + 1 = ____

8 + 2 = ____

3 + 5 = ____

6 + 3 = ____

6 + 2 = ____

4 + 5 = ____

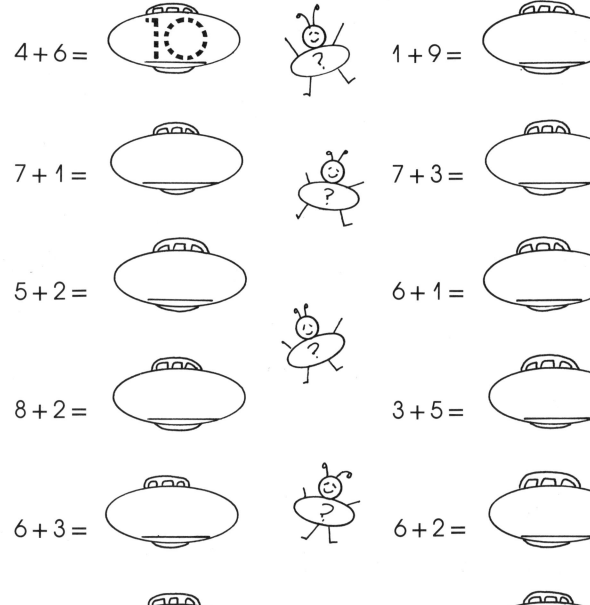

1 + 7 = ____

Addition Review Name_______________

Work all problems. Connect dots from smallest to largest answer.

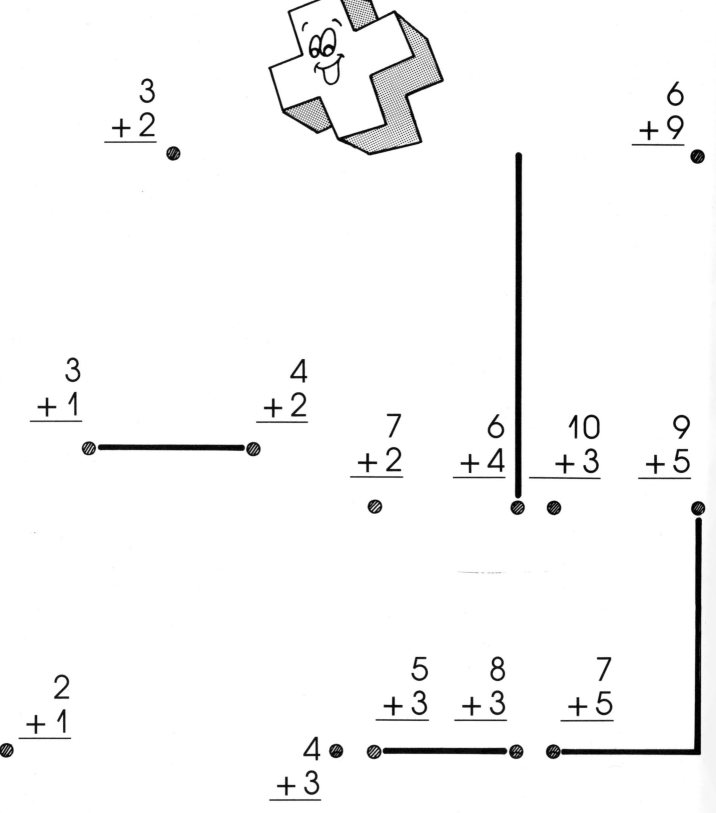

$$\begin{array}{r} 3 \\ +2 \\ \hline \end{array}$$

$$\begin{array}{r} 6 \\ +9 \\ \hline \end{array}$$

$$\begin{array}{r} 3 \\ +1 \\ \hline \end{array}$$

$$\begin{array}{r} 4 \\ +2 \\ \hline \end{array}$$

$$\begin{array}{r} 7 \\ +2 \\ \hline \end{array}$$

$$\begin{array}{r} 6 \\ +4 \\ \hline \end{array}$$

$$\begin{array}{r} 10 \\ +3 \\ \hline \end{array}$$

$$\begin{array}{r} 9 \\ +5 \\ \hline \end{array}$$

$$\begin{array}{r} 2 \\ +1 \\ \hline \end{array}$$

$$\begin{array}{r} 5 \\ +3 \\ \hline \end{array}$$

$$\begin{array}{r} 8 \\ +3 \\ \hline \end{array}$$

$$\begin{array}{r} 7 \\ +5 \\ \hline \end{array}$$

$$\begin{array}{r} 4 \\ +3 \\ \hline \end{array}$$

Commutative Property

Name ____________________________

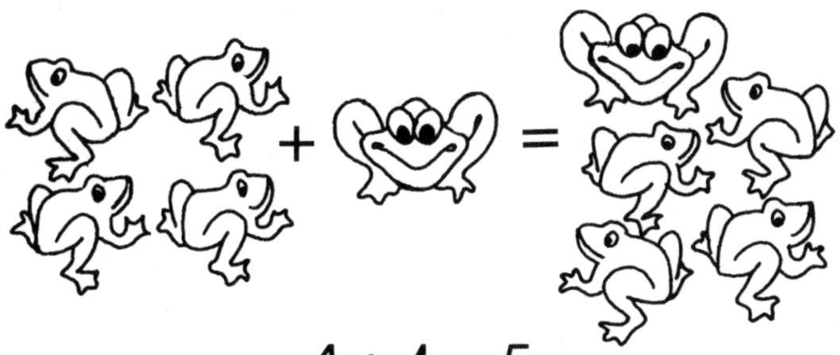

$4 + 1 = 5$

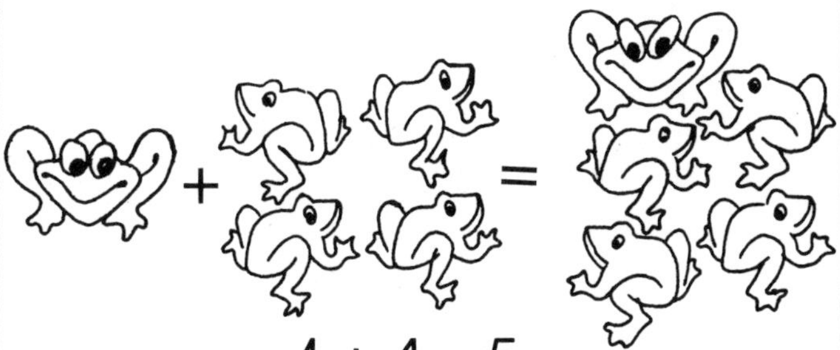

$1 + 4 = 5$

$3 + 1 =$ ______

$1 + 3 =$ ______

$4 + 1 =$ ______

$1 + 4 =$ ______

$2 + 1 =$ ______

$1 + 2 =$ ______

$3 + 2 =$ ______

$2 + 3 =$ ______

Add. Use code to color frogs.

2 green 3 purple 4 yellow 5 red

$1 + 1 =$ ______ 

$2 + 1 =$ ______ 

$3 + 2 =$ ______ 

$2 + 2 =$ ______ 

$2 + 1 =$ ______ 

$2 + 3 =$ ______ 

$1 + 3 =$ ______ 

$3 + 1 =$ ______ 

Subtraction (1-5)

Name ______________________

$3 - 2 = 1$

$$\begin{array}{r} 3 \\ -\,2 \\ \hline 1 \end{array}$$

5 – 1 = ______ 3 – 1 = ______ 5 – 2 = ______

4 – 1 = ______ 2 – 1 = ______ 4 – 2 = ______

3 – 2 = ______ 4 – 3 = ______ 5 – 3 = ______

Subtract. Use code to color worms. **1—red** **3—yellow** **2—orange** **4—brown**

5 – 1 = ◯

$$\begin{array}{r} 5 \\ -\,1 \\ \hline \end{array}$$

4 – 2 = ◯

$$\begin{array}{r} 4 \\ -\,2 \\ \hline \end{array}$$

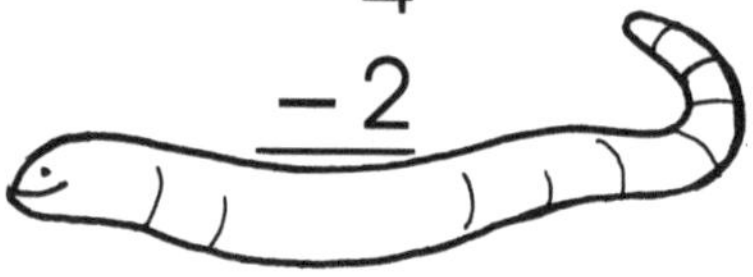

5 – 2 = ◯

$$\begin{array}{r} 5 \\ -\,2 \\ \hline \end{array}$$

3 – 1 = ◯

$$\begin{array}{r} 3 \\ -\,1 \\ \hline \end{array}$$

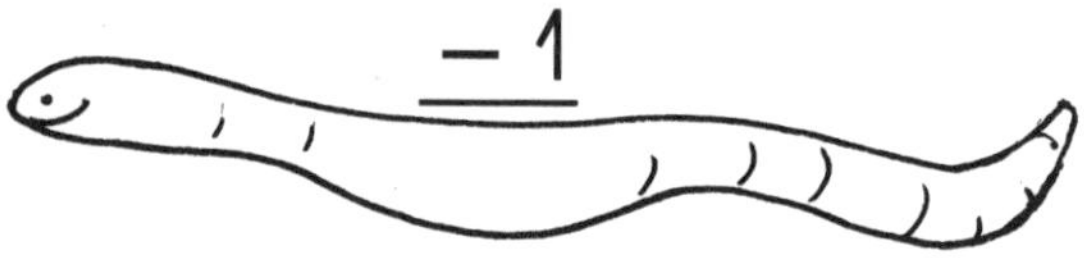

4 – 3 = ◯

$$\begin{array}{r} 4 \\ -\,3 \\ \hline \end{array}$$

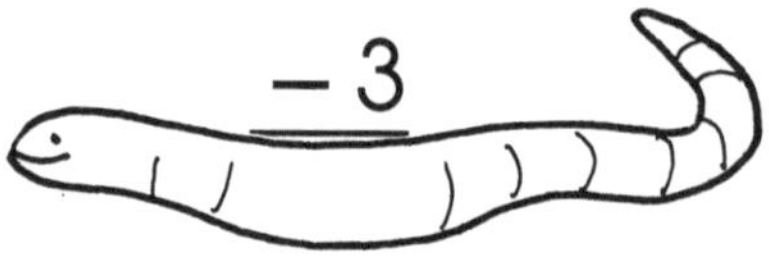

5 – 3 = ◯

$$\begin{array}{r} 5 \\ -\,3 \\ \hline \end{array}$$

2 – 1 = ◯

$$\begin{array}{r} 2 \\ -\,1 \\ \hline \end{array}$$

4 – 1 = ◯

$$\begin{array}{r} 4 \\ -\,1 \\ \hline \end{array}$$

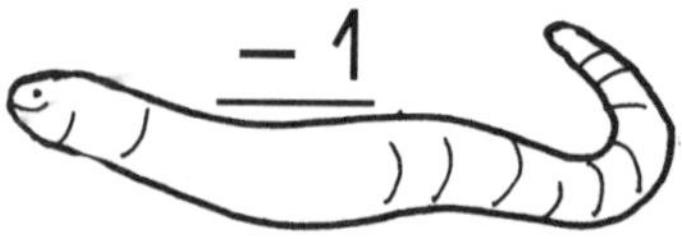

3 – 2 = ◯

$$\begin{array}{r} 3 \\ -\,2 \\ \hline \end{array}$$

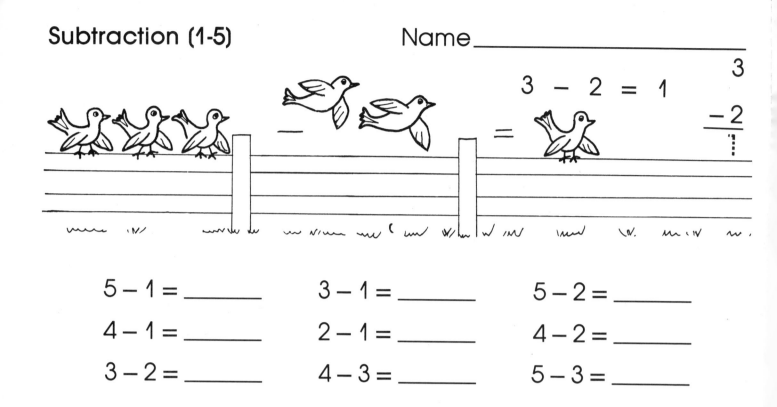

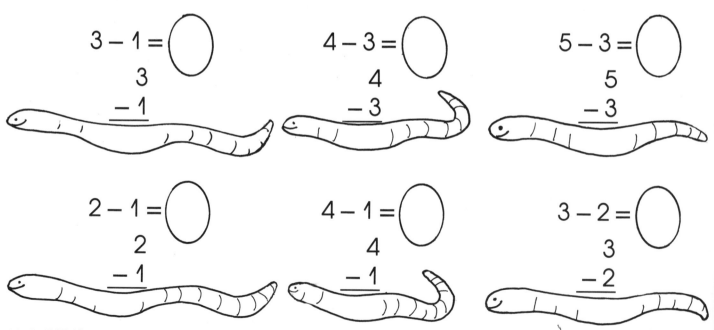

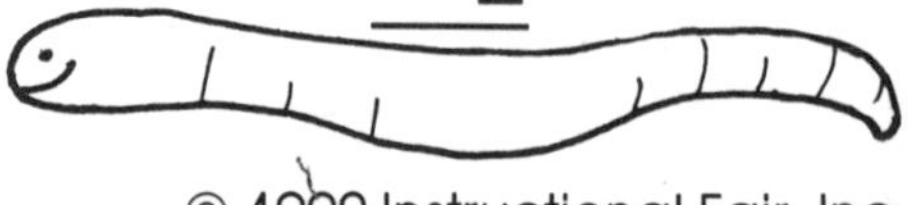

Name ____________________

Count the nuts.
Write answer on blank.
Circle problems with same answer.

1

$\begin{array}{r}2\\-1\end{array}$ $5-4$ $\begin{array}{r}5\\-2\end{array}$

$3-2$

$\begin{array}{r}2\\-2\end{array}$ $4-1$

$5-2$ $\begin{array}{r}5\\-1\end{array}$

$5-1$

$5-4$

$\begin{array}{r}5\\-2\end{array}$

$4-0$

$4-2$ $\begin{array}{r}5\\-3\end{array}$

$\begin{array}{r}4\\-1\end{array}$

$3-1$

$5-0$ $\begin{array}{r}2\\-2\end{array}$

$\begin{array}{r}5\\-1\end{array}$ $\begin{array}{r}4\\-3\end{array}$

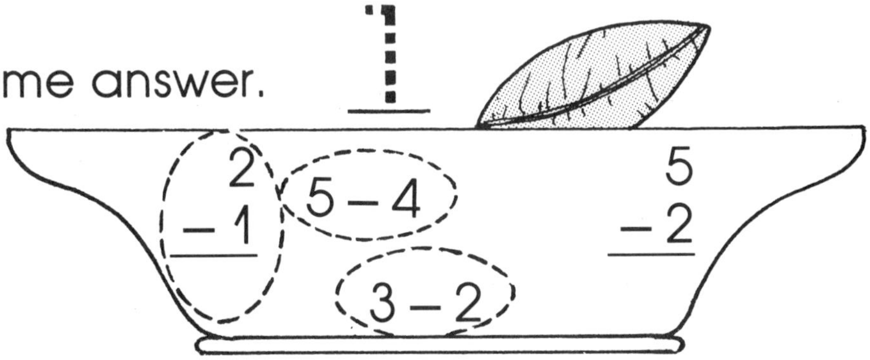

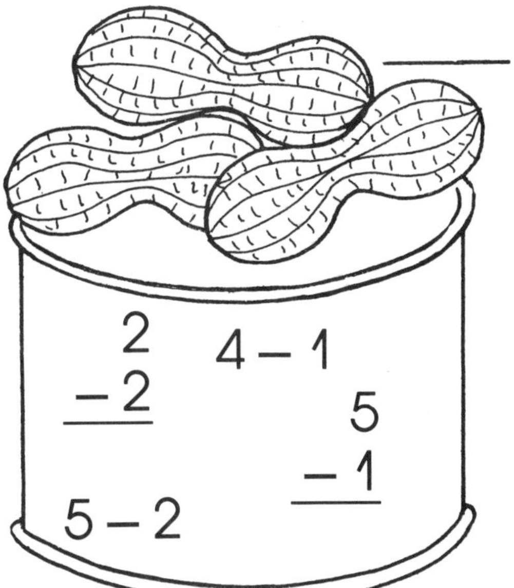

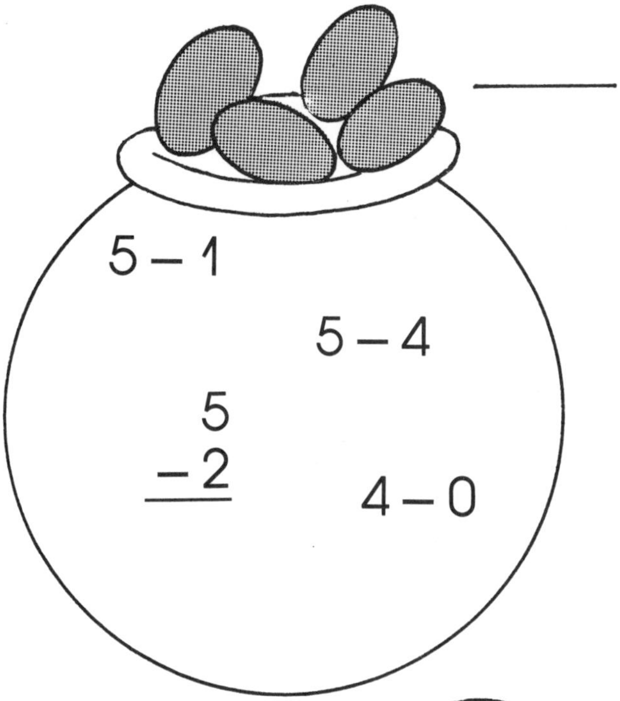

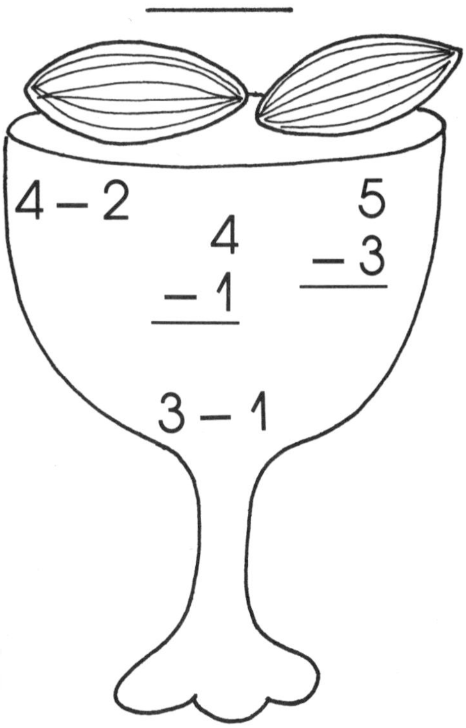

Subtraction Review

Name_____

Work problems.
Use code to color.

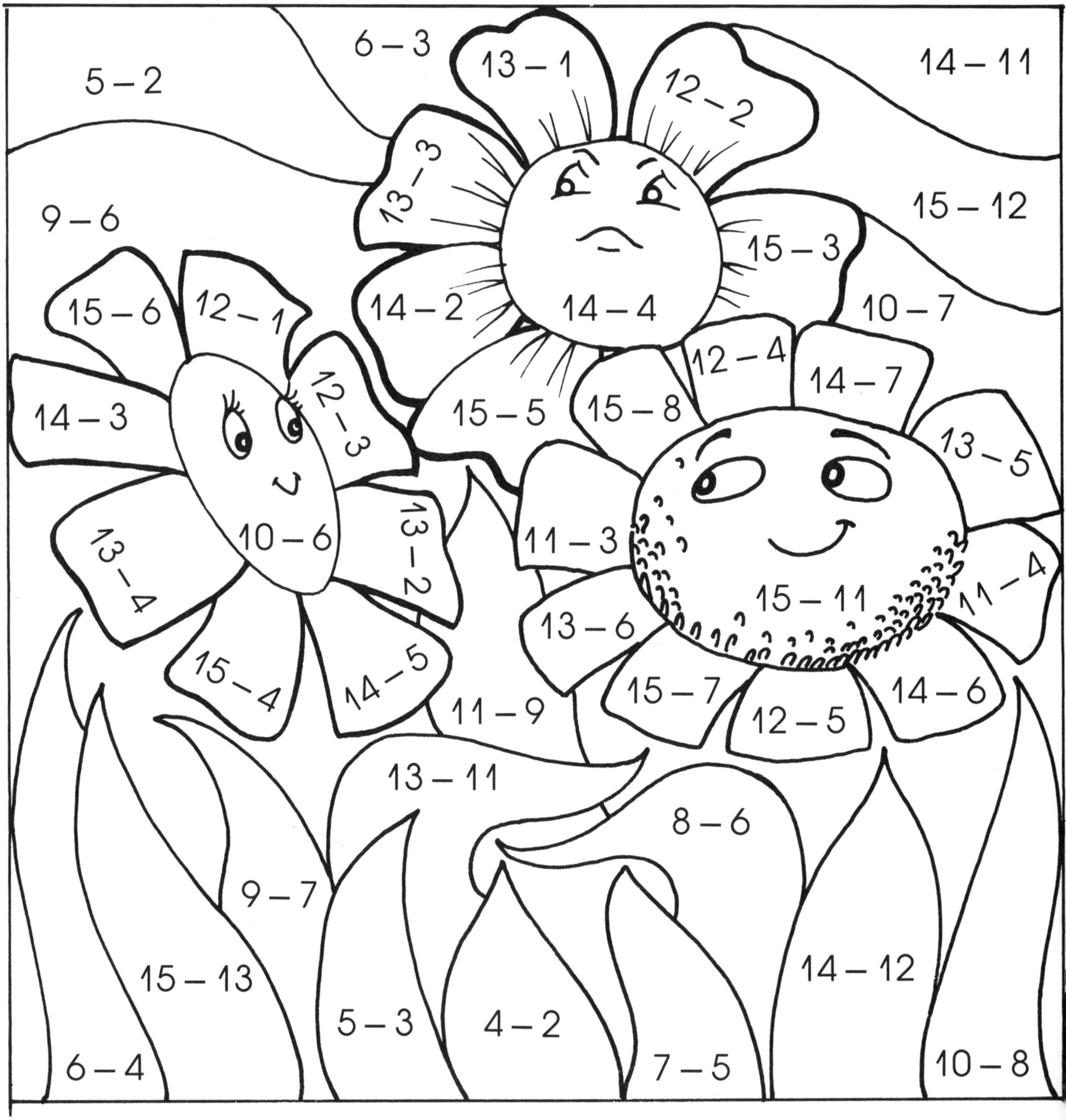

Addition and Subtraction Review

Name ________________________

Color answer:

- 2—red
- 3—blue
- 4—yellow
- 5—green

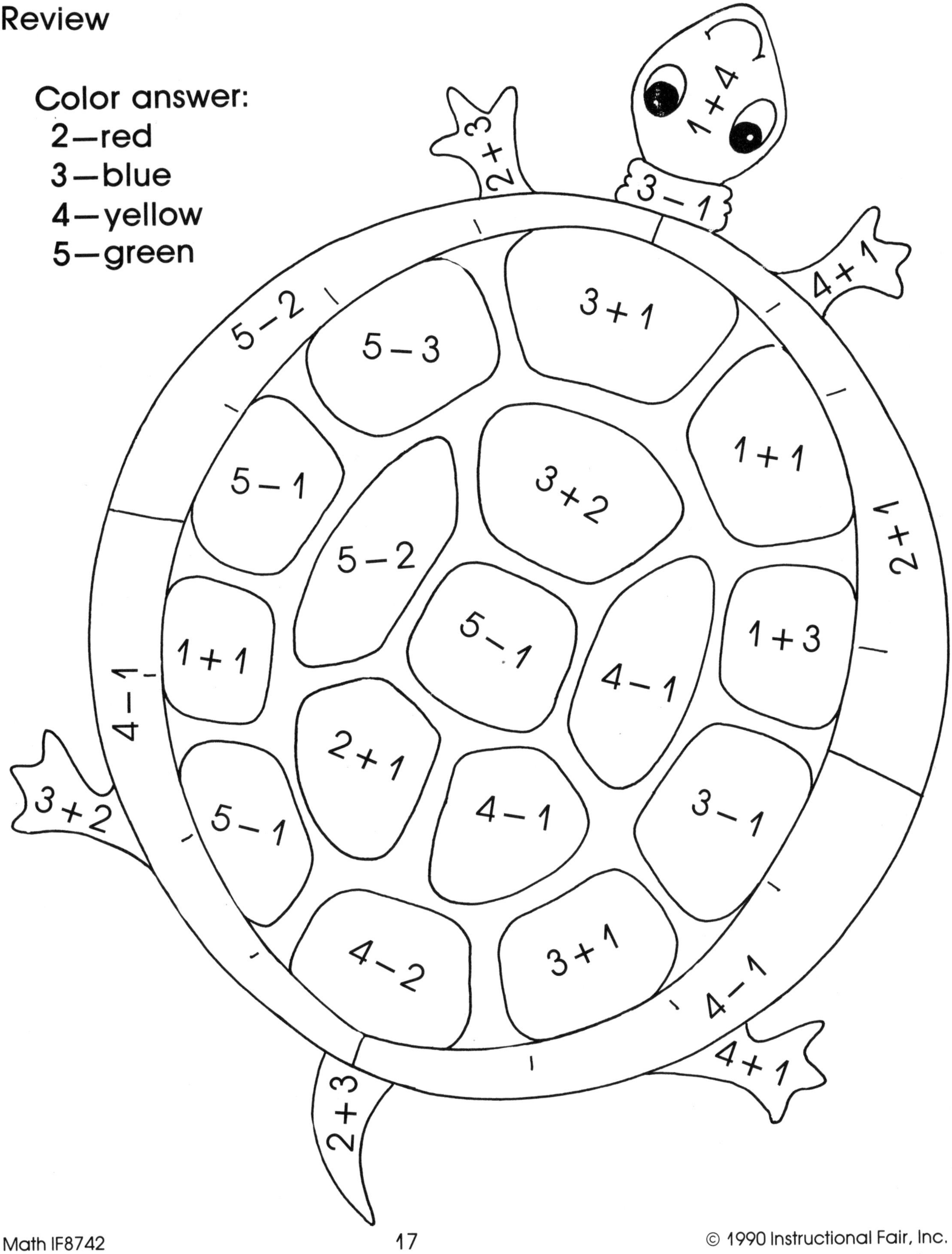

Zero Concept

$3 + 0 = 3$

$3 - 0 = 3$

$4 + 0 = 4$

$4 - 0 = 4$

$\underline{2} + 0 = \underline{2}$

$\underline{2} - 0 = \underline{2}$

$1 + 0 = \underline{}$ $1 - 0 = \underline{}$

$9 + 0 = \underline{}$ $5 - 0 = \underline{}$

$7 + 0 = \underline{}$ $8 - 0 = \underline{}$

$10 + 0 = \underline{}$ $2 - 0 = \underline{}$

$3 + 0 = \underline{}$ $9 + 0 = \underline{}$

$5 + 0 = \underline{}$ $4 - 0 = \underline{}$

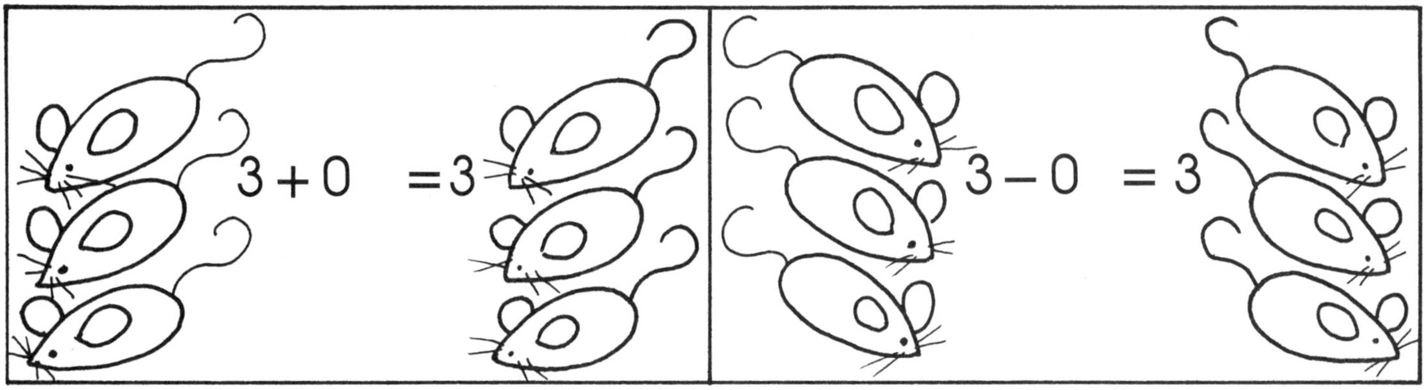

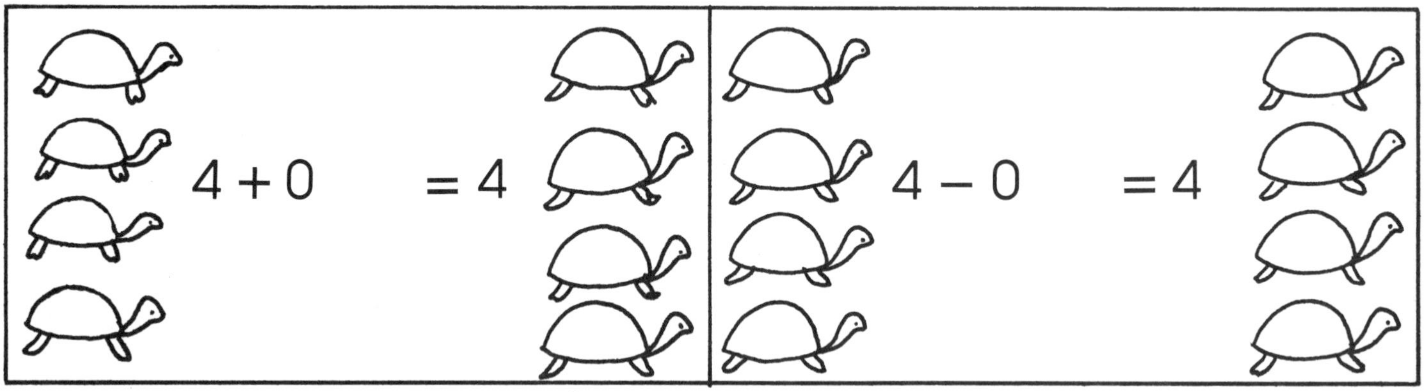

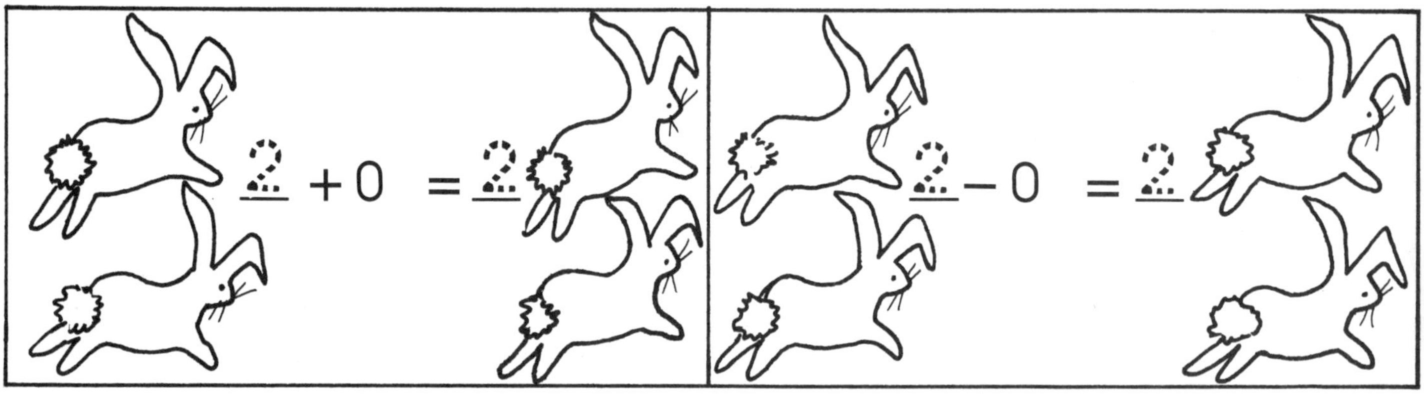

Subtraction (6-10)

Name _____

$9 - 2 = 7$

$$\begin{array}{r} 7 \\ -1 \\ \hline 6 \end{array}$$

Subtract. Use code to color.

6—orange   9—green
7—red   10—purple
8—yellow

$11 - 1 =$	$\begin{array}{r} 9 \\ -1 \\ \hline \end{array}$	$8 - 1 =$
$10 - 4 =$	$\begin{array}{r} 9 \\ -2 \\ \hline \end{array}$	$\begin{array}{r} 10 \\ -1 \\ \hline \end{array}$
$10 - 2 =$	$11 - 2 =$	$\begin{array}{r} 10 \\ -3 \\ \hline \end{array}$

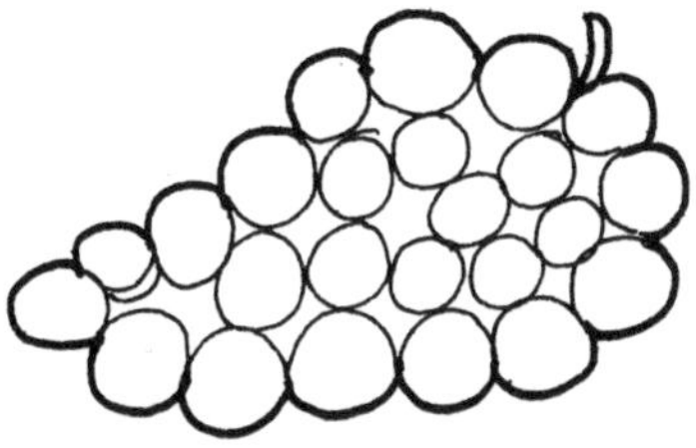

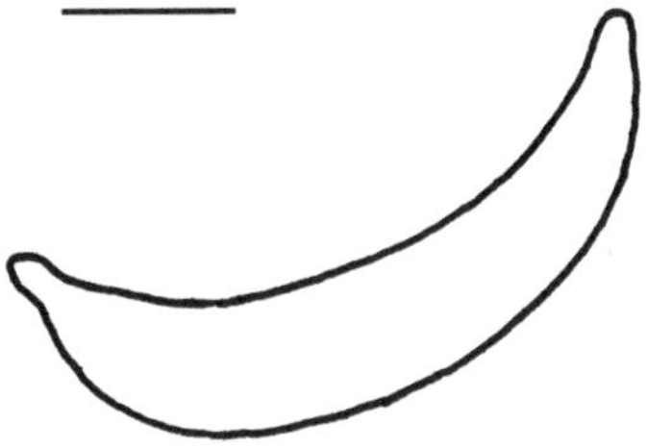

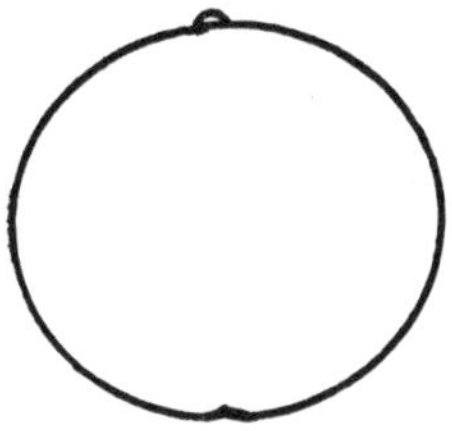

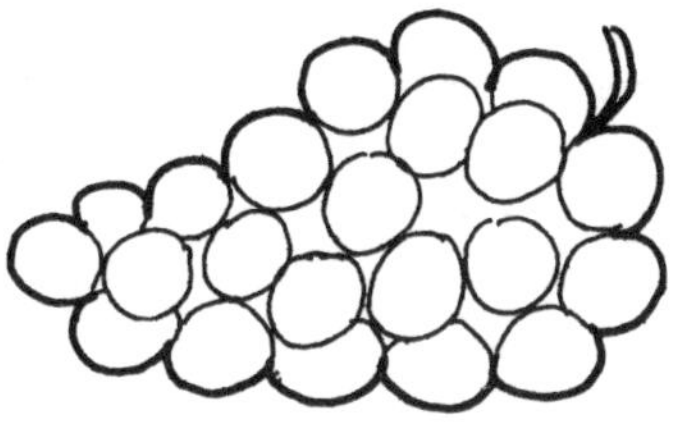

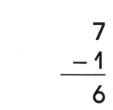

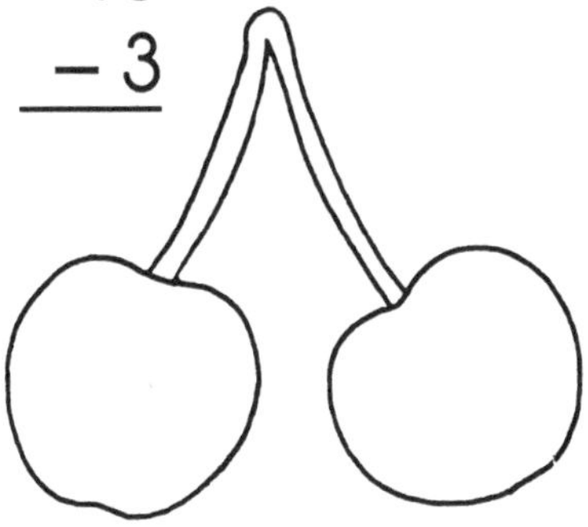

 Name ____________

Count the candy.
Write number on blank.
Circle problems with same answer.

10 – 1
10 – 4
11
– 2
9
– 1

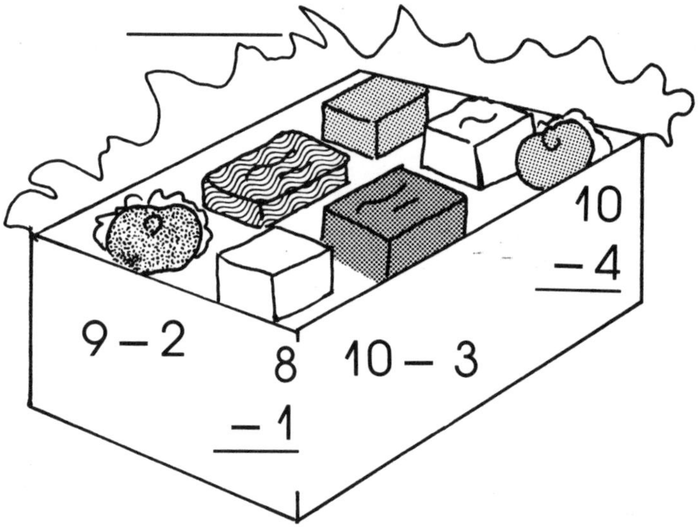
10
– 4
9 – 2
8
– 1
10 – 3

10
– 4
7 – 2
8
– 2
8 – 2

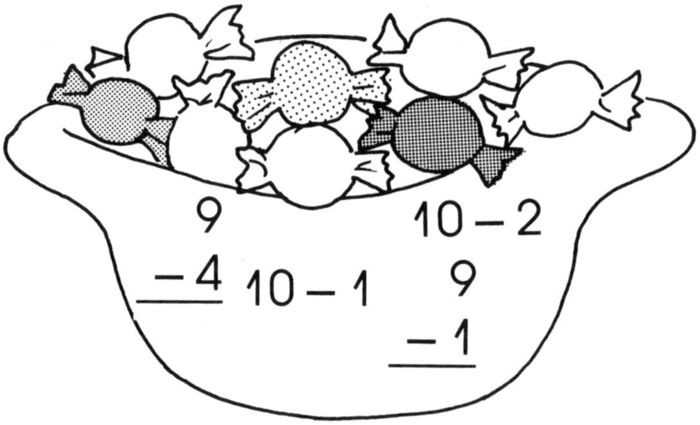
9
– 4
10 – 1
10 – 2
9
– 1

Review
Addition and Subtraction

Name________________________

Add or subract.
Use code to color each part of picture.

6—yellow
7—red
8—green
9—blue
10—orange

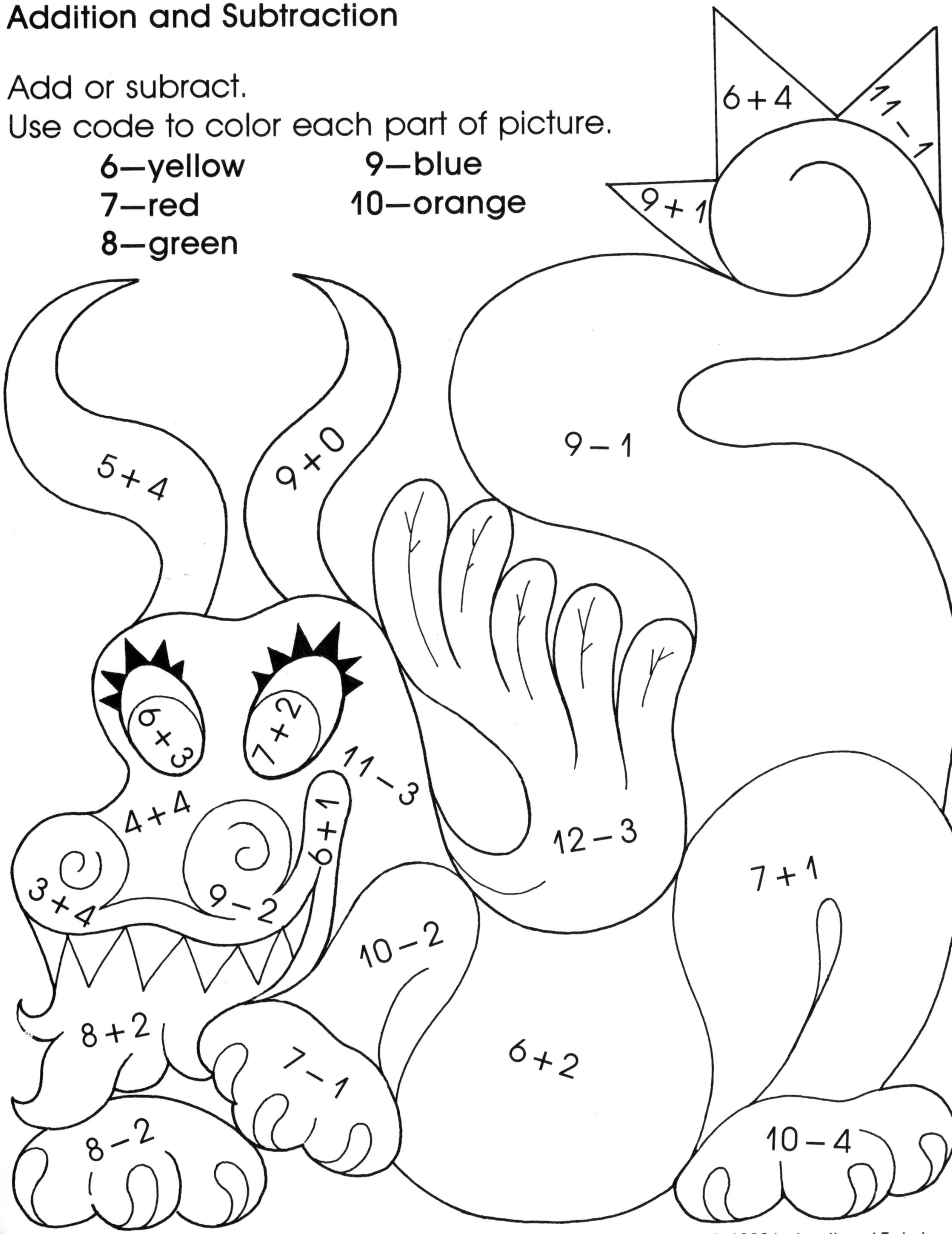

Addition and Subtraction Review

Name____________________

Add or subtract.
Use code to color picture.

1—yellow
2—blue
3—red
4—brown
5—green
6—orange
7—black
8—purple

Magic Squares

Name____________________

+

6	2	8
3	4	7
9	6	15

−

11	2	9
6	1	5
5	1	4

+

5	2	
3	4	

+

9	3	
2	1	

+

8	1	
2	3	

+

2	1	
3	6	

−

13	6	
3	2	

−

15	6	
9	3	

−

12	5	
3	2	

Addition and Subtraction Review

Name____________________________

Work problems. Use color code to find the Secret Word!

15—yellow	**12**—green
14—orange	**11**—blue
13—red	

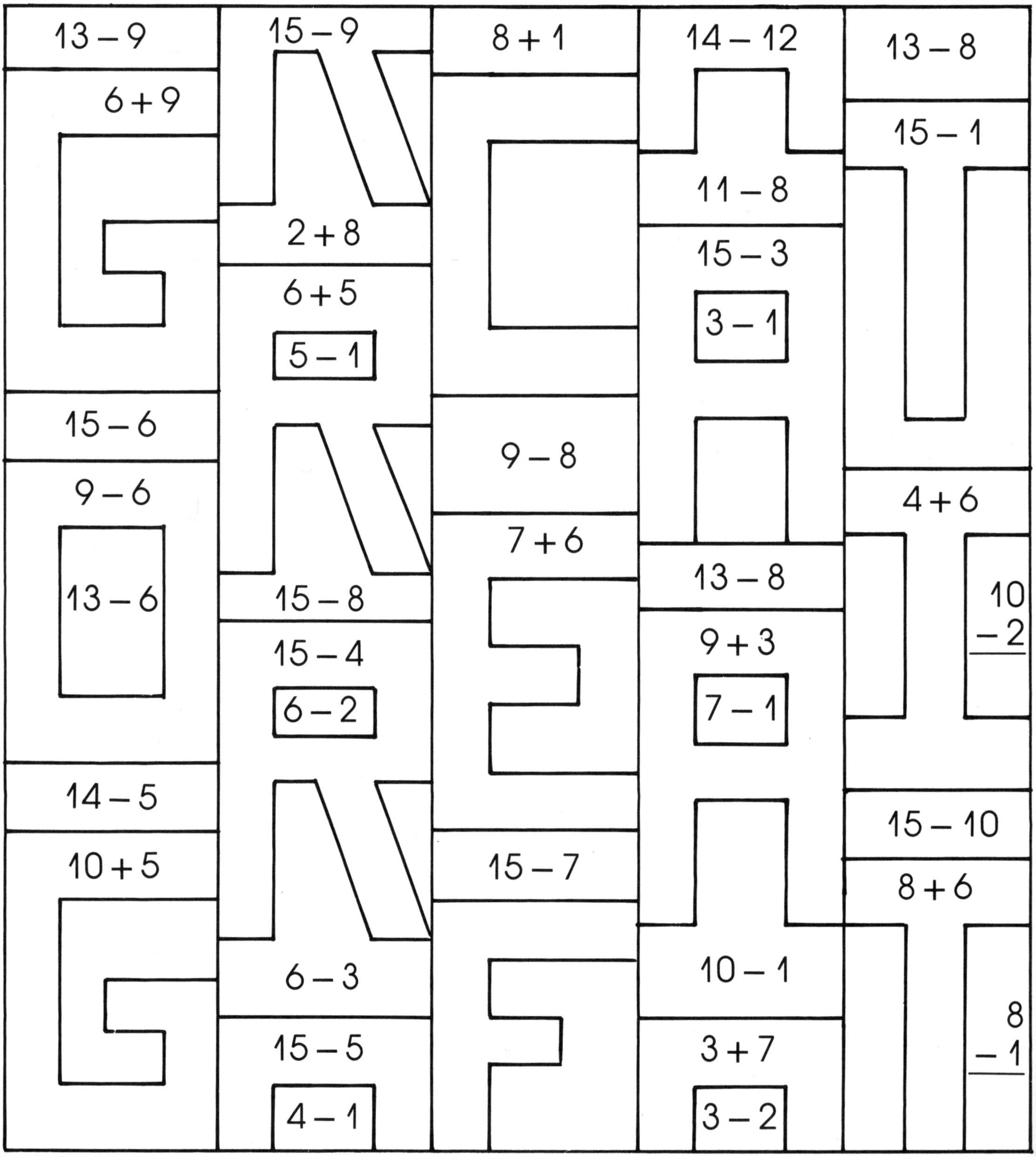

Ordinal Numbers

Name_____

Circle the ordinal number word for each treat.

1.

2.

3.

4.

16.

 third, sixteenth, fifth

5.

 fifteenth, fourth, first

 twelfth, second, seventh

15.

third, eleventh, fifteenth

6.

eighth, first, tenth

14.

sixteenth, thirteenth, third

7.

ninth, second, thirteenth

13.

 sixth, seventh, ninth,

8.

12.

11.

10.

9.

Name ______________________

Color the **ninth** flag red.
Write **O** on the **second** flag.
Color the **eighth** flag blue.
Write **D** on the **fourth** flag.
Color the **sixth** flag yellow.
Write **G** on the **first** flag.
Color the **tenth** flag purple.
Write **O** on the **third** flag.
Color the **seventh** flag green.
Color the **fifth** flag orange.

Ordinal Numbers

Name________________________

Number the circles in order, beginning at **START.**

Follow these directions:

Color the ninth blue.
Draw a □ on the eleventh.
Put a red X on the third.
Color the sixteenth purple.
Put a green ○ on the fifth.
Color the thirteenth orange.
Put 3 lines in the sixth.
Color the tenth red striped.
Color the first green.
Put 6 black dots on the fourth.
Color the eighth 3 colors.
Put 2 green lines on the twelfth.
Put an orange △ on the fifteenth.
Color the second the same as the ninth.
Draw ☺ on the fourteenth.
Put 2 brown X 's on the seventh.

1

START ←

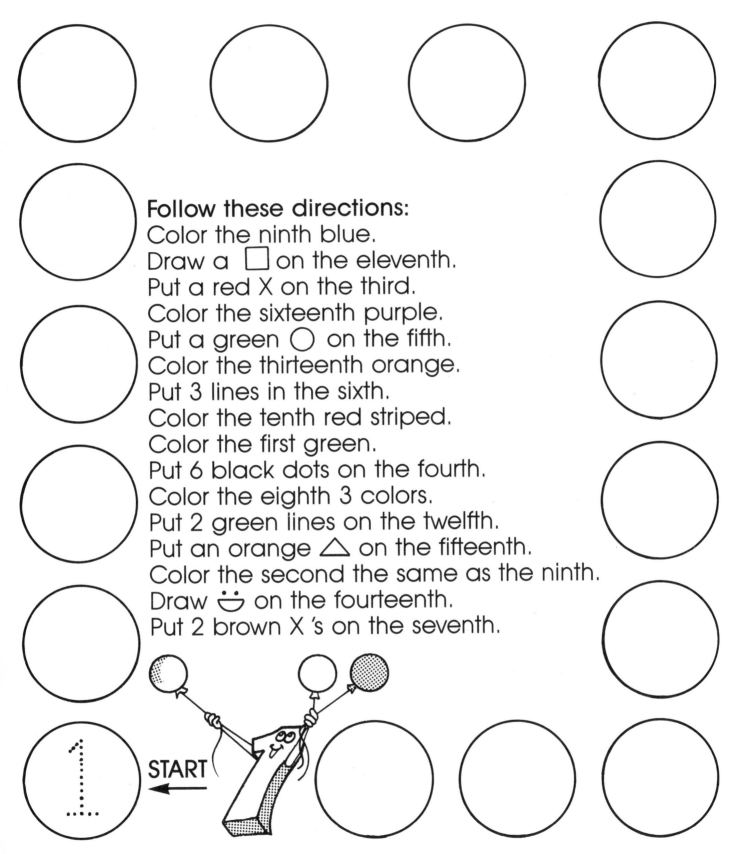

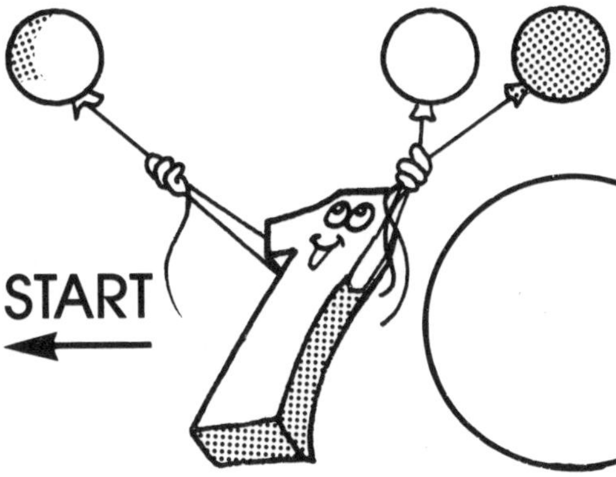

Place Value: Tens and Ones

Name ______________________________

1 2

tens ones

12

tens ones

tens ones

tens ones

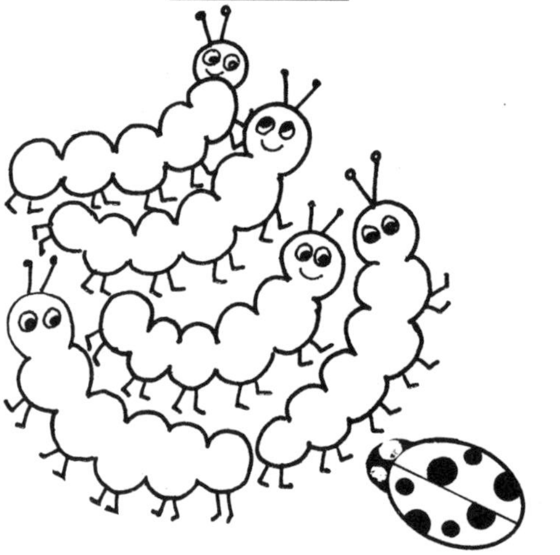

tens ones

tens ones

tens ones

tens ones

tens ones

Place Value: Tens and Ones

Name ____________________

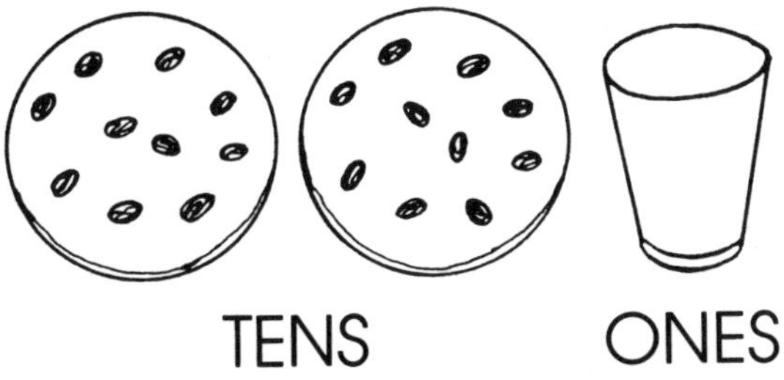

tens ones

2 tens 1 ones __2__ __1__ = __21__

tens ones

2 tens 8 ones __2__ __8__ = __28__

4 tens 6 ones ____ ____ = ____

5 tens 7 ones ____ ____ = ____

3 tens 8 ones ____ ____ = ____

9 tens 1 one ____ ____ = ____

1 ten 4 ones ____ ____ = ____

6 tens 2 ones ____ ____ = ____

8 tens 5 ones ____ ____ = ____

7 tens 9 ones ____ ____ = ____

tens ones

8 tens 3 ones ____ ____ = ____

7 tens 4 ones ____ ____ = ____

1 ten 7 ones ____ ____ = ____

6 tens 3 ones ____ ____ = ____

5 tens 3 ones ____ ____ = ____

2 tens 6 ones ____ ____ = ____

9 tens 5 ones ____ ____ = ____

3 tens 6 ones ____ ____ = ____

4 tens 2 ones ____ ____ = ____

38 = __3__ tens __8__ ones

57 = ____ tens ____ ones

15 = ____ tens ____ ones

65 = ____ tens ____ ones

88 = ____ tens ____ ones

46 = ____ tens ____ ones

29 = ____ tens ____ ones

71 = ____ tens ____ ones

21 = ____ tens ____ ones

13 = ____ tens ____ ones

Place Value Review Name ______________________

Color one of the two balloons.

Here's how:

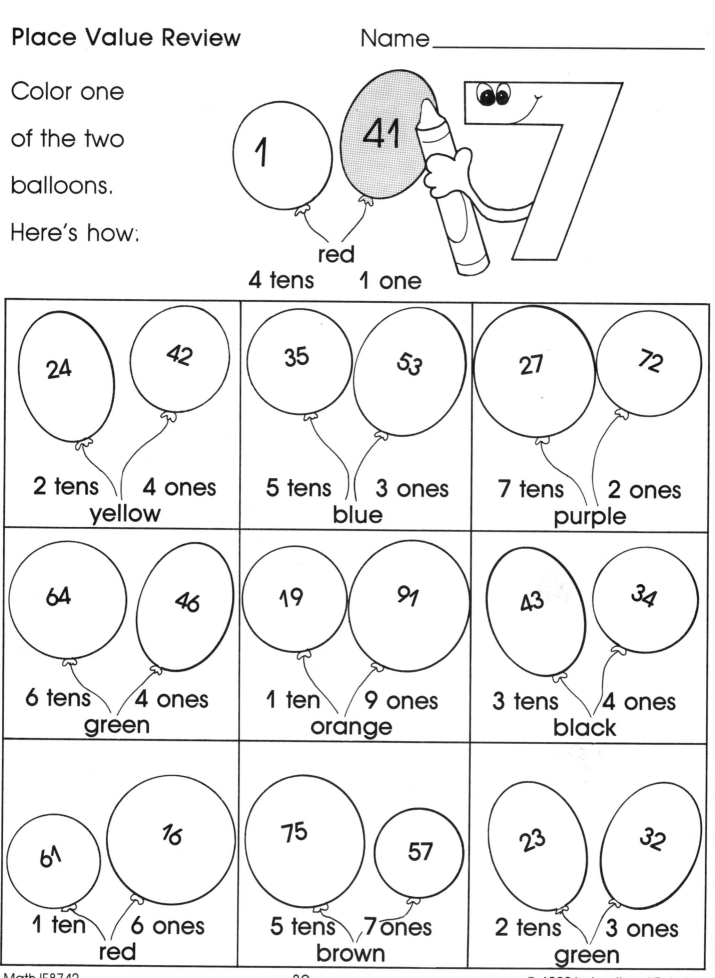

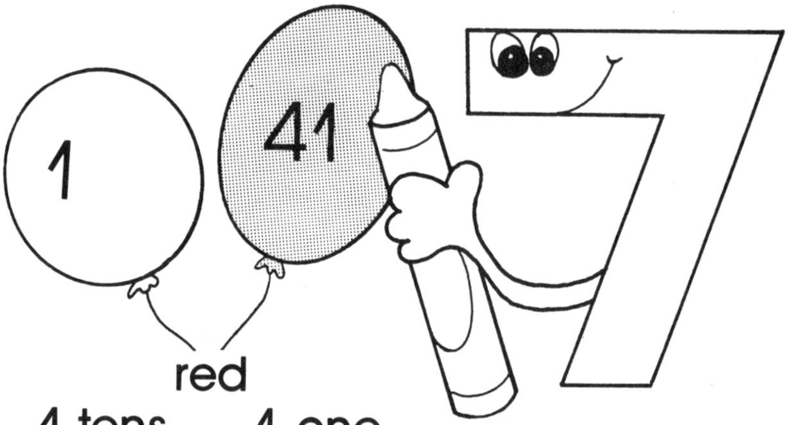

red

4 tens 1 one

24 42 2 tens 4 ones yellow	35 53 5 tens 3 ones blue	27 72 7 tens 2 ones purple
64 46 6 tens 4 ones green	19 91 1 ten 9 ones orange	43 34 3 tens 4 ones black
61 16 1 ten 6 ones red	75 57 5 tens 7 ones brown	23 32 2 tens 3 ones green

Sequencing Numbers

Name ______________________

Put the numbers on each house in order.

28, 25, 27, 26

____

36, 38, 37

____

15, 17, 16, 18

____

32, 34, 33, 35, 36

____

17, 19, 18

____

66, 68, 67

____

65, 61, 63, 64, 62

____

41, 43, 42

____

75, 78, 77, 76

____

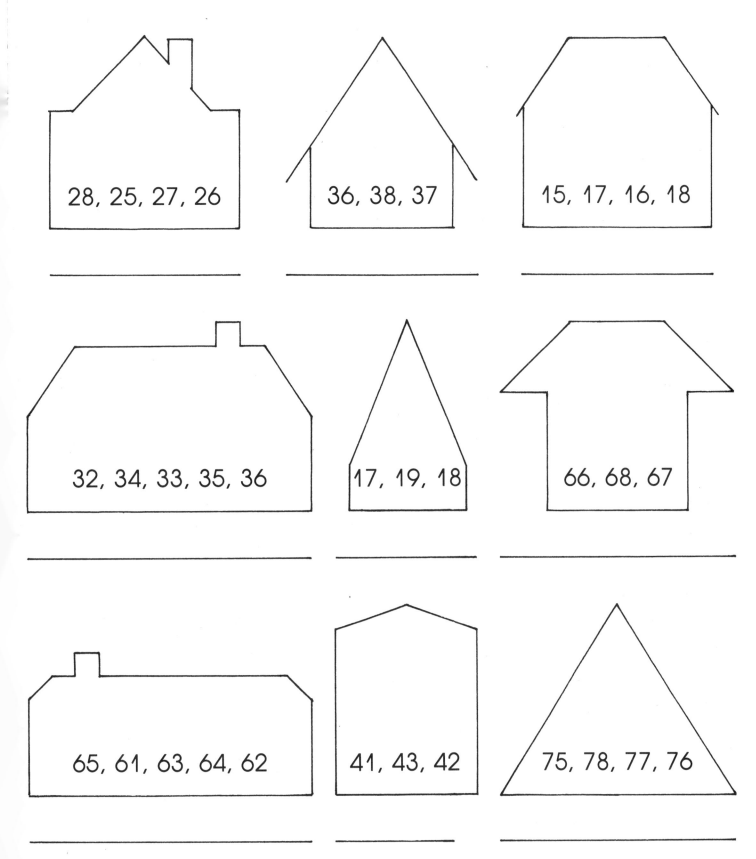

Greater Than; Less Than

Name________________________

Which number is greater?

[62] or 34	21 or 52	79 or 97
55 or 62	45 or 15	88 or 87
91 or 19	29 or 36	57 or 69

Which number is less?

[22] or 29	63 or 50	44 or 14
82 or 56	39 or 93	58 or 85
42 or 43	99 or 100	1 or 2

> greater than   < less than

>			<	
____	____	13, 35	____	____
____	____	21, 46	____	____
____	____	56, 37	____	____
____	____	45, 15	____	____

Number Discrimination

Name _____

In the shapes, circle the smallest number.

Draw a square around the largest number.

4 5 9 2 3 8

Square: 3 8 4 10

Diamond: 2 9 7 5

Circle: 7 12 20 5 3 16 6

Rectangle: 11 14 10 9 18

Triangle (middle): 15 9 36 10 13

Square (right): 34 23 38 42 28

Triangle (left): 25 11 42 33 18

Circle (bottom): 26 46 19 32

Parallelogram: 22 35 45 42 11 25

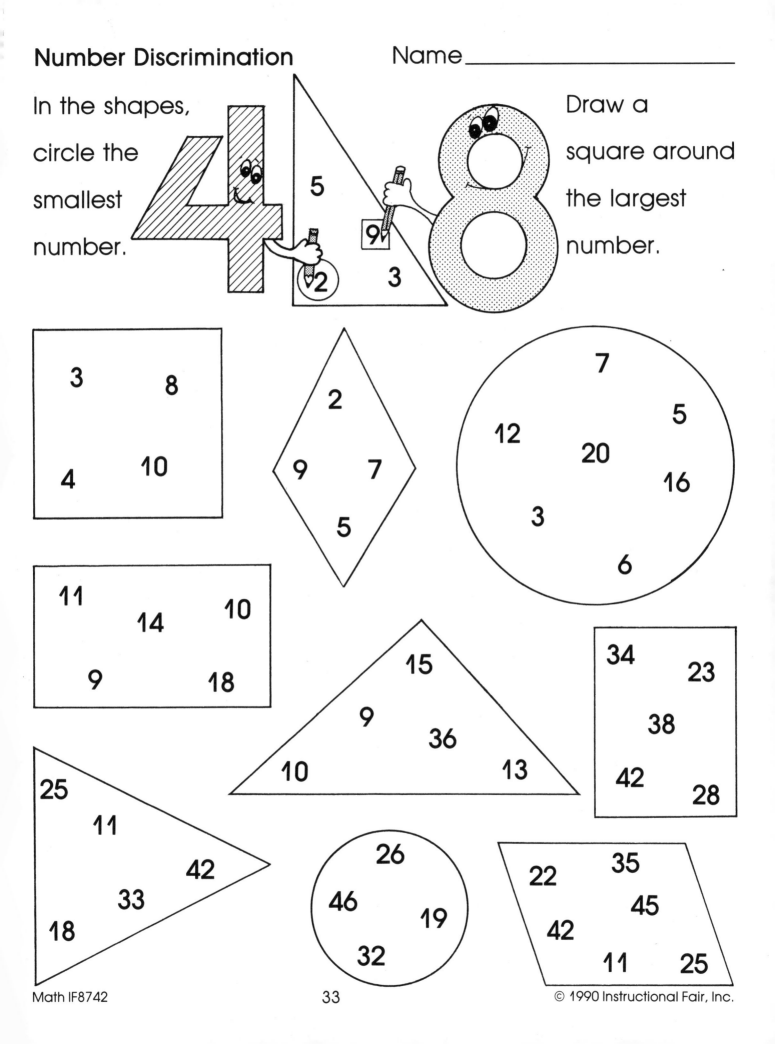

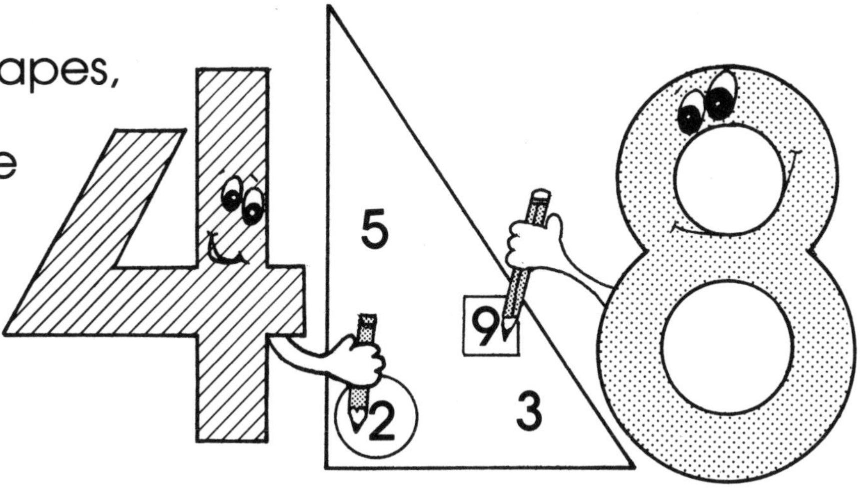

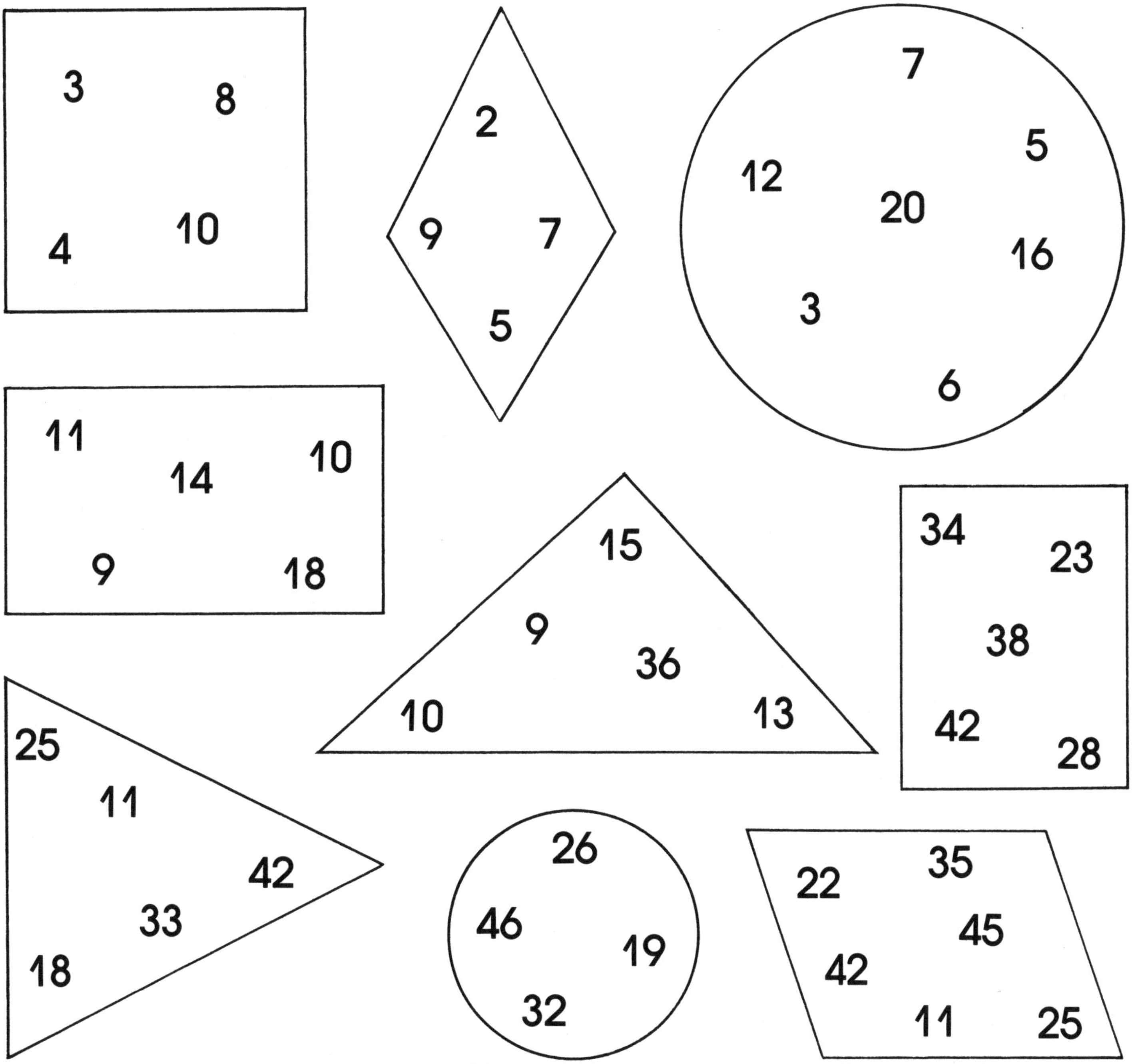

Name ____________________

Color second ball brown.

Color sixth ball yellow.

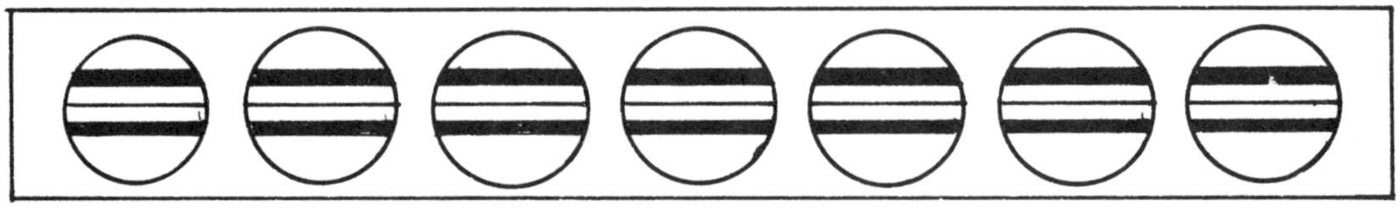

Color fourth ball orange.

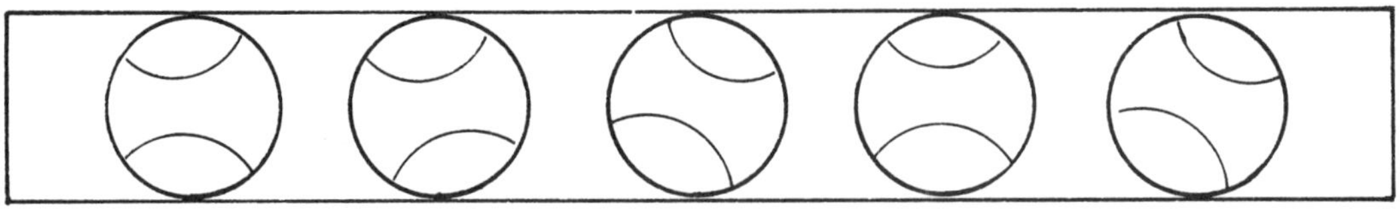

Color first ball black.

Color third ball blue.

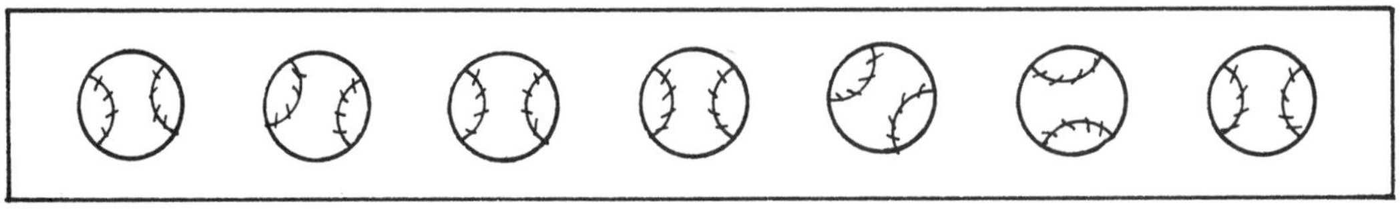

Color fifth ball green.

Color seventh ball purple.

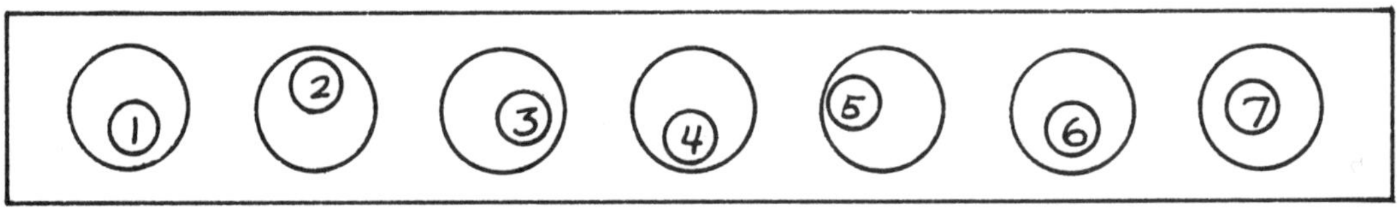

Color eighth ball pink.

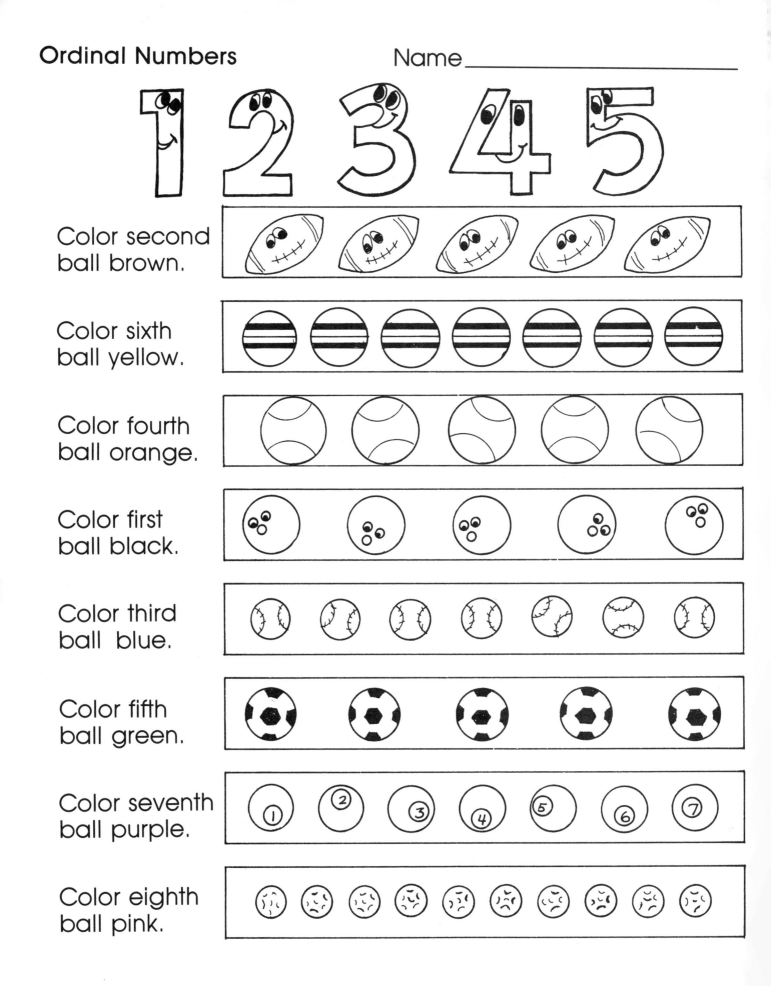

Counting by Tens

Name________________________

Color the road the bus takes to school counting by 10's.

Counting by 5's

Name ____________________

Fill in the big road signs by 5's to get to the circus.

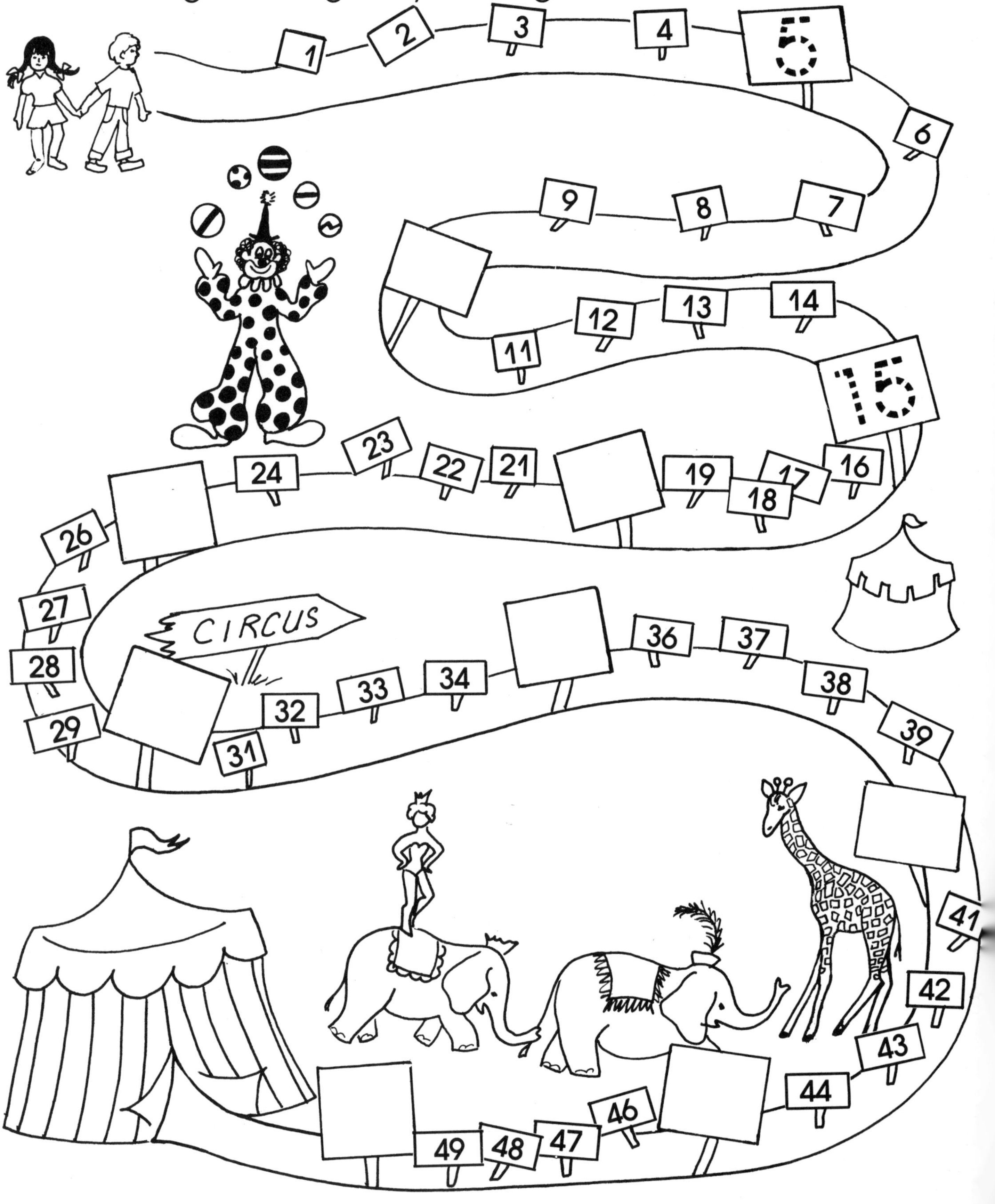

Counting by 2's and 5's

Name ____________________________

Write and count by 2's.

2		6							

Write and count by 5's.

5		15							

Connect the dots by 2's.

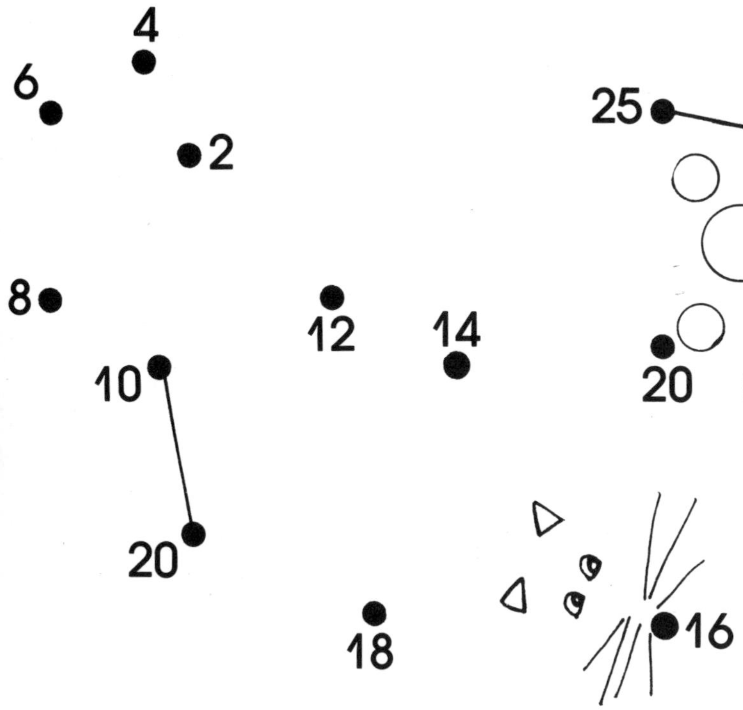

Connect the dots by 5's.

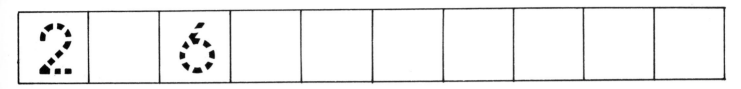

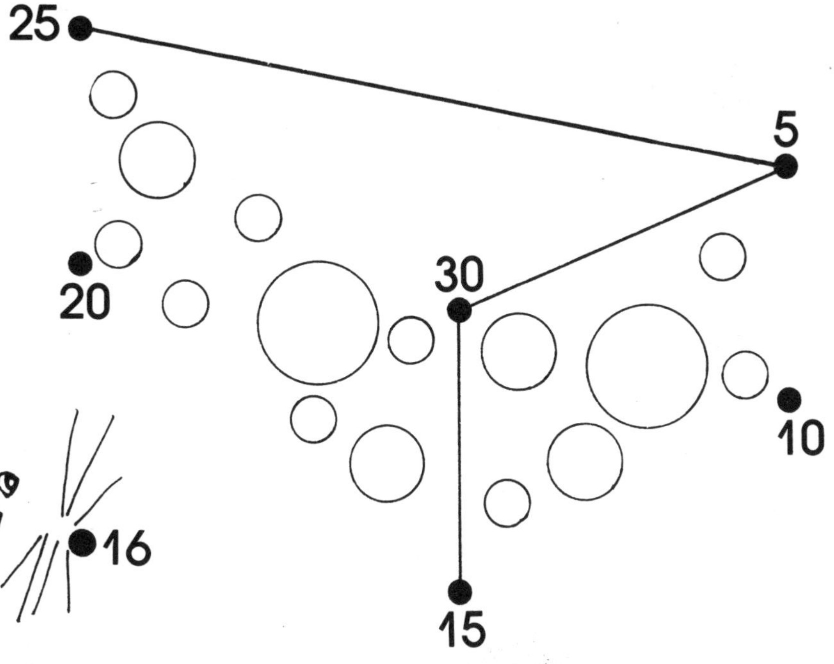

Shape Recognition

Name ____________________

Color:

brown yellow green red

 Name ____________________________

Color:

squares —— **green**
rectangles —— **yellow**
circles —— **red**
triangles —— **blue**

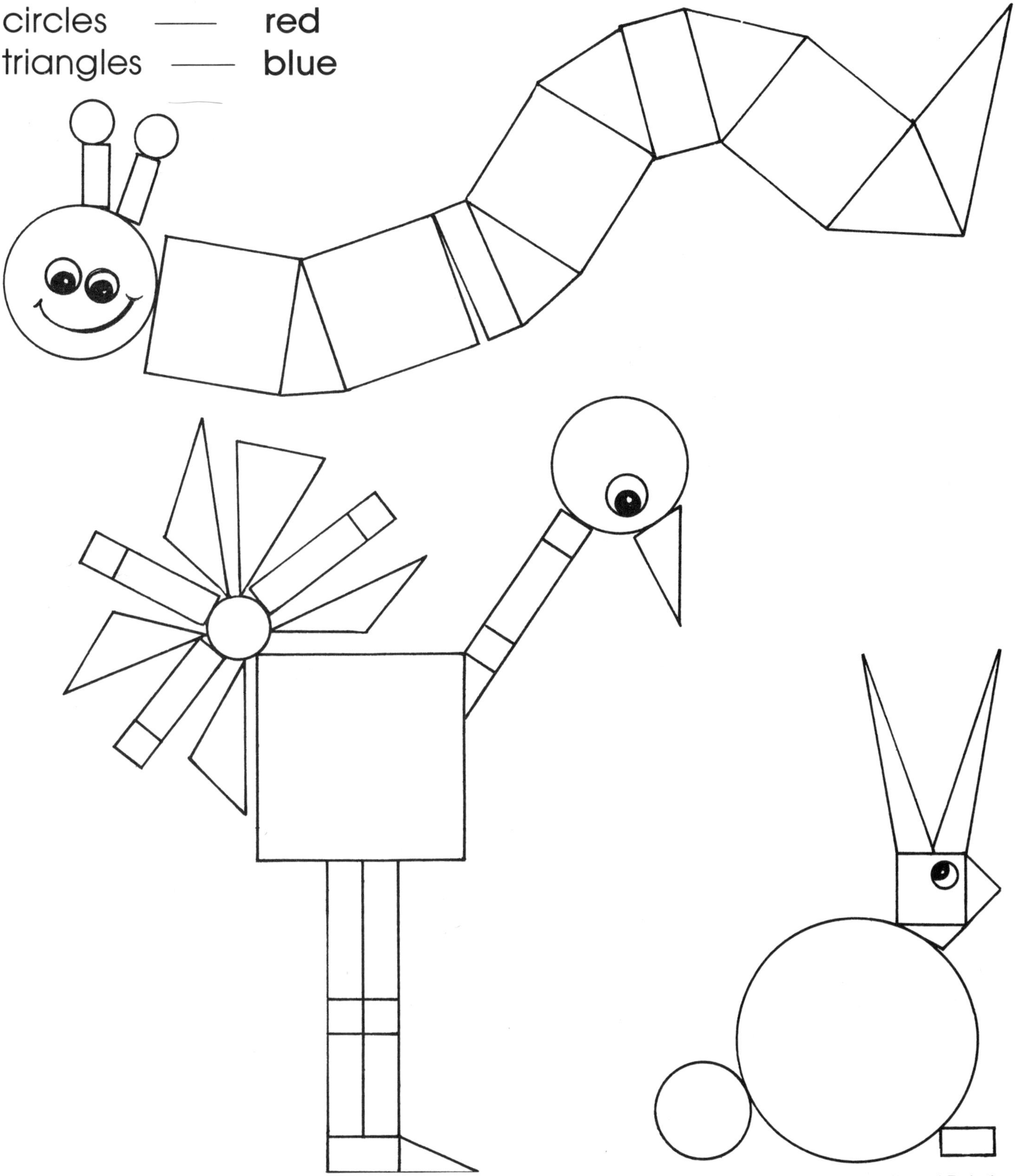

Shape Discrimination Name ______________________

How many circles? ○ ______ How many triangles? △ ______

How many rectangles? ▯ ______ How many squares? □ ______

Color toys.

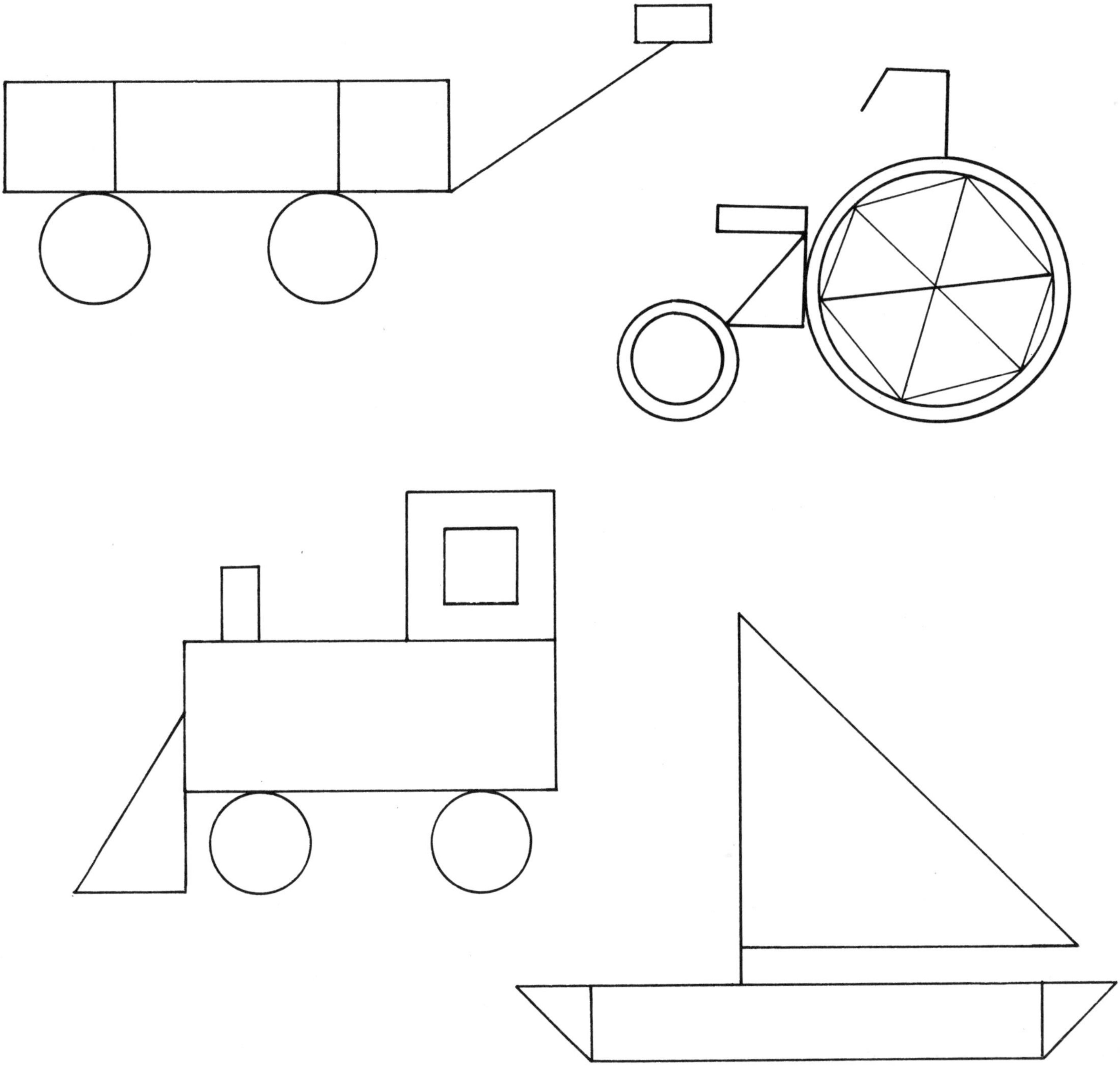

 Name________________________

Color the ones in each row that are the same size and shape. Write **T** for triangle, **R** for rectangle and **S** for square.

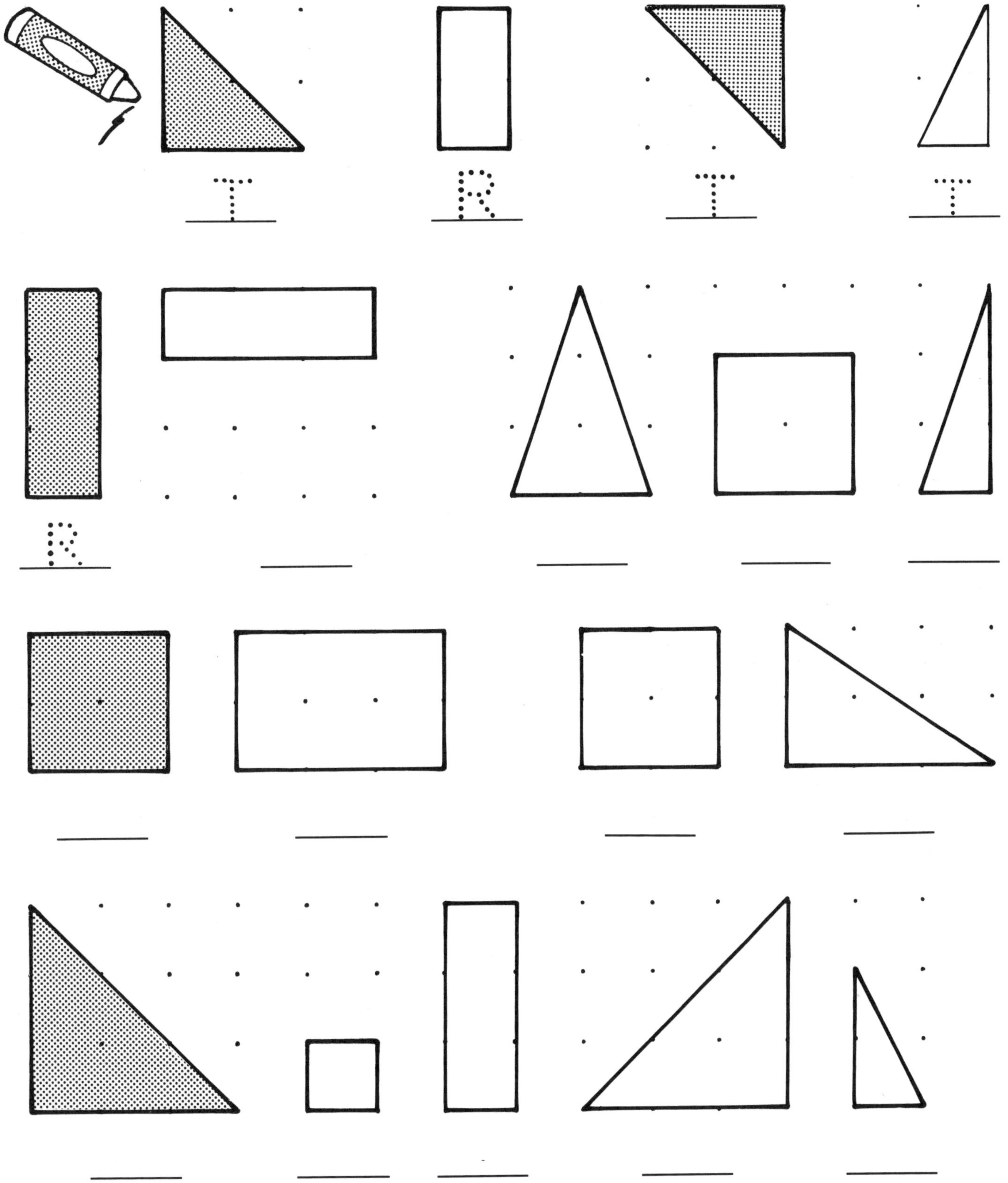

Geometry: Location Name ______________________

top-bottom

inside-outside

left-right

Color top green and bottom brown.

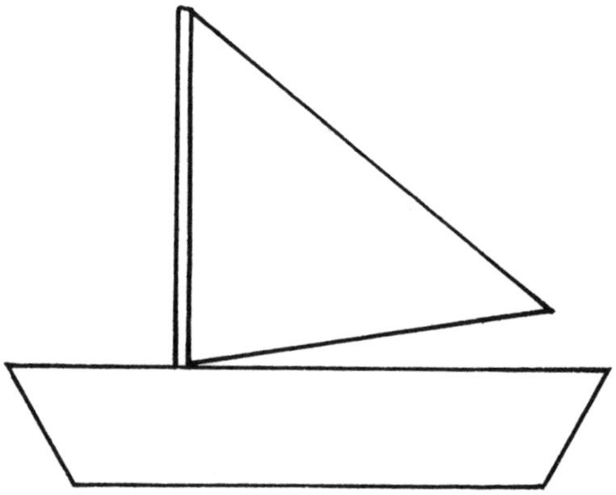

Color inside yellow and outside blue.

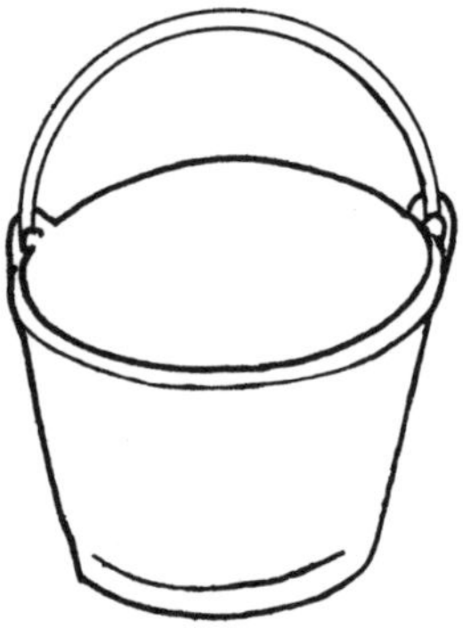

Color left red and right purple.

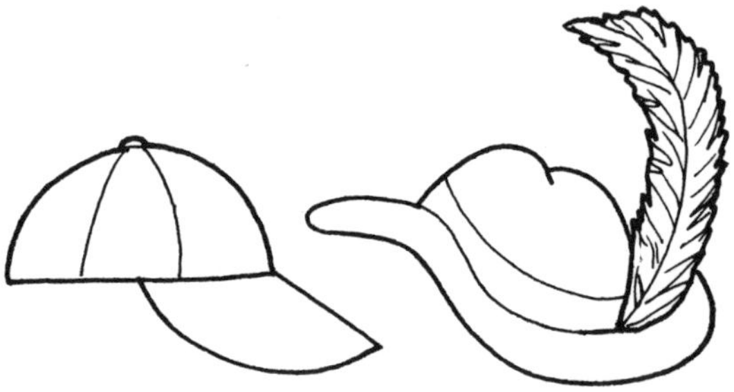

$$4 \quad + \quad 7 \quad = \quad 11$$

Add.

$3 + 9 = \underline{12}$

$6 + 7 = \underline{}$

$6 + 5 = \underline{}$

$5 + 7 = \underline{}$

$4 + 9 = \underline{}$

$9 + 6 = \underline{}$

$7 + 7 = \underline{}$

$7 + 8 = \underline{}$

$6 + 8 = \underline{}$

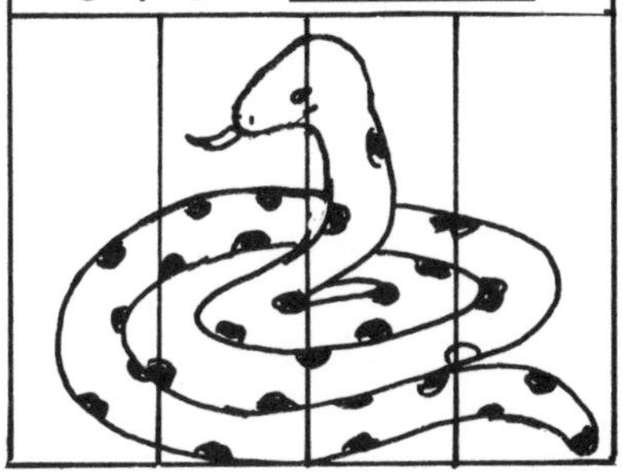

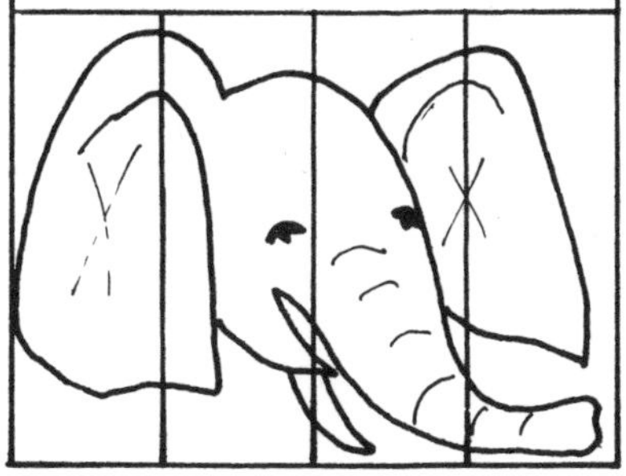

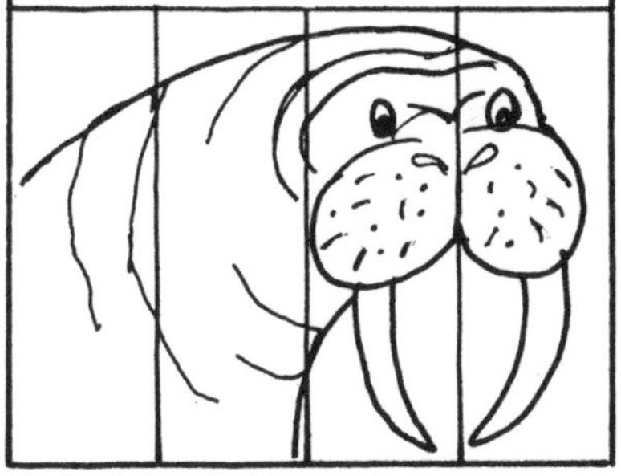

Addition (2-15)

Name ____________________

Match.

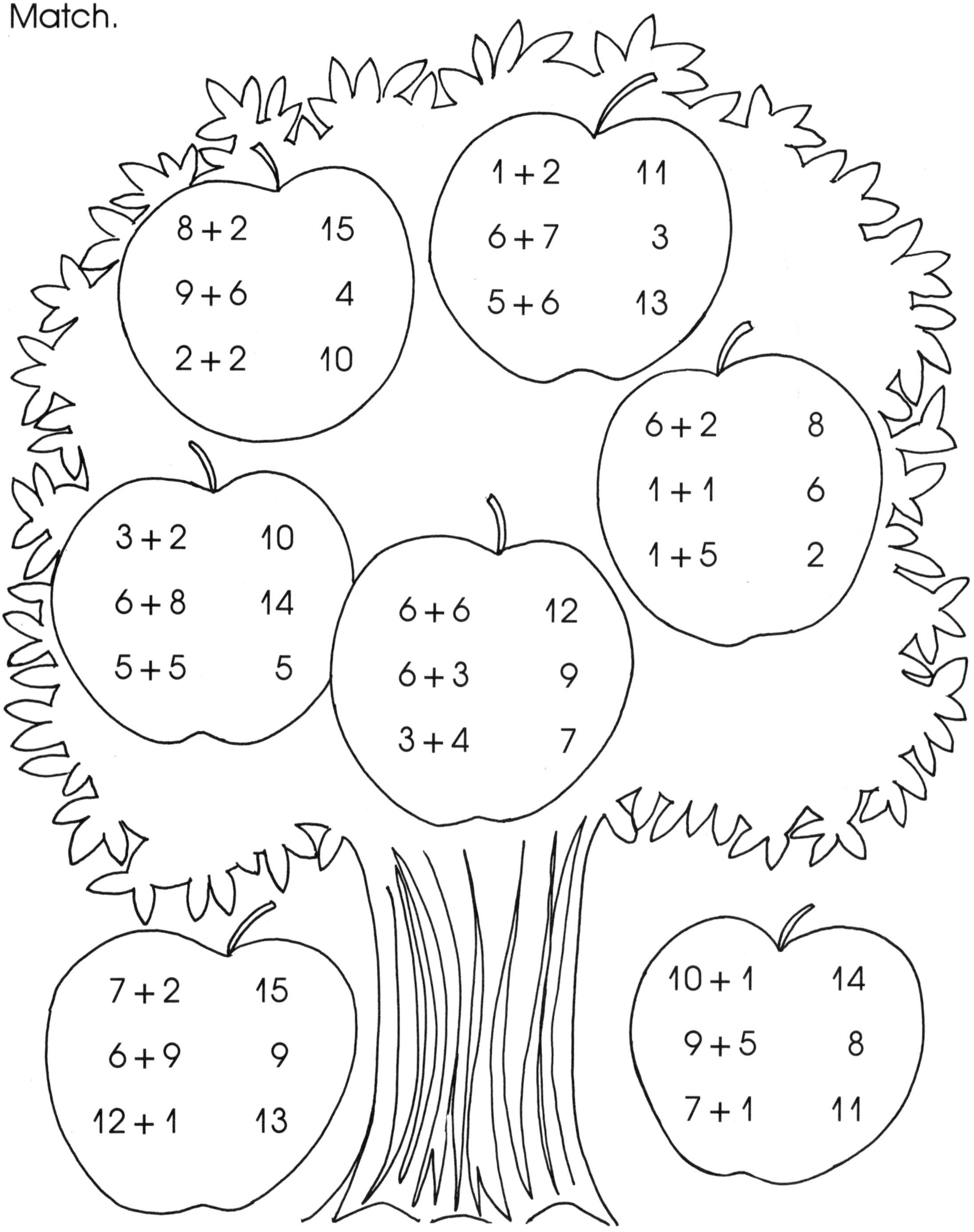
8 + 2 15
9 + 6 4
2 + 2 10
1 + 2 11
6 + 7 3
5 + 6 13
6 + 2 8
1 + 1 6
1 + 5 2
3 + 2 10
6 + 8 14
5 + 5 5
6 + 6 12
6 + 3 9
3 + 4 7
7 + 2 15
6 + 9 9
12 + 1 13
10 + 1 14
9 + 5 8
7 + 1 11

Column Addition

Work problem. Use color codes to find secret problem.

$$\begin{array}{r} 3 \\ 1 \\ +\,5 \\ \hline \end{array}$$

$$\begin{array}{r} 2 \\ 2 \\ 1 \\ +\,6 \\ \hline \end{array}$$

10 – pink	13 – green
11 – red	14 – blue
12 – yellow	15 – orange

$$\begin{array}{r} 1 \\ 6 \\ +\,2 \\ \hline \end{array}$$

$$\begin{array}{r} 8 \\ 3 \\ +\,4 \\ \hline \end{array}$$

$$\begin{array}{r} 4 \\ 3 \\ +\,2 \\ \hline \end{array}$$

$$\begin{array}{r} 6 \\ 2 \\ +\,1 \\ \hline \end{array}$$

$$7 + 1 + 1 = \underline{\quad}$$

$$1 + 4 + 1 + 1 = \underline{\quad}$$

$$\begin{array}{r} 6 \\ 1 \\ 4 \\ +\,2 \\ \hline \end{array}$$

$$\begin{array}{r} 4 \\ 6 \\ 3 \\ +\,1 \\ \hline \end{array}$$

$$\begin{array}{r} 1 \\ 5 \\ 2 \\ +\,1 \\ \hline \end{array}$$

$$6 + 5 + 1 = \underline{\quad}$$

$$\begin{array}{r} 2 \\ 6 \\ +\,2 \\ \hline \end{array}$$

$$\begin{array}{r} 4 \\ 3 \\ +\,2 \\ \hline \end{array}$$

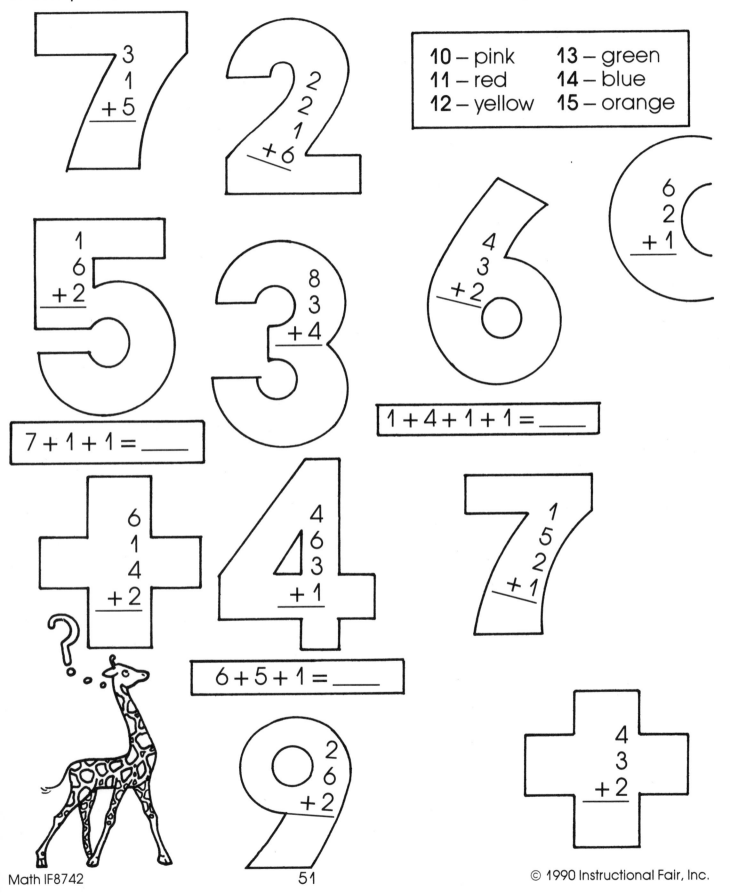

Name ____________________

Add. ⟨2⟩ and [7] = (9)
⟨2⟩ and [4] = (6)

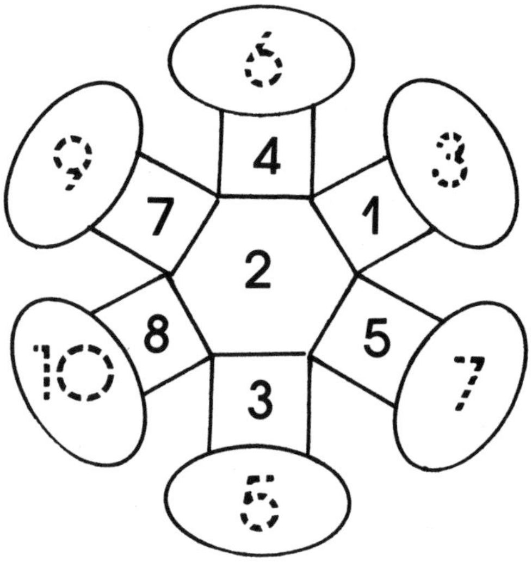

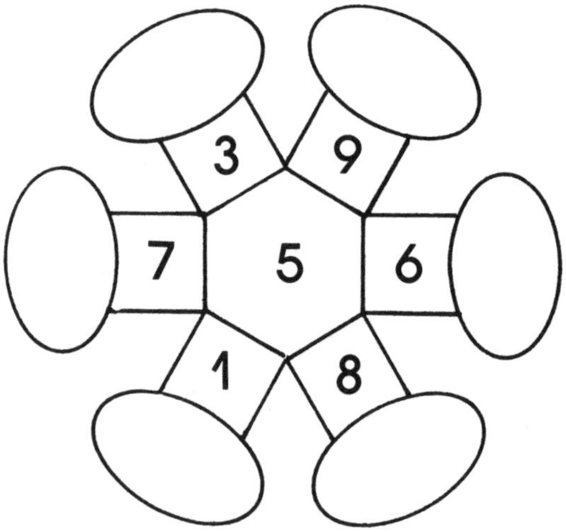

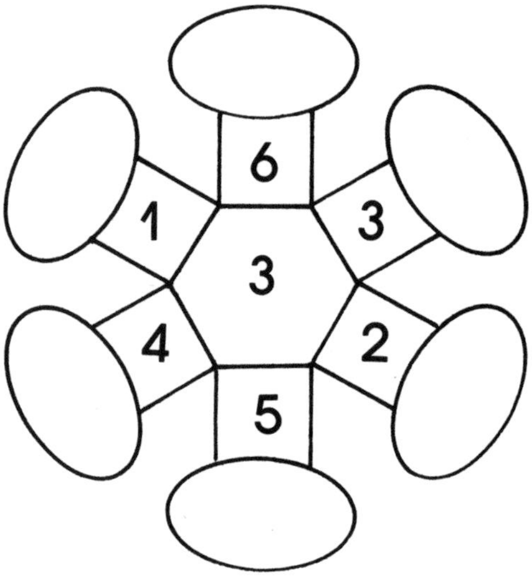

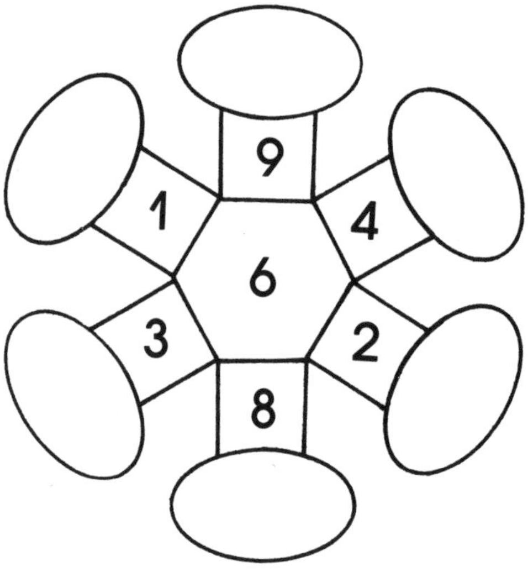

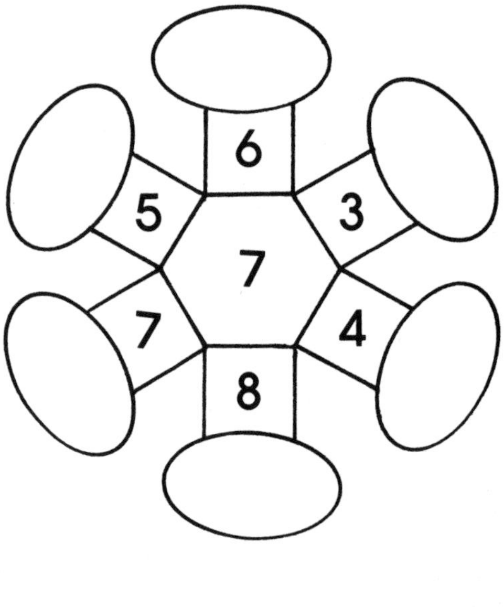

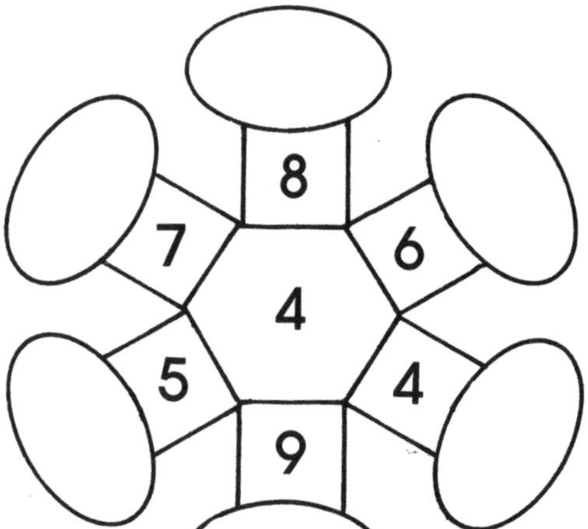

Subtraction (10-15)

Name ____________________

Count crayons. Write number on blank.
Circle problems that name answer.

____

12 – 1

13 – 3 =

15 – 5

12 – 2 =

13 – 3

11 – 1

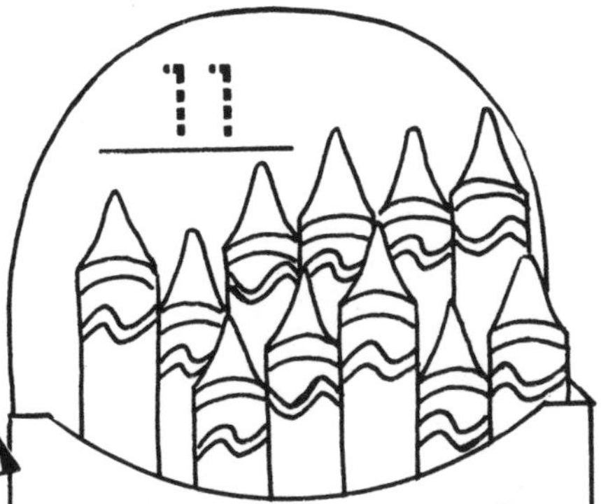

11

13 – 2 =

14 – 3

15 – 4 =

13 – 2

15 – 5 =

12 – 1 =

____

15 – 2 =

14 – 1

14 – 2

14 – 1 =

15 – 2

15 – 3 =

____

14 – 2

15 – 4 =

13 – 1

15 – 3

14 – 2 =

14 – 4 =

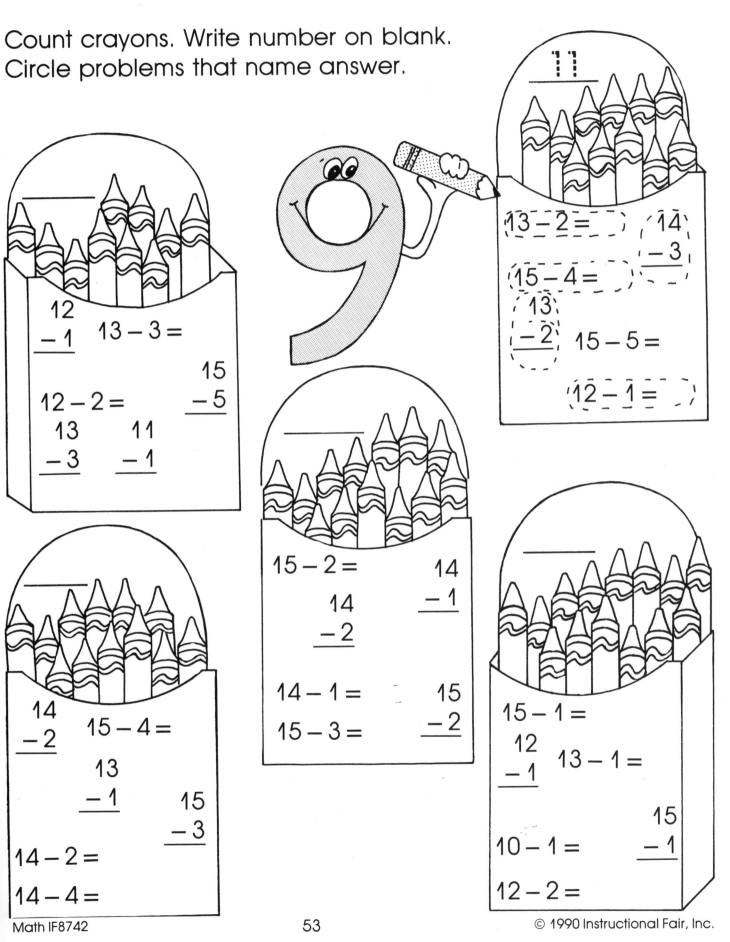

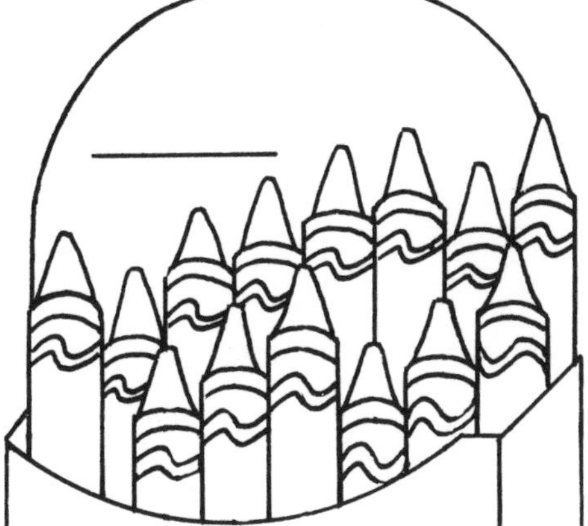

____

15 – 1 =

12 – 1

13 – 1 =

15 – 1

10 – 1 =

12 – 2 =

Commutative Property Name ______________________

Add. Use code to color truck cabs.

11—purple
12—orange
13—green
14—blue
15—red

3 + 8 = ______
8 + 3 = ______

6 + 5 = ______
5 + 6 = ______

8 + 6 = ______
6 + 8 = ______

9 + 5 = ______
5 + 9 = ______

9 + 4 = ______
4 + 9 = ______

8 + 4 = ______
4 + 8 = ______

8 + 7 = ______
7 + 8 = ______

7 + 6 = ______
6 + 7 = ______

4 + 7 = ______
7 + 4 = ______

9 + 3 = ______
3 + 9 = ______

6 + 9 = ______
9 + 6 = ______

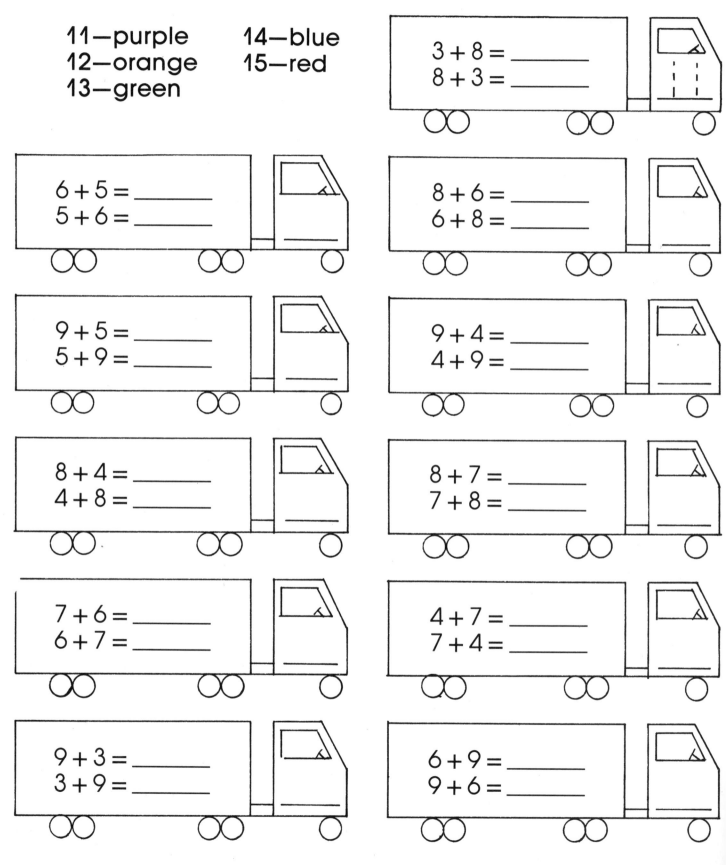

 Name ____________________

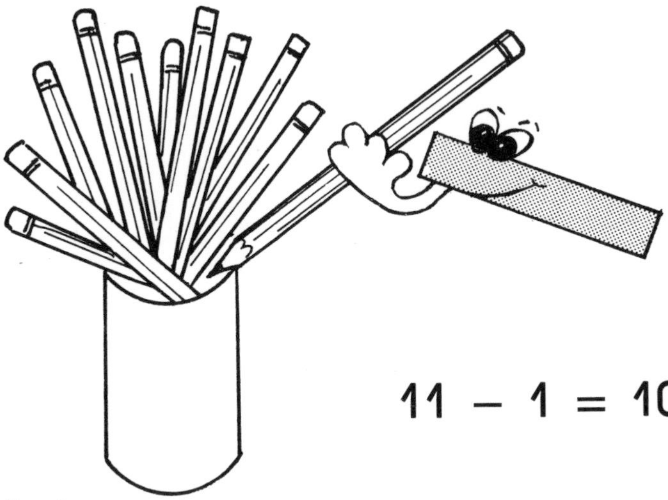

11 − 1 = 10

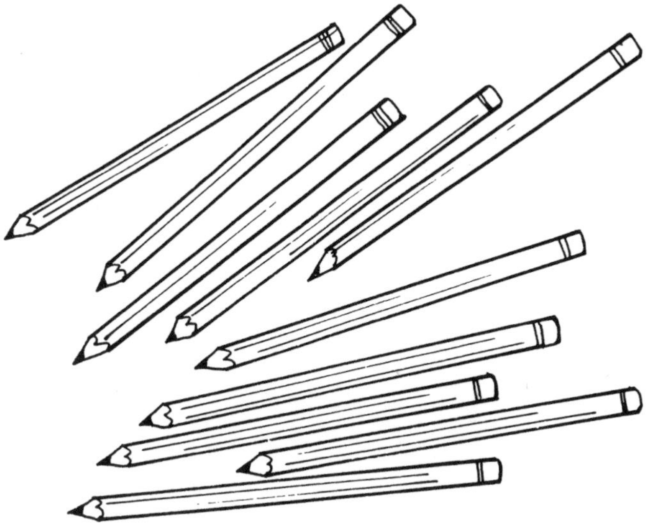

Subtract.

Use code to color crayons.

10—red
11—blue
12—green
13—yellow
14—orange
15—purple

$$\begin{array}{r} 11 \\ -\ 1 \\ \hline \end{array}$$

11 − 1 = 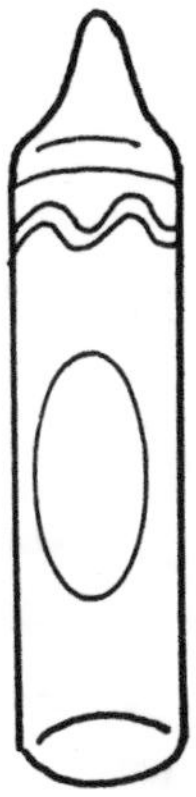

14 − 1 = 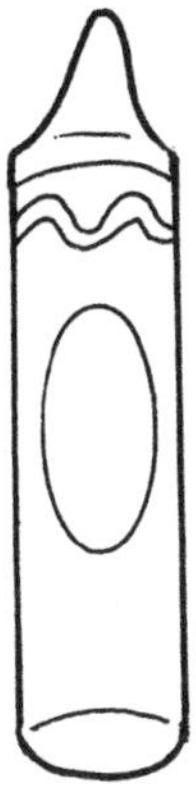

15 − 0 = 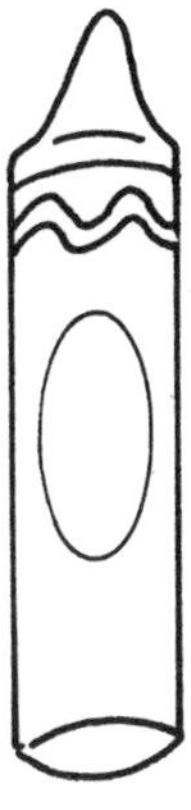

15 − 1 = 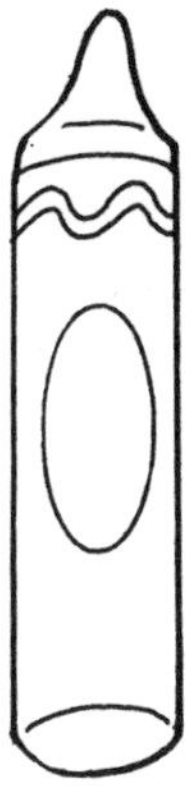

$$\begin{array}{r} 14 \\ -\ 1 \\ \hline \end{array}$$

$$\begin{array}{r} 15 \\ -\ 0 \\ \hline \end{array}$$

$$\begin{array}{r} 15 \\ -\ 1 \\ \hline \end{array}$$

13 − 3 = 

14 − 2 = 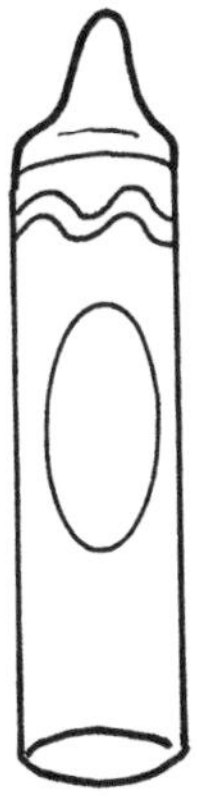

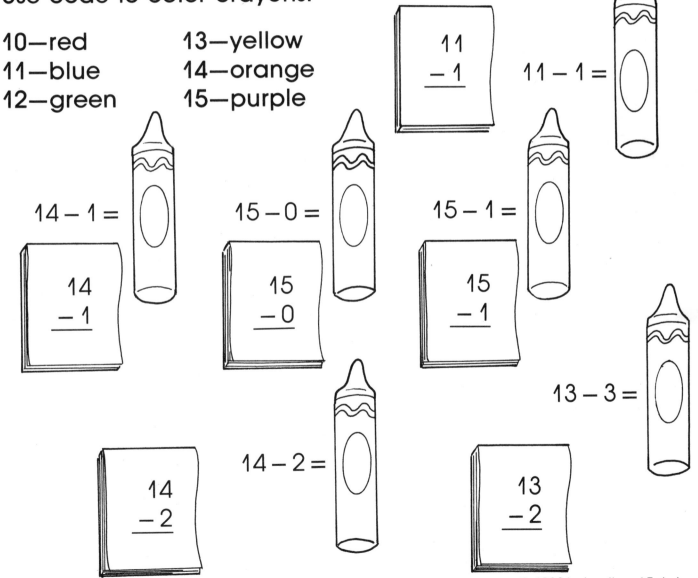

$$\begin{array}{r} 14 \\ -\ 2 \\ \hline \end{array}$$

$$\begin{array}{r} 13 \\ -\ 2 \\ \hline \end{array}$$

Addition and Subtraction Review

Name________________________

Add or subtract.
Use code to color eggs.

6—green	9—orange
7—blue	10—red
8—yellow	

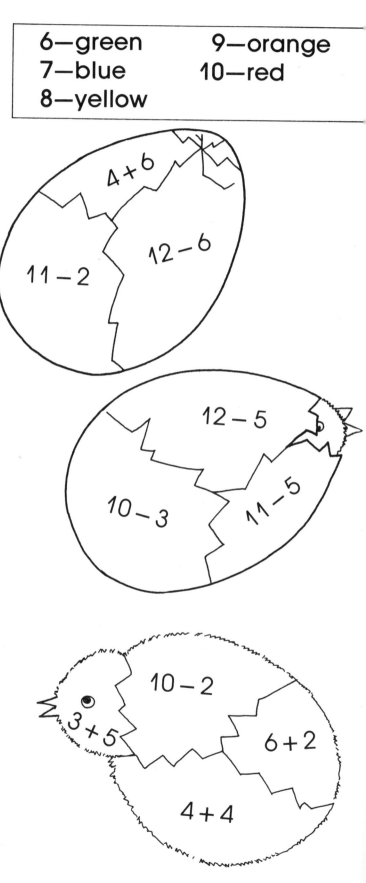

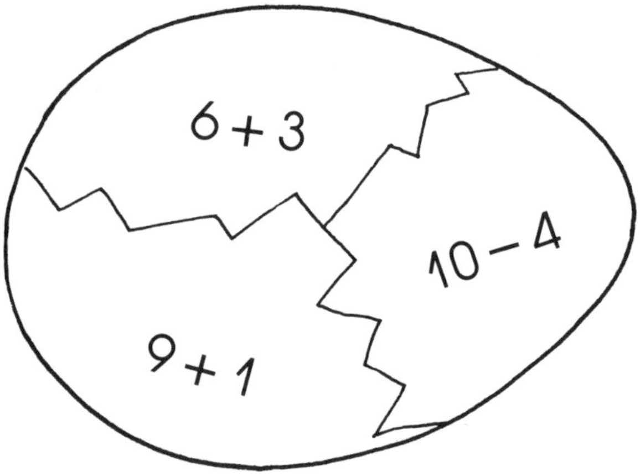

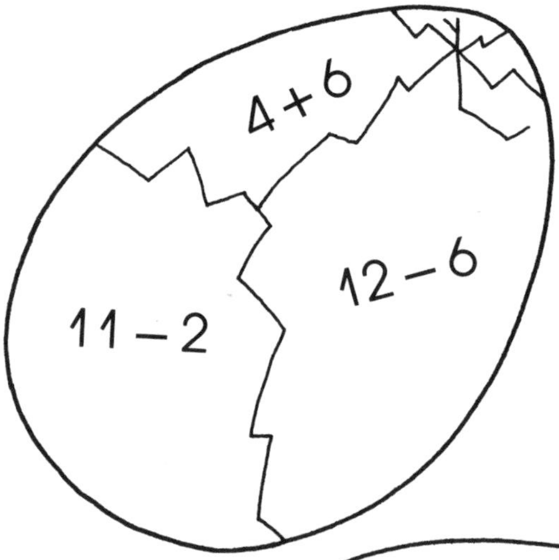

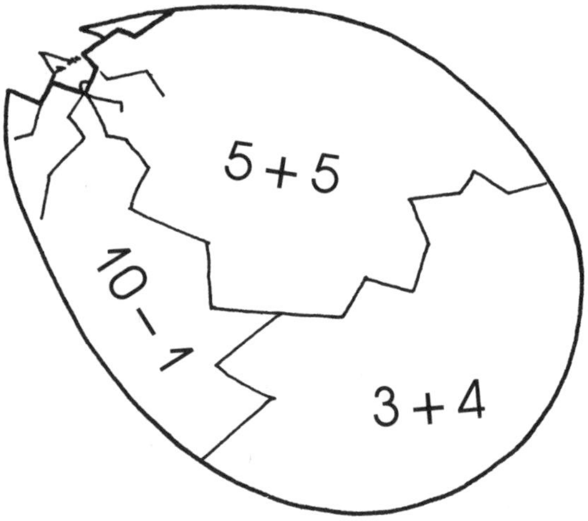

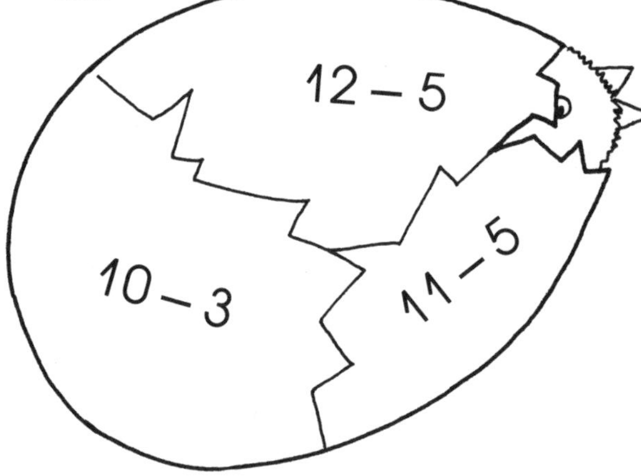

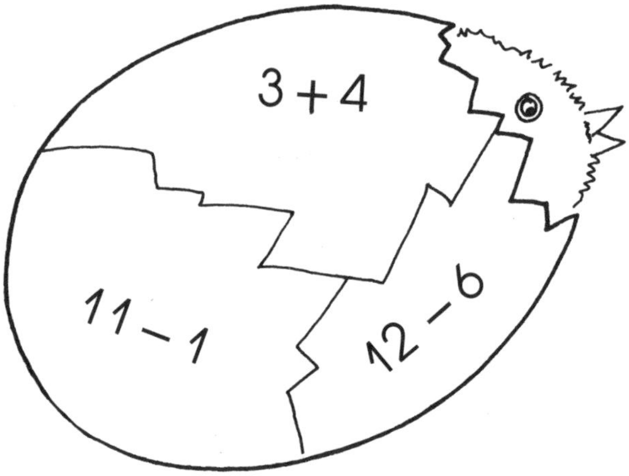

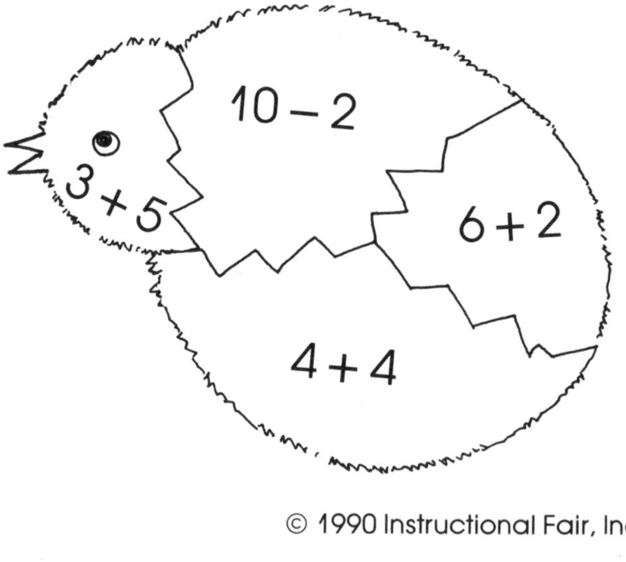

Subtraction Review

Name ______________________

Subtract. Use code to color jellybeans.

4—white
5—orange
6—red
7—blue
8—green
9—purple
10—brown
11—black
12—pink
13—yellow

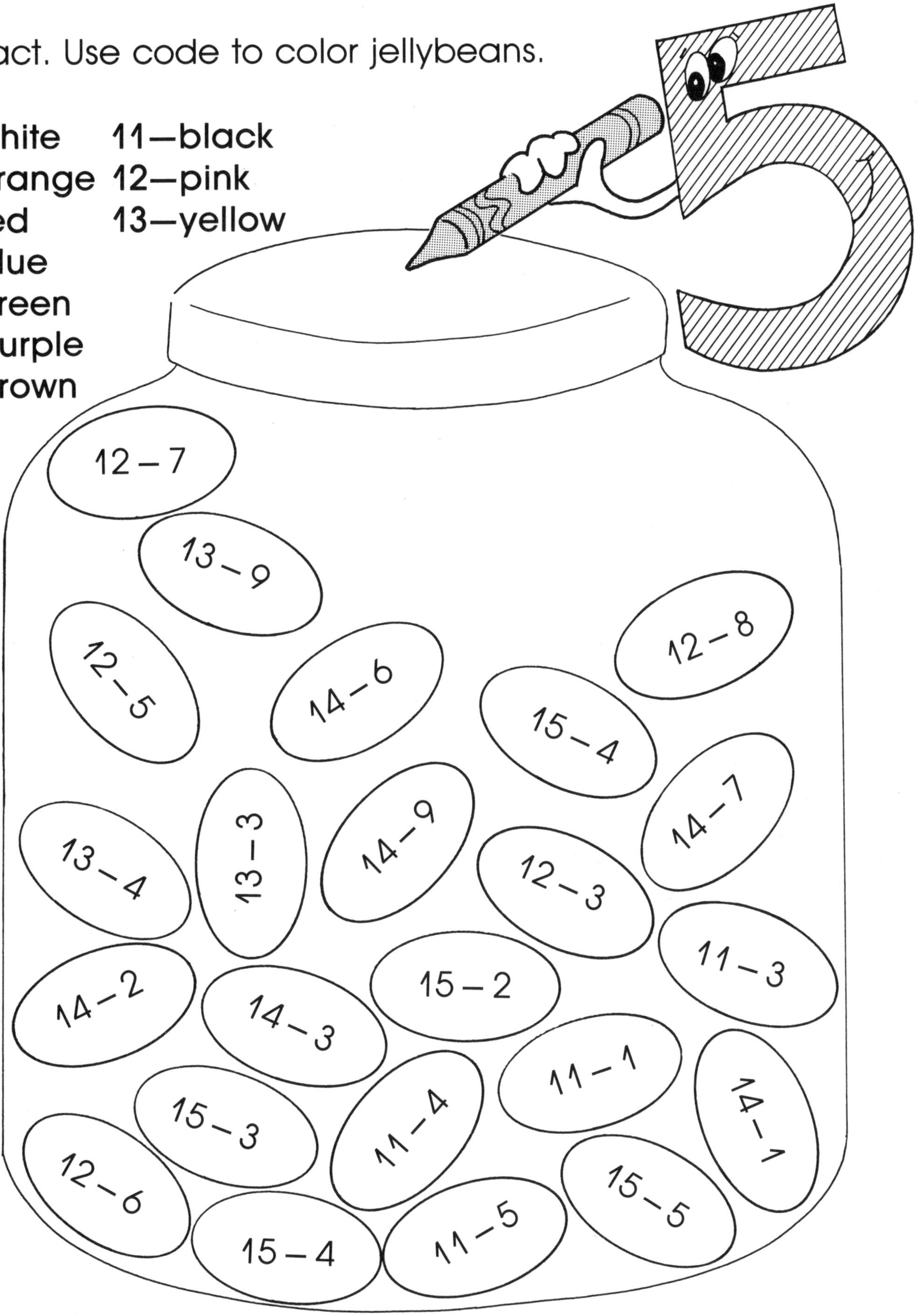
12 – 7
13 – 9
12 – 5
14 – 6
12 – 8
15 – 4
13 – 4
13 – 3
14 – 9
12 – 3
14 – 7
14 – 2
14 – 3
15 – 2
11 – 3
15 – 3
11 – 4
11 – 1
14 – 1
12 – 6
15 – 4
11 – 5
15 – 5

Subtraction Review

Name ______________________________

Join dots 1-15 in order.
Use code to color picture

7—purple	12—green
8—yellow	14—brown
9—red	15—blue
10—orange	

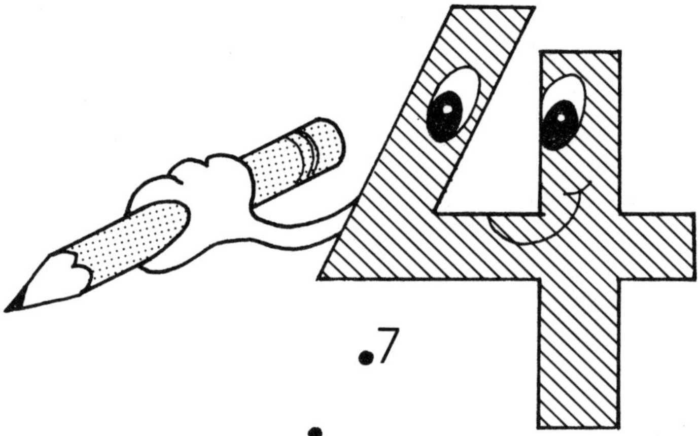

6 • 7 • 13 • 12 •

12 – 4 15 – 7 11 – 2 13 – 5

5 • 14 •

14 – 6 9 – 1 15 – 0 11 • 8 •

11 – 4 13 – 6 12 – 3

15 • 15 – 8 13 – 3 14 – 2

14 – 7 15 – 3 10 – 2 10 •

13 – 1 12 – 5 8 – 1 15 – 1 11 – 3 9 •

4 • 15 – 7

1 •

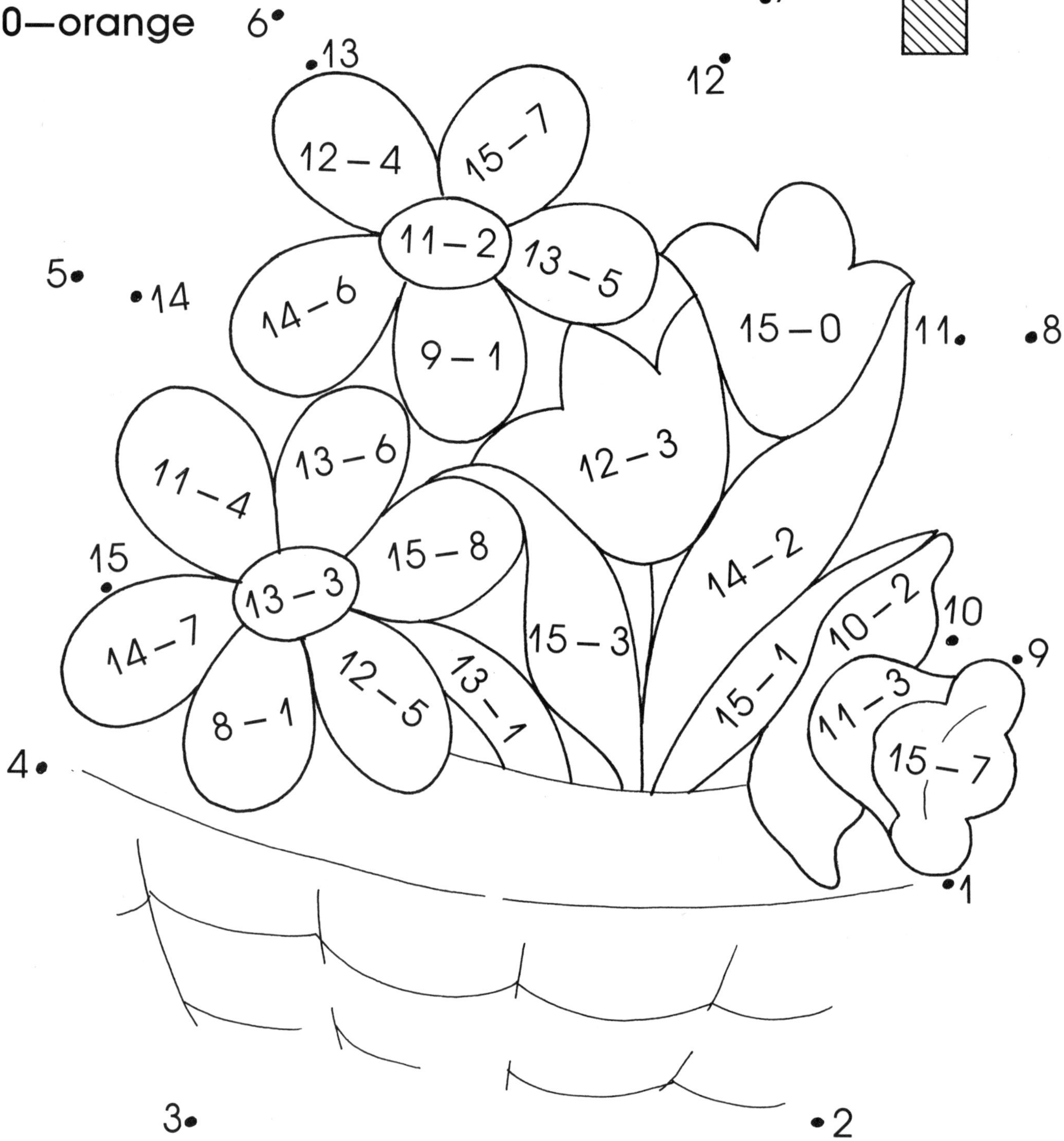

3 • 2 •

Addition and Subtraction Review

Name ______________________

Add or subtract.
Use code to color.

5—blue
6—purple
7—brown
8—green
9—yellow
10—orange
11—red
12—black

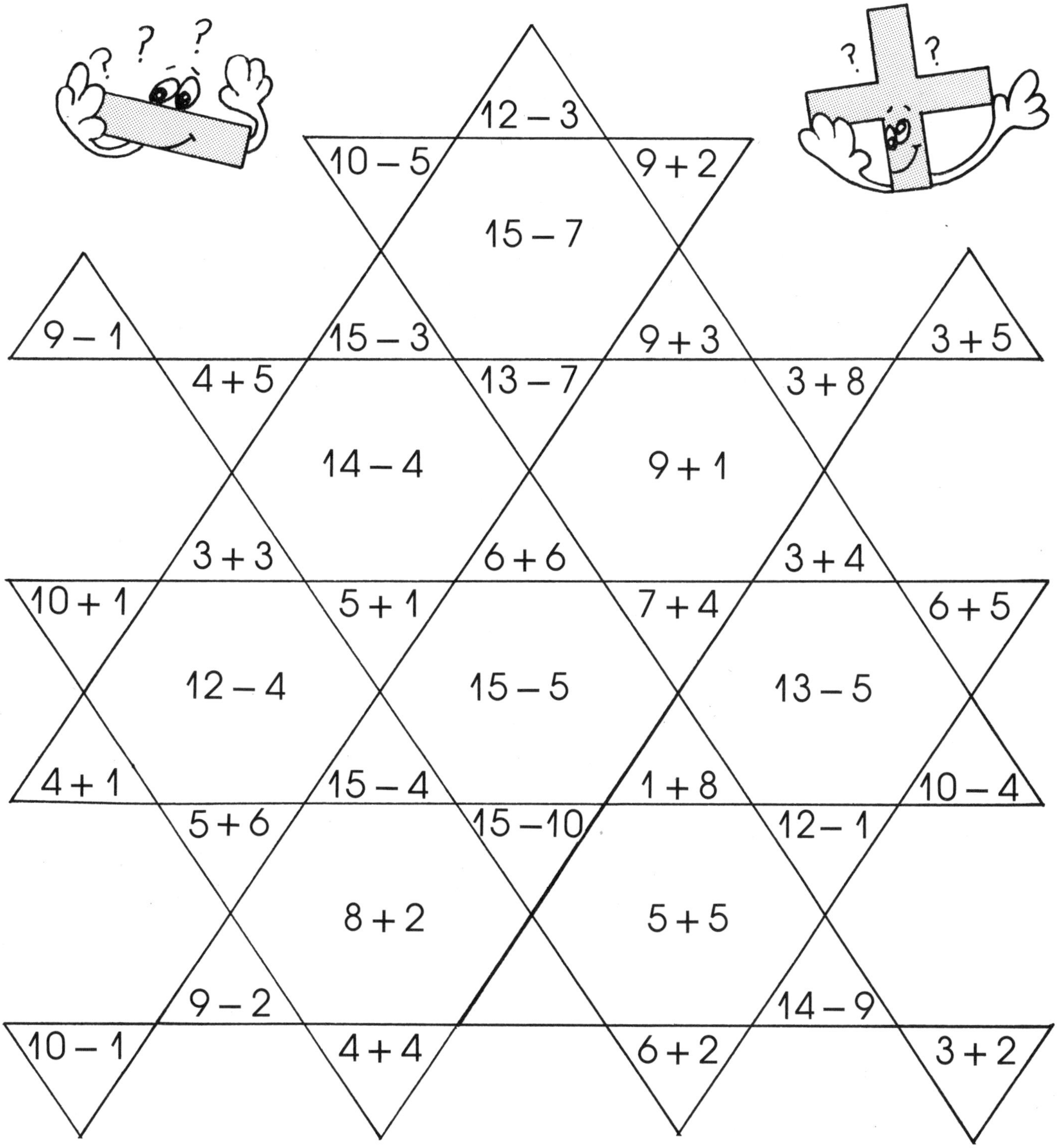

12 – 3
10 – 5
9 + 2
15 – 7
9 – 1
15 – 3
9 + 3
3 + 5
4 + 5
13 – 7
3 + 8
14 – 4
9 + 1
3 + 3
6 + 6
3 + 4
10 + 1
5 + 1
7 + 4
6 + 5
12 – 4
15 – 5
13 – 5
4 + 1
15 – 4
1 + 8
10 – 4
5 + 6
15 – 10
12 – 1
8 + 2
5 + 5
9 – 2
14 – 9
10 – 1
4 + 4
6 + 2
3 + 2

Adding 3 Digits

Name ____________________

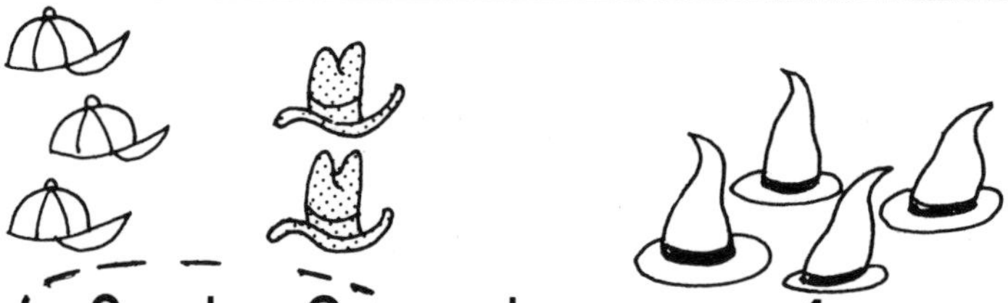

(3 + 2) + 4 = 9

5 + 4

Add.

4 + 2 + 5

(4 + 2) + 5

6 + 5 = ______

3 + 1 + 5

(3 + 1) + 5

4 + 5 = ______

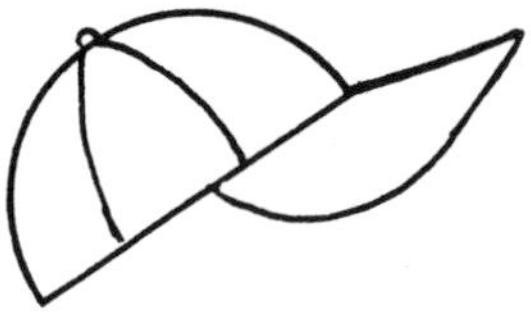

2 + 6 + 2

(2 + 6) + 2

_____ + 2 = ______

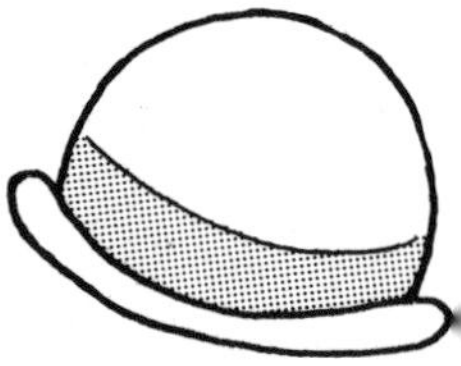

Color hats:

9—red
10—blue
11—orange
12—green
13—purple
14—yellow

3 + 4 + 6

_____ + 6 = ______

3 + 6 + 5

_____ + 5 = ______

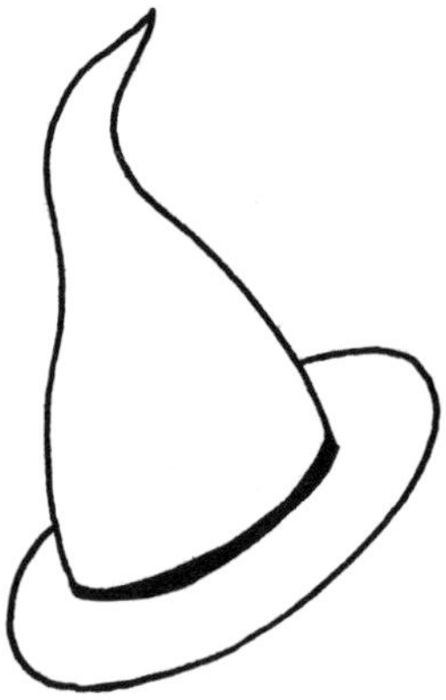

3 + 2 + 4

_____ + 4 = ______

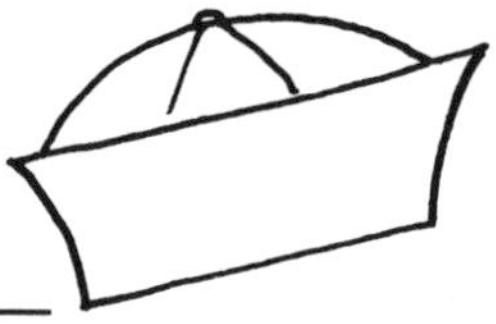

2 + 3 + 6

_____ + 6 = ______

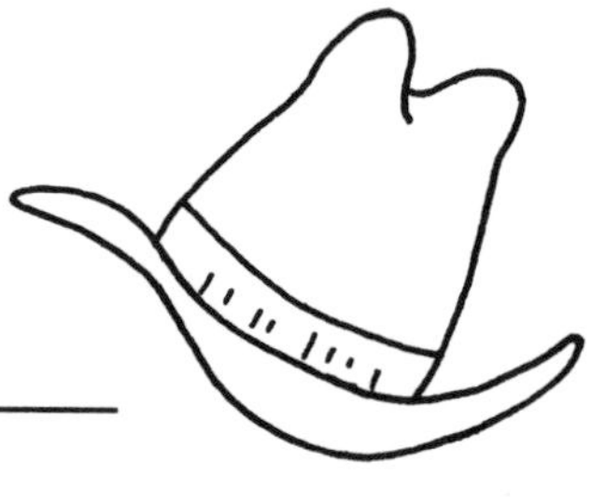

5 + 3 + 4

_____ + 4 = ______

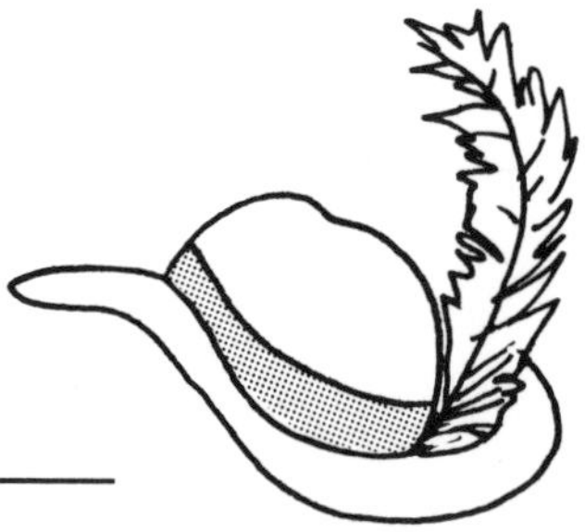

6 + 3 + 1

_____ + 1 = ______

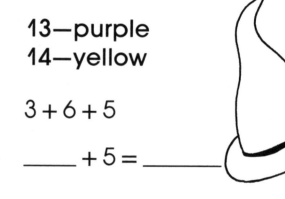

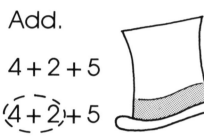

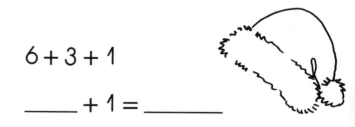

Adding 3 Digits

$$4 + 3 = 7 \qquad 7 + 1 = 8$$

$4 + 3 + 1$	$\begin{array}{r} 4 \\ 3 \\ +1 \\ \hline \end{array}$	$9 + 1 + 2$	$\begin{array}{r} 9 \\ 1 \\ +2 \\ \hline \end{array}$
___ $+ 1 =$ ___		___ $+ 2 =$ ___	
$5 + 1 + 2$	$\begin{array}{r} 5 \\ 1 \\ +2 \\ \hline \end{array}$	$6 + 7 + 2$	$\begin{array}{r} 6 \\ 7 \\ +2 \\ \hline \end{array}$
___ $+ 2 =$ ___		___ $+ 2 =$ ___	
$1 + 3 + 9$	$\begin{array}{r} 1 \\ 3 \\ +9 \\ \hline \end{array}$	$5 + 6 + 1$	$\begin{array}{r} 5 \\ 6 \\ +1 \\ \hline \end{array}$
___ $+ 9 =$ ___		___ $+ 1 =$ ___	
$1 + 3 + 4$	$\begin{array}{r} 1 \\ 3 \\ +4 \\ \hline \end{array}$	$2 + 9 + 1$	$\begin{array}{r} 2 \\ 9 \\ +1 \\ \hline \end{array}$
___ $+ 4 =$ ___		___ $+ 1 =$ ___	

$\begin{array}{r} 3 \\ 4 \\ +7 \\ \hline \end{array}$	$\begin{array}{r} 5 \\ 3 \\ +1 \\ \hline \end{array}$	$\begin{array}{r} 4 \\ 4 \\ +1 \\ \hline \end{array}$	$\begin{array}{r} 2 \\ 3 \\ +3 \\ \hline \end{array}$	$\begin{array}{r} 3 \\ 5 \\ +1 \\ \hline \end{array}$
$\begin{array}{r} 4 \\ 1 \\ +2 \\ \hline \end{array}$	$\begin{array}{r} 6 \\ 1 \\ +3 \\ \hline \end{array}$	$\begin{array}{r} 7 \\ 1 \\ +5 \\ \hline \end{array}$	$\begin{array}{r} 8 \\ 1 \\ +2 \\ \hline \end{array}$	$\begin{array}{r} 9 \\ 1 \\ +1 \\ \hline \end{array}$

Adding 3 Digits

Name ______________________

Add the 3 numbers.

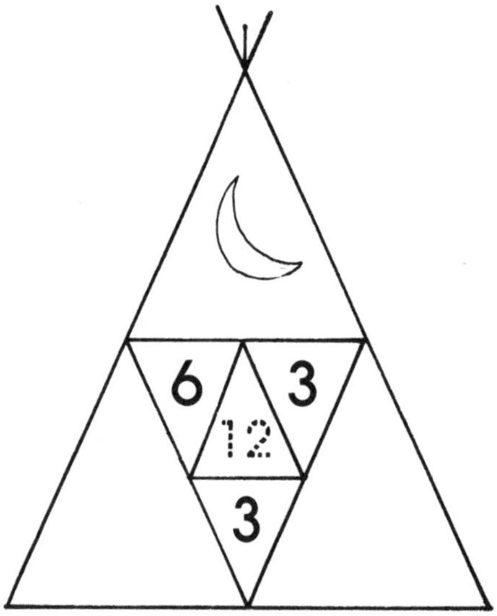

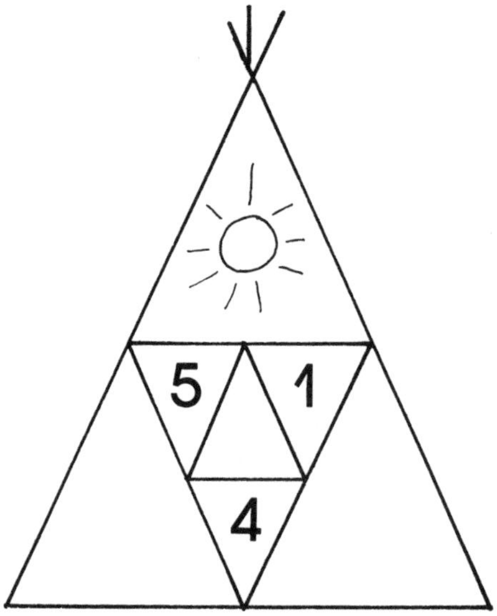

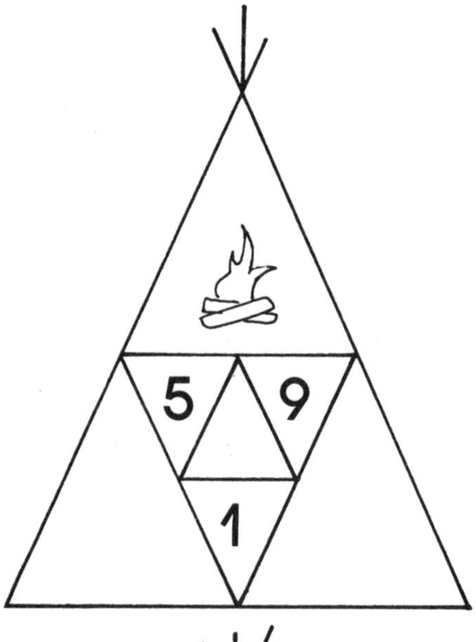

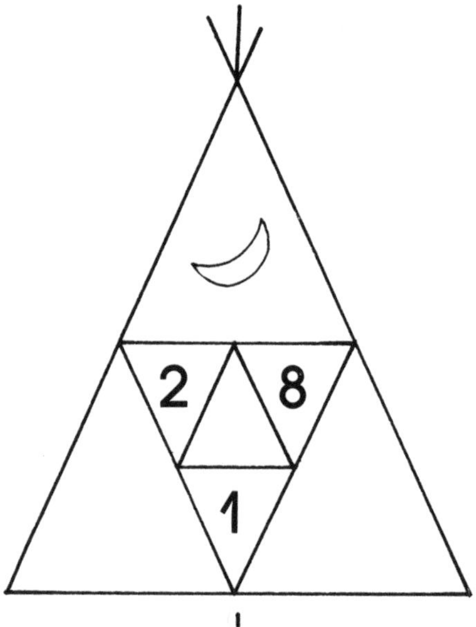

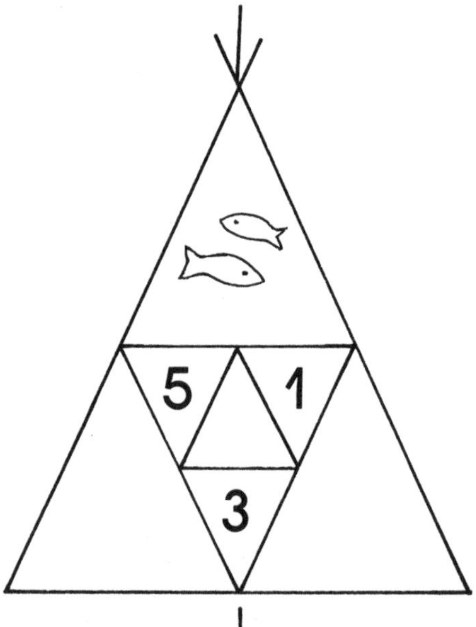

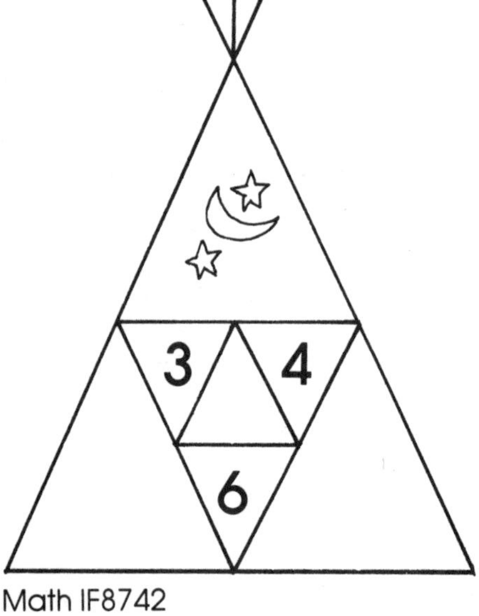

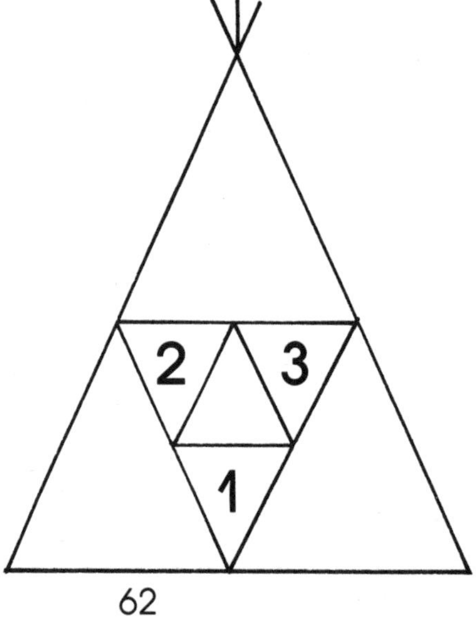

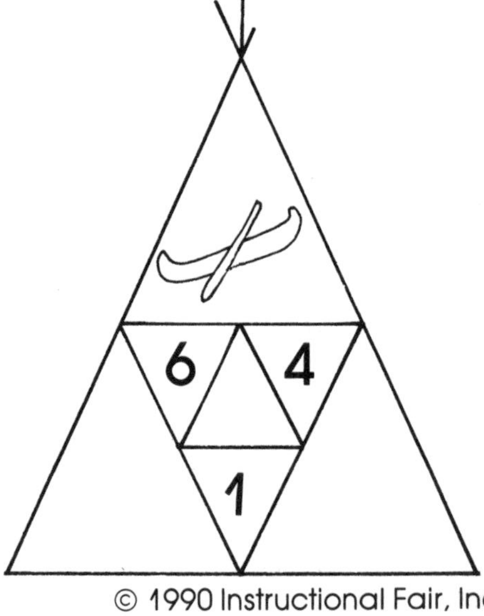

Addition and Subtraction Review

Name ______________________

1	2	3	4	5	6	7	8	9	10	11	12	13	14	15
H	I	C	A	N	T	S	O	B	D	M	G	Y	R	U

Work problems. Use code for secret message.

1		1	6	2		14	5	15		4
+ 1		+ 2	− 2	+ 3		− 10	+ 5	− 5		− 2
☐		☐	☐	☐		☐	☐	☐ .		☐

5	2	10		14	9	6	11	15	3	14	3
− 2	+ 2	− 5		− 7	+ 6	+ 3	− 5	− 1	+ 1	− 11	+ 3
☐	☐	☐		☐	☐	☐	☐	☐	☐	☐	☐ .

5		10	13	4		6	14		13	6	3	9
− 3		− 7	− 9	+ 1		+ 4	− 6		− 2	+ 2	+ 4	− 3
☐		☐	☐	☐		☐	☐		☐	☐	☐	☐

11	4	10	4	15	9	6	6
− 7	+ 1	+ 3	+ 2	− 14	− 7	− 1	+ 6
☐	☐	☐	☐	☐	☐	☐	☐ !

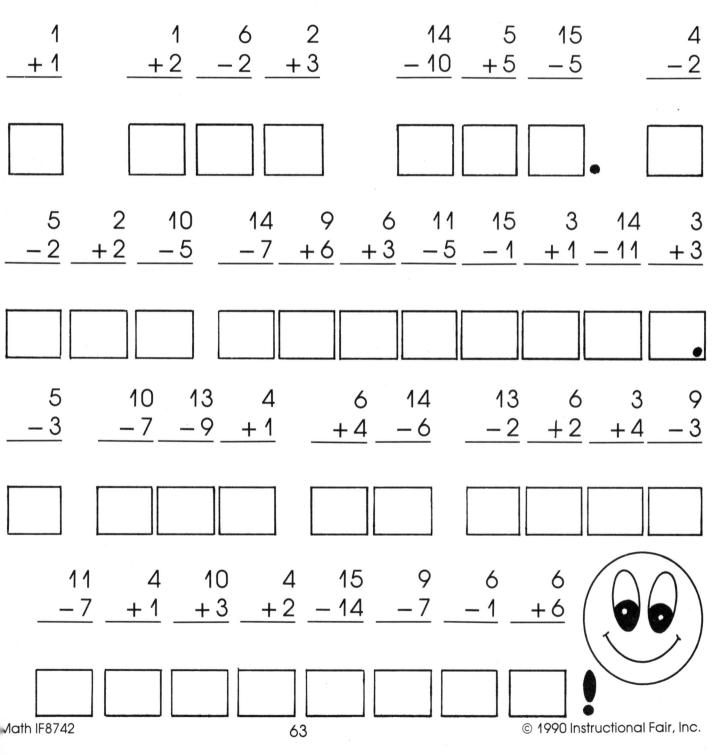

Number Word Review

Name ______________________

Add or subtract.
Write number words of answers in puzzle.

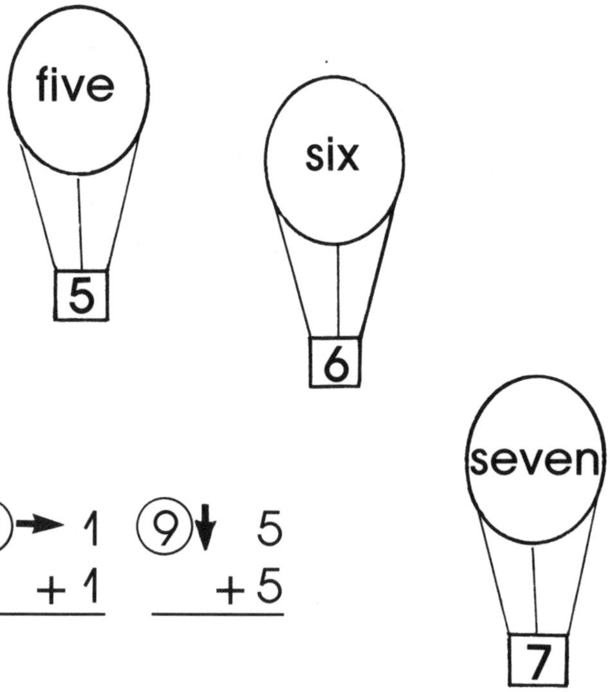

1. $11 - 5 =$ ___
2. $4 + 1 =$ ___
3. $3 + 5 =$ ___
4. $13 - 10 =$ ___
5. $9 - 5 =$ ___
6. $14 - 7 =$ ___
7. $11 - 10 =$ ___
8. $15 - 6 =$ ___
9. → $1 + 1 =$ ___
9. ↓ $5 + 5 =$ ___

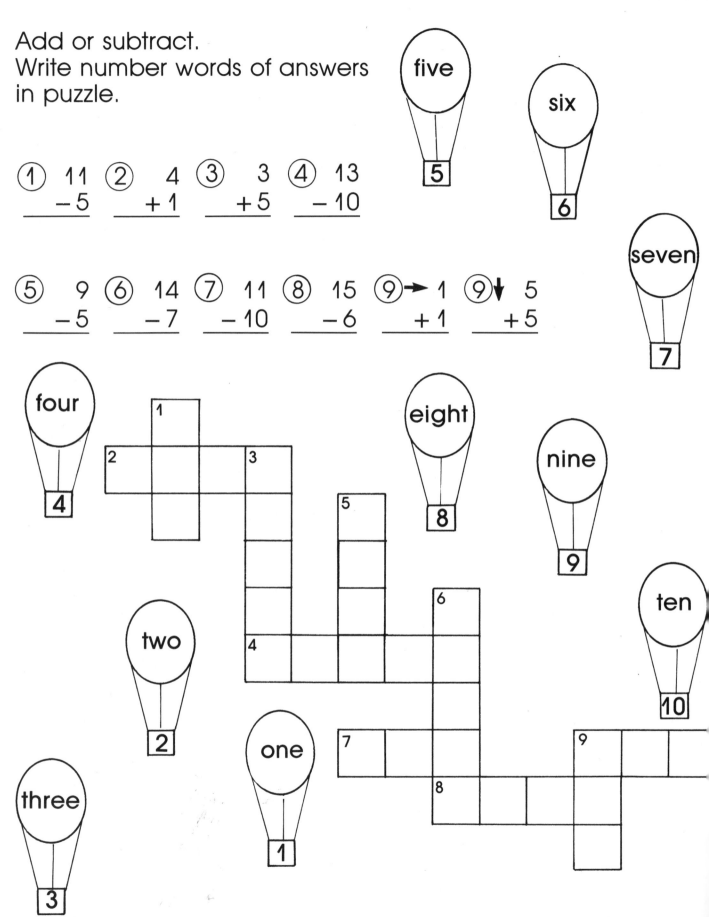

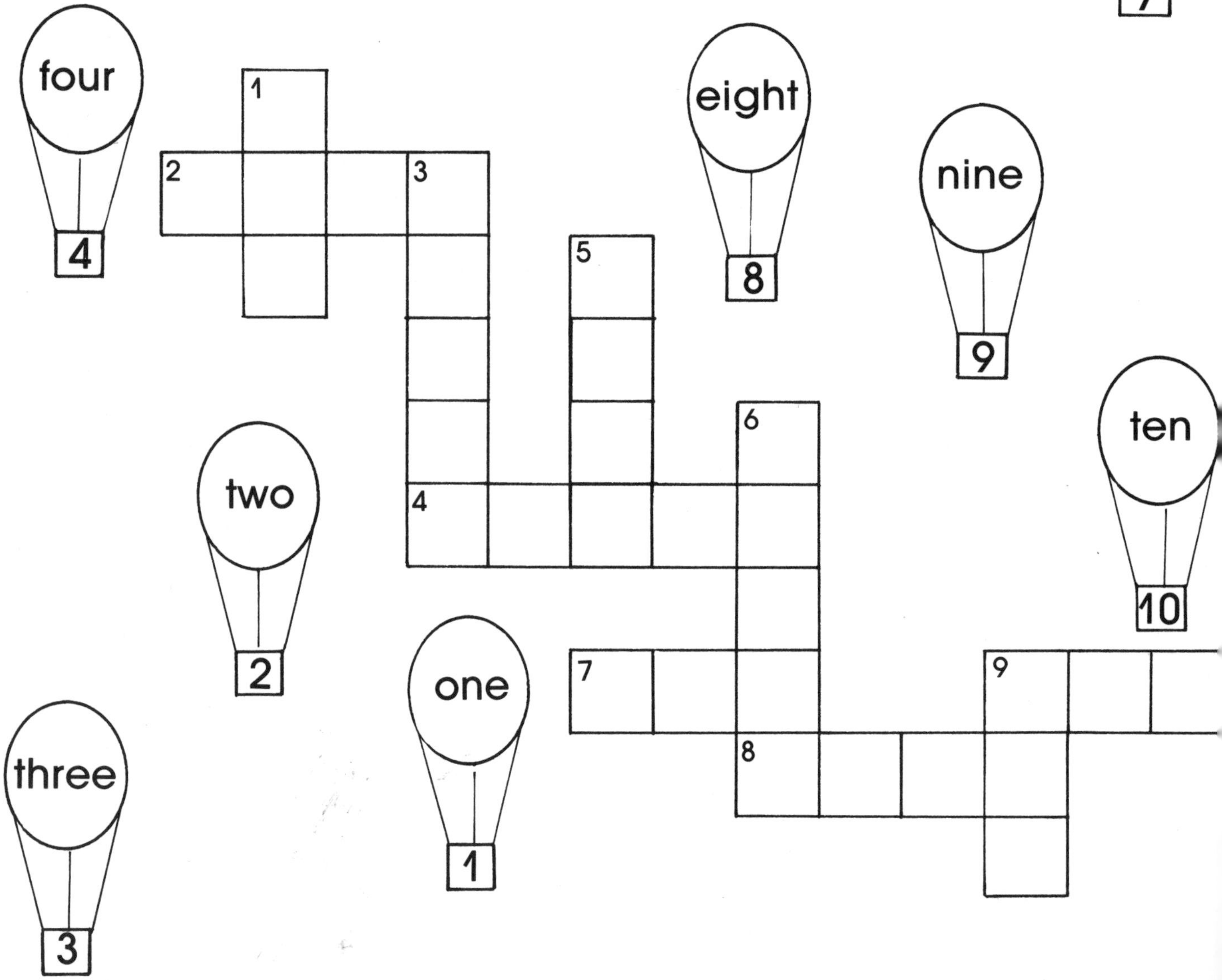

Addition and Subtraction Review

Name ______________________

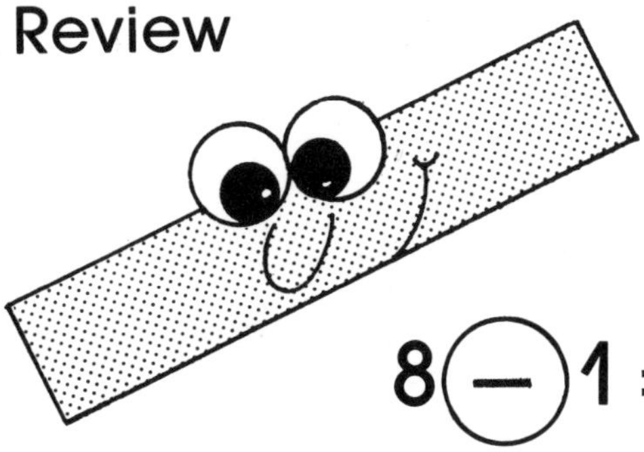

8 (−) 1 = 7

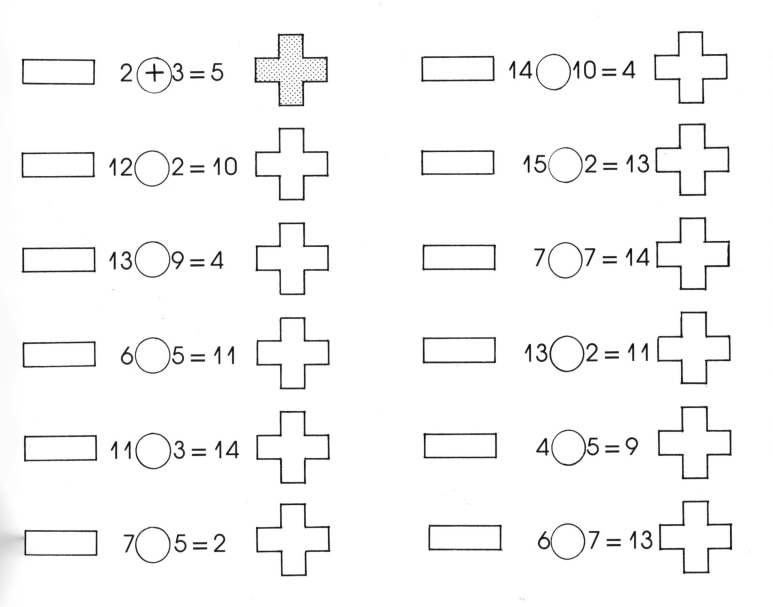

8 (+) 1 = 9

Write + or − in circle.
Color the correct symbol for each problem. The first one has been done for you.

2 (+) 3 = 5	14 ◯ 10 = 4
12 ◯ 2 = 10	15 ◯ 2 = 13
13 ◯ 9 = 4	7 ◯ 7 = 14
6 ◯ 5 = 11	13 ◯ 2 = 11
11 ◯ 3 = 14	4 ◯ 5 = 9
7 ◯ 5 = 2	6 ◯ 7 = 13

Ordinal Number Review

Name ______________________

Color the **first** animal orange.
Draw a blue **X** under the **fourth** animal.
Draw a black □ around the **fifth** animal.
Color the **sixth** animal red with blue spots.
Color the **fourth** animal green.
Draw a yellow hat on the **first** animal.
Color the **fifth** animal purple.
Draw brown tennis shoes on the **second** animal.
Draw a blue ○ around the **sixth** animal.
Color the **second** animal yellow.
Color the **third** animal blue.

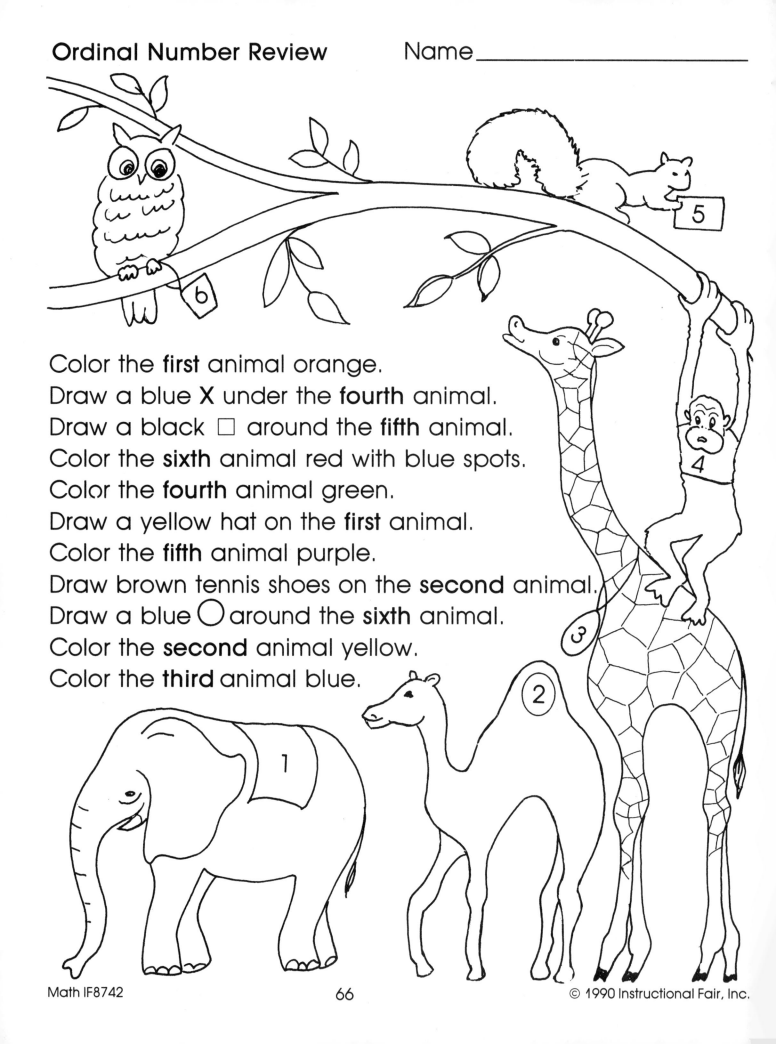

Addition and Subtraction Review

Name ____________________

Work problems.
Join dots from smallest number to largest number.
Watch out! Some numbers are missing!

15
− 14

5
+ 9

10
+ 5

12
− 10

2
+ 2

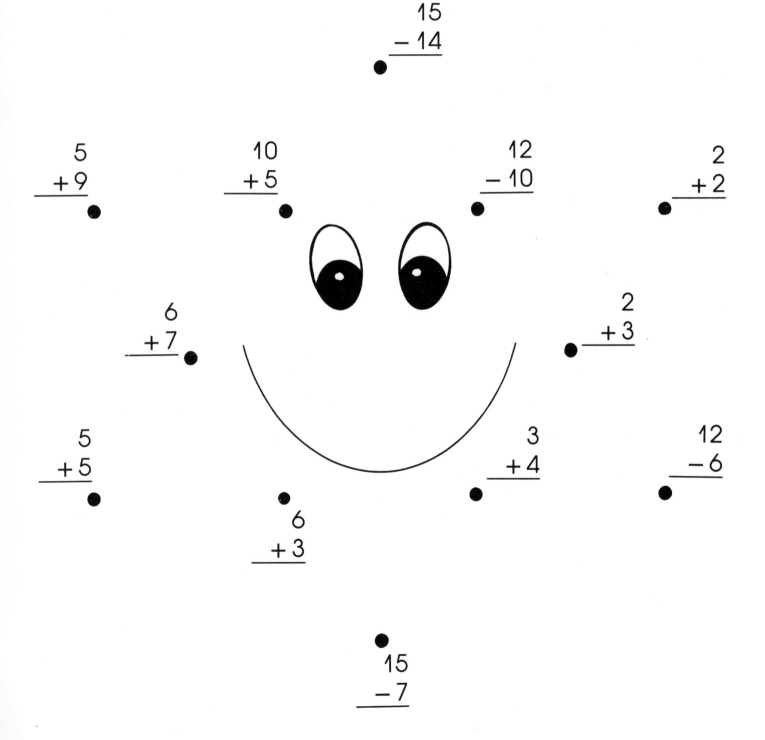

6
+ 7

2
+ 3

5
+ 5

3
+ 4

12
− 6

6
+ 3

15
− 7

Greater Than; Less Than Review

Name ____________________

greater than

less than

*Think of the signs always being open toward the larger number.

Write each problem.

___3___ > ___2___ ______ < ______ ______ > ______

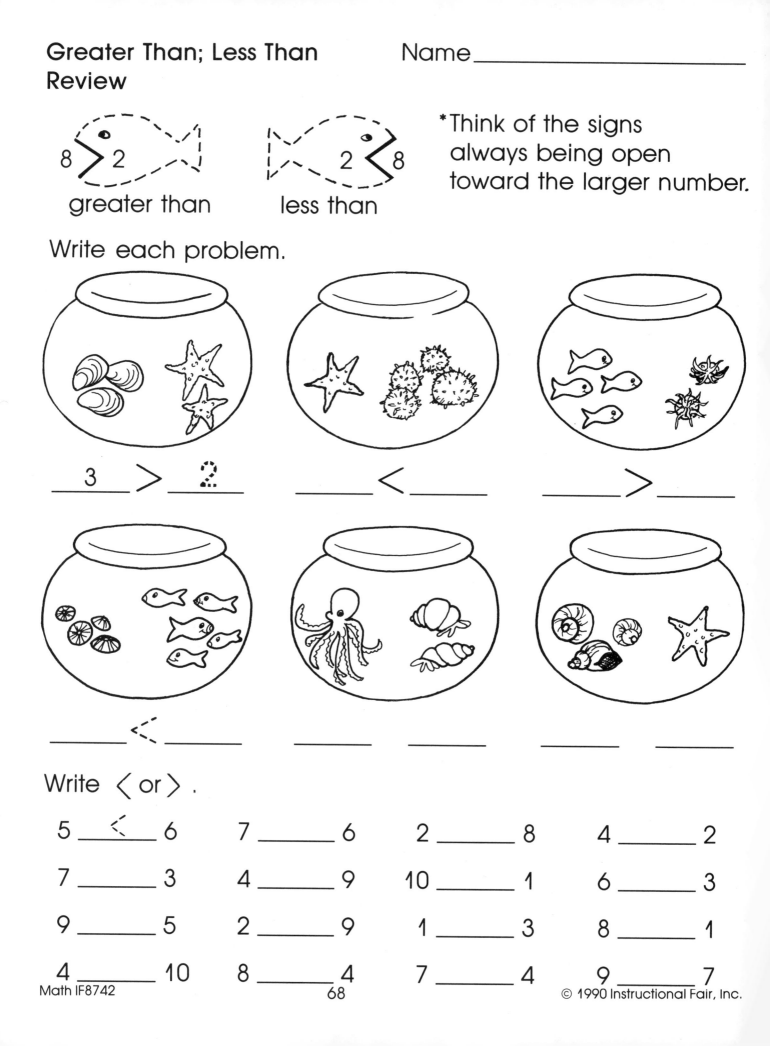

______ < ______ ______ ______ ______ ______

Write < or > .

5 ___<___ 6	7 ______ 6	2 ______ 8	4 ______ 2
7 ______ 3	4 ______ 9	10 ______ 1	6 ______ 3
9 ______ 5	2 ______ 9	1 ______ 3	8 ______ 1
4 ______ 10	8 ______ 4	7 ______ 4	9 ______ 7

Addition and Subtraction Review

Name ____________________

Work problems to win the race.

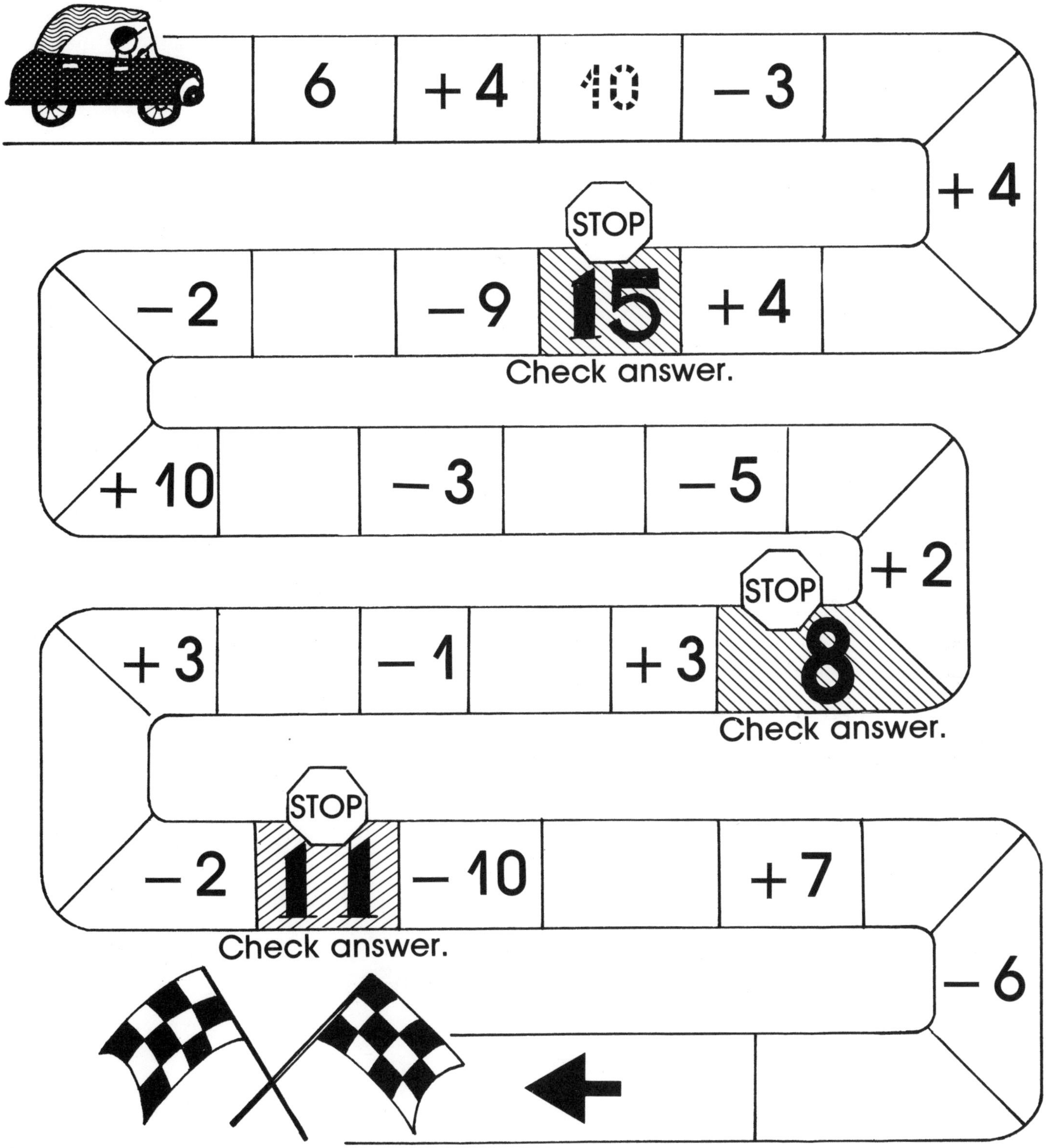

Name____________________

hundreds 3 | tens 4 | ones 5

345

hundred	tens	ones		
8	7	6	=	8 hundreds 7 tens 6 ones
3	2	9	=	___ hundreds ___ ones ___ tens
7	4	5	=	___ ones ___ hundreds ___ tens
1	9	2	=	___ tens ___ ones ___ hundreds
3	8	4	=	___ hundreds ___ tens ___ ones
5	___	___	=	___ hundreds 6 tens 7 ones
___	___	___	=	2 hundreds 1 ten 3 ones
___	4	___	=	4 hundreds ___ tens 1 one
___	___	6	=	8 hundreds 2 tens ___ ones

Name________________________

Connect dots that number 201-205, 526-533, 791-798, 662-670.

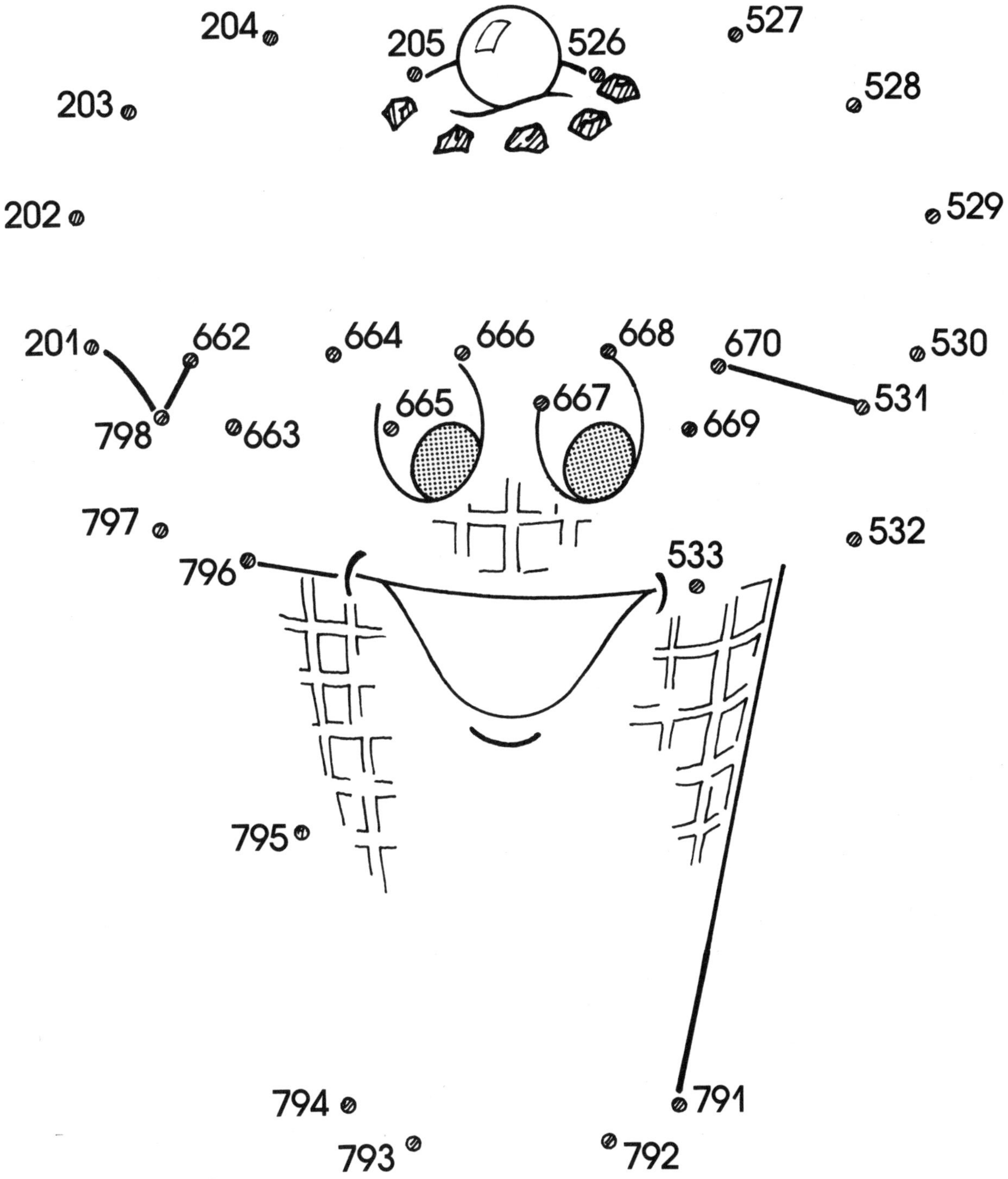

Counting by Twos, Fives and Tens

Name_____

Circle numbers counting by twos.

| 1, ②, 3, 4, 5, 6, 7, |
| 8, 9, 10, 11, 12, 13, |
| 14, 15, 16, 17, 18, 19, |
| 20, 21, 22, 23, 24 |

Count by 2's.

2 , 4 , ___ , ___ , ___ , ___ , ___ , ___ , ___ , ___

Put △ around numbers counting by fives.

| 1, 2, 3, 4, △5△ 6, 7, 8, 9, |
| 10, 11, 12, 13, 14, 15, 16, |
| 17, 18, 19, 20, 21, 22, |
| 23, 24, 25, 26, 27, |
| 28, 29, 30, 31, 32, 33, |
| 34, 35, 36, 37, 38, 39, 40 |

Count by 5's.

5 , 10 , ___ , ___ , ___ , ___ , ___ , ___ , ___

Put ☐ around numbers counting by 10's.

| 1, 2, 3, 4, 5, 6, 7, 8, 9, [10,] 11, |
| 12, 13, 14, 15, 16, 17, 18, 19, |
| 20, 21, 22, 23, 24, 25, 26, |
| 27, 28, 29, 30, 31, 32, 33 |

Count by 10's.

10 , ___ , ___ , ___ , ___ , ___ , ___ , ___

Counting by Twos, Fives and Tens

Name____________________

Finish counting.
Start with:

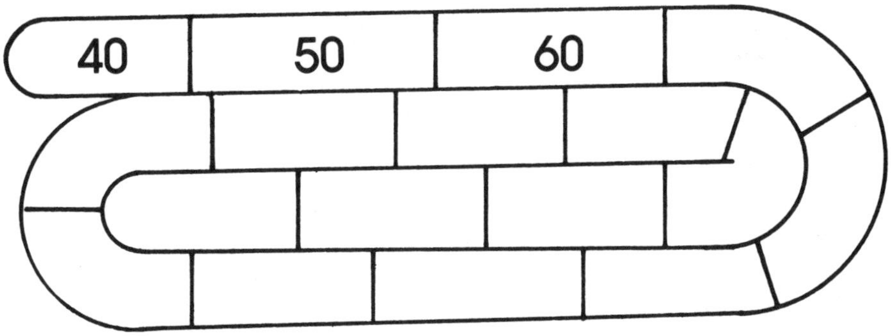

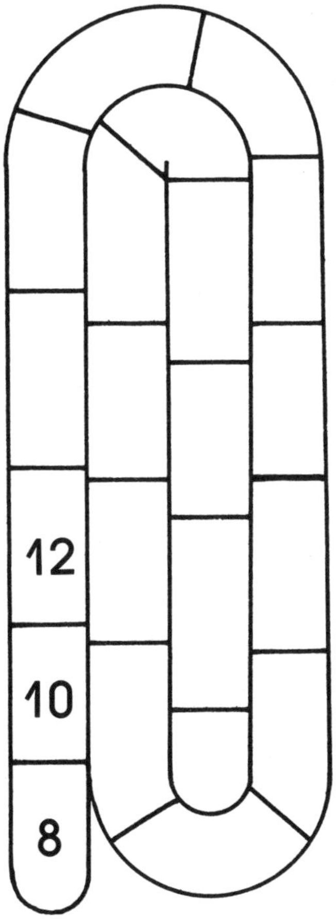

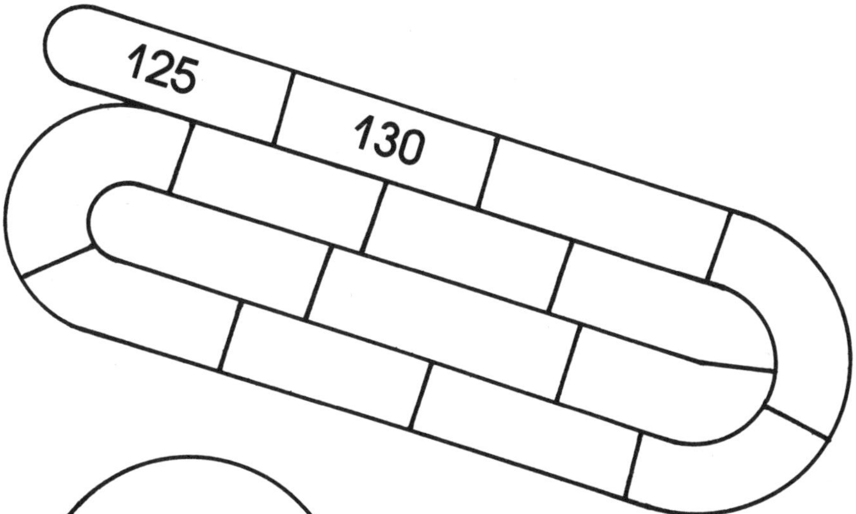

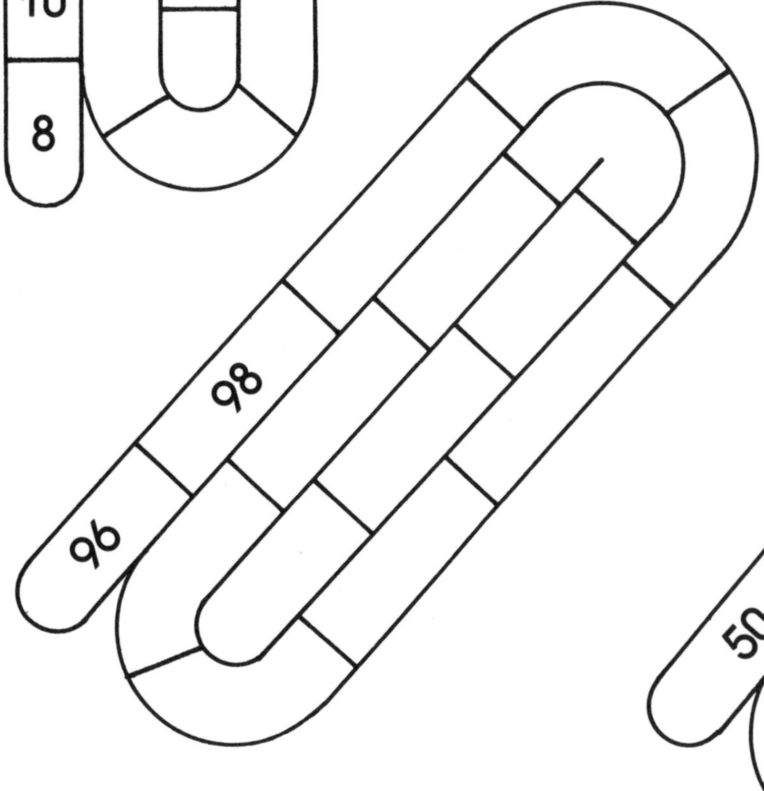

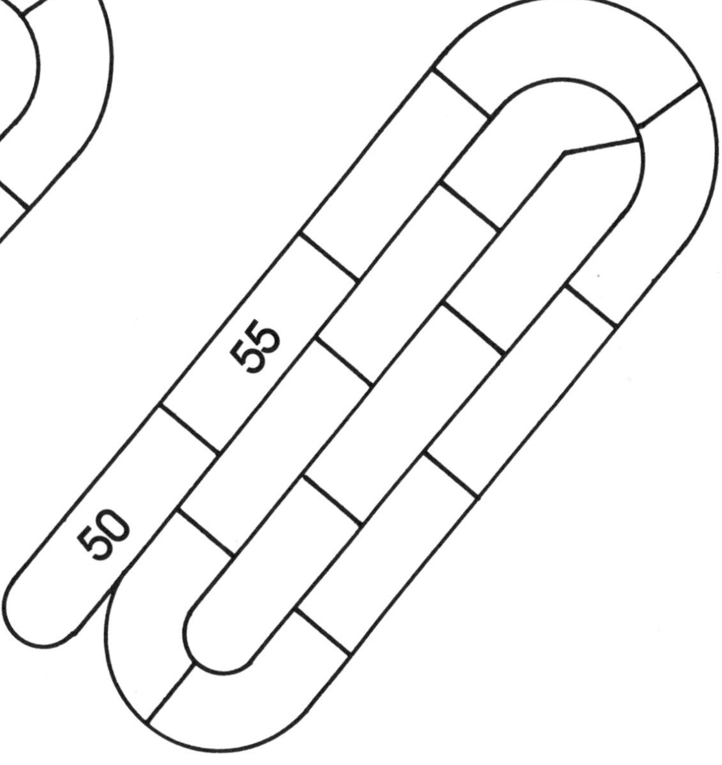

Counting by Twos, Fives and Tens

Name_______________

Number of 's found.  = 5

 = 20

 = ______

 = ______

Number of 's found.  = 10

 = ______

 = ______

 = ______

Number of 's found.  = 2

 = ______

 = ______

 = ______

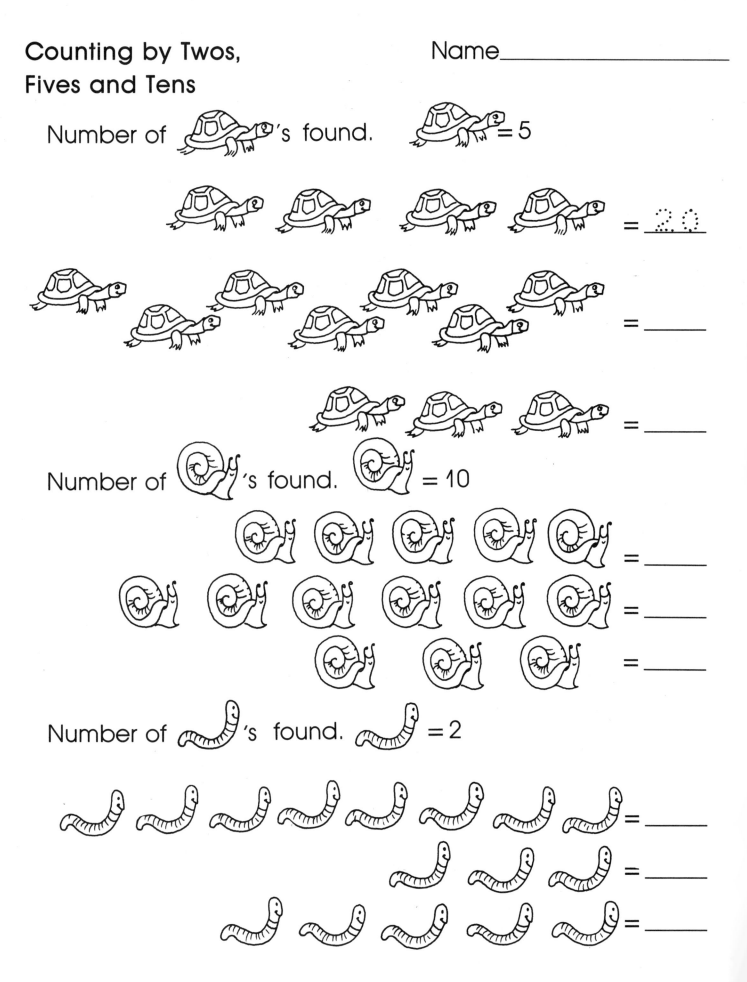

Two-Digit Addition

Name________________________

Add ones first. $4+2=6$

tens	ones
2	4
+3	2
	6

Then, add tens. $2+3=5$

tens	ones
2	4
+3	2
5	6

tens	ones
1	7
+2	1

tens	ones
3	4
+5	2

tens	ones
	5
+6	2

tens	ones
	6
+5	2

tens	ones
2	0
+4	0

tens	ones
5	1
+	8

tens	ones
7	2
+1	7

tens	ones
4	7
+2	1

tens	ones
2	5
+6	2

tens	ones
4	2
+2	4

tens	ones
8	3
+1	4

tens	ones
3	2
+2	5

tens	ones
4	4
+3	1

tens	ones
	8
+3	1

tens	ones
6	2
+1	7

tens	ones
8	2
+	7

Two-Digit Addition

Name____________________

Remember to add ones first. Then, add tens.

tens	ones
3	1
+2	2

tens	ones
	5
+6	2

tens	ones
3	5
+2	3

tens	ones
4	0
+5	0

tens	ones
5	0
+1	9

tens	ones
2	7
+	2

tens	ones
6	0
+2	8

tens	ones
5	2
+2	5

tens	ones
2	7
+6	0

tens	ones
6	3
+2	1

tens	ones
5	1
+3	1

tens	ones
4	5
+3	1

tens	ones
4	4
+3	5

tens	ones
2	4
+3	2

tens	ones
6	5
+1	1

tens	ones
7	3
+1	4

tens	ones
7	3
+	6

Two-Digit Addition

Name______________________________

Add ones first.
6 + 6 = 12

REGROUP

12 = 1 ten and 2 ones

tens	ones
1	
7	6
+	6
	2

tens	ones
1	
7	6
+	6
8	2

---

tens	ones
1	
2	4
+	7
	1

tens	ones
1	
	8
+ 3	5
	3

tens	ones
	9
+ 4	3

tens	ones
5	4
+	7

tens	ones
6	3
+	8

tens	ones
5	4
+	7

tens	ones
	5
+ 4	9

tens	ones
8	8
+	5

tens	ones
7	2
+	8

tens	ones
	7
+ 2	6

tens	ones
5	4
+	7

tens	ones
2	6
+	9

tens	ones
	9
+ 4	4

tens	ones
7	2
+	9

tens	ones
6	5
+	6

tens	ones
6	3
+	7

Two-Digit Addition

Add ones first.
8 + 5 = 13

REGROUP

13 = 1 ten and 3 ones
Then, add tens.

tens	ones
3	8
+ 2	5
	3

tens	ones
3	8
+ 2	5
6	3

---

tens	ones
2	9
+ 3	4
	3

tens	ones
5	5
+ 2	8

tens	ones
2	5
+ 4	6

tens	ones
4	5
+ 2	5

tens	ones
6	7
+ 1	3

tens	ones
7	4
+ 1	8

tens	ones
3	2
+ 4	8

tens	ones
3	7
+ 1	6

tens	ones
3	4
+ 2	9

tens	ones
5	1
+ 2	9

tens	ones
6	2
+ 2	9

tens	ones
6	6
+ 2	5

tens	ones
5	3
+ 2	7

tens	ones
4	6
+ 2	5

tens	ones
2	8
+ 1	7

tens	ones
7	3
+ 1	9

Two-Digit Addition

Name_____

T	N	O	I	G	A	E	L	H	S
61	53	92	44	65	31	76	84	52	80

Why did the turtle cross the road?

```
  45        48                  28        57        38
+ 16      + 44               + 37      + 19      + 23
----      ----               ----      ----      ----
  61
  [T]      [ ]                 [ ]       [ ]       [ ]
```

```
  59        59                  24        36        49
+  2      + 33               + 37      + 16      + 27
----      ----               ----      ----      ----

  [ ]      [ ]                 [ ]       [ ]       [ ]
```

```
  51        29        38        29        38
+ 29      + 23      + 38      + 55      + 46
----      ----      ----      ----      ----

  [ ]      [ ]       [ ]       [ ]       [ ]
```

```
  36        36        22        33        18        67        19
+ 44      + 25      +  9      + 28      + 26      + 25      + 34
----      ----      ----      ----      ----      ----      ----

  [ ]      [ ]       [ ]       [ ]       [ ]       [ ]       [ ]  !
```

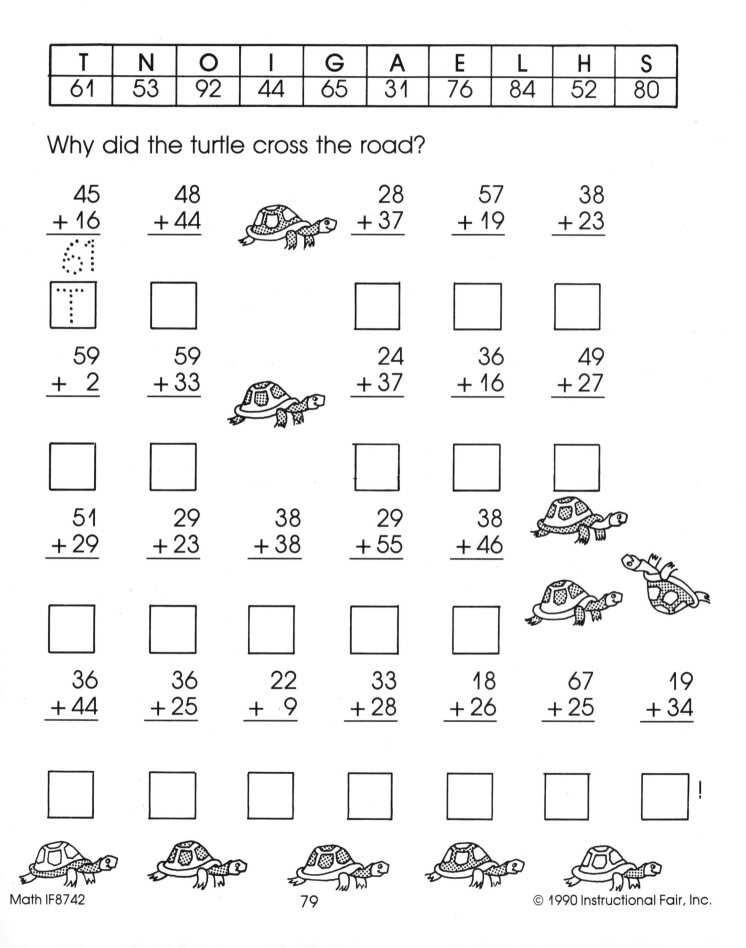

Two-Digit Subtraction

Name____________________

Subtract ones first.
5 – 1 = 4
Then, subtract tens.
6 – 4 = 2

tens	ones
4	5
– 2	1
	4

tens	ones
4	5
– 2	1
2	4

tens	ones
7	2
– 5	1
	1

tens	ones
9	6
– 3	3

tens	ones
8	8
– 5	7

tens	ones
7	4
– 4	4

tens	ones
6	9
– 2	8

tens	ones
9	5
– 1	5

tens	ones
5	8
– 3	5

tens	ones
8	7
– 3	6

tens	ones
2	7
– 1	5

tens	ones
8	2
– 6	1

tens	ones
7	7
– 5	6

tens	ones
6	3
– 5	2

tens	ones
8	6
– 3	2

tens	ones
9	9
– 4	5

tens	ones
4	6
– 2	3

tens	ones
2	9
– 1	3

Two-Digit Subtraction

Name____________________

Remember to subtract ones first. Then, subtract tens.

tens	ones
4	8
− 2	3
2	5

tens	ones
6	2
− 4	1

tens	ones
4	5
− 3	5

tens	ones
2	9
− 1	5

tens	ones
6	3
− 4	2

tens	ones
8	7
− 5	6

tens	ones
7	5
− 3	4

tens	ones
5	8
− 4	5

tens	ones
4	9
− 1	3

tens	ones
3	9
− 2	1

tens	ones
8	8
− 1	8

tens	ones
6	5
− 5	4

tens	ones
8	1
− 6	0

tens	ones
7	6
− 5	3

tens	ones
9	7
− 8	3

tens	ones
5	8
− 2	3

tens	ones
5	6
− 4	5

Name_____

Work problems. Use color code. **25**—blue, **31**—yellow,
57—green, **14**—orange, **21**—brown, **11**—red

$$\begin{array}{r} 47 \\ -22 \\ \hline \end{array}$$

$$\begin{array}{r} 52 \\ -21 \\ \hline \end{array}$$

$$\begin{array}{r} 25 \\ -11 \\ \hline \end{array}$$

$$\begin{array}{r} 62 \\ -31 \\ \hline \end{array}$$

$$\begin{array}{r} 77 \\ -20 \\ \hline \end{array}$$

$$\begin{array}{r} 51 \\ -40 \\ \hline \end{array}$$

$$\begin{array}{r} 55 \\ -34 \\ \hline \end{array}$$

$$\begin{array}{r} 69 \\ -12 \\ \hline \end{array}$$

$$\begin{array}{r} 98 \\ -41 \\ \hline \end{array}$$

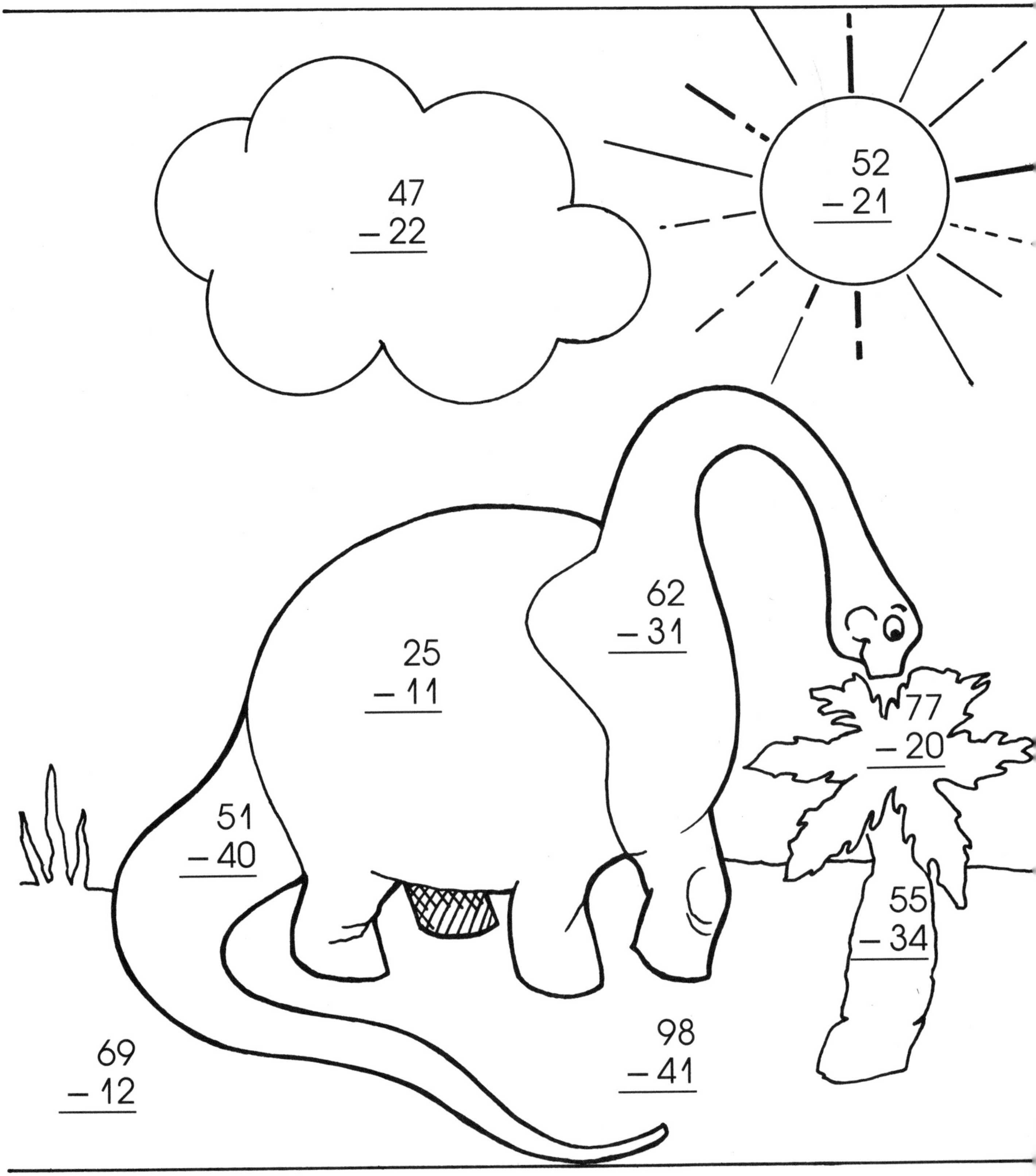

Two-Digit Subtraction

Name ______________________________

tens	ones
4	2
−	7

You cannot subtract 7 from 2.

REGROUP
Take 1 ten from tens.

tens	ones
3	
~~4~~	2
−	8

Add 1 ten (10) to ones. (10 + 2 = 12)

tens	ones
3	12
~~4~~	~~2~~
−	7

Next, subtract ones. (12 − 7 = 5)

tens	ones
3	12
~~4~~	~~2~~
−	7
	5

Then, subtract tens. (3 − 0 = 3)

tens	ones
3	12
~~4~~	~~2~~
−	7
3	5

NOW, it's your turn!

---

tens	ones
3	4
−	6

You cannot subtract ___ from ___ .

REGROUP
Take 1 ten from tens.

tens	ones
3	4
−	6

Add 1 ten to ones. (10 + ___ = ___)

tens	ones
3	4
−	6

Next, subtract ones.
14 − ___ = ___
Then, subtract tens.

tens	ones
3	4
−	6

Name________________________

REGROUP

tens	ones
3	16
~~4~~	~~6~~
− 1	9

Subtract ones.
16 − 9 = 7

tens	ones
3	16
~~4~~	~~6~~
− 1	9
	7

Subtract tens.

tens	ones
3	16
~~4~~	~~6~~
− 1	9
2	7

---

tens	ones
9	6
− 4	8

tens	ones
5	3
− 2	5

tens	ones
3	1
− 1	5

tens	ones
6	4
− 2	7

tens	ones
8	4
− 5	5

tens	ones
7	2
− 3	7

tens	ones
6	5
− 1	7

tens	ones
4	8
− 2	9

tens	ones
7	7
− 2	9

tens	ones
8	1
− 2	8

tens	ones
7	5
− 5	8

tens	ones
3	2
− 1	8

tens	ones
4	2
− 1	3

tens	ones
5	6
− 2	7

tens	ones
3	5
− 1	9

tens	ones
2	5
− 1	9

Two-Digit Subtraction

Name____________________

Remember:

REGROUP

Subtract ones.
Subtract tens.

tens	ones
6	14
~~7~~	~~4~~
− 2	8
4	6

$\begin{array}{r} 57 \\ -29 \\ \hline \end{array}$	$\begin{array}{r} 86 \\ -37 \\ \hline \end{array}$	$\begin{array}{r} 98 \\ -49 \\ \hline \end{array}$	$\begin{array}{r} 75 \\ -26 \\ \hline \end{array}$
$\begin{array}{r} 66 \\ -18 \\ \hline \end{array}$	$\begin{array}{r} 41 \\ -18 \\ \hline \end{array}$	$\begin{array}{r} 32 \\ -18 \\ \hline \end{array}$	$\begin{array}{r} 45 \\ -17 \\ \hline \end{array}$
$\begin{array}{r} 92 \\ -36 \\ \hline \end{array}$	$\begin{array}{r} 82 \\ -54 \\ \hline \end{array}$	$\begin{array}{r} 65 \\ -38 \\ \hline \end{array}$	$\begin{array}{r} 73 \\ -56 \\ \hline \end{array}$
$\begin{array}{r} 57 \\ -18 \\ \hline \end{array}$	$\begin{array}{r} 46 \\ -29 \\ \hline \end{array}$	$\begin{array}{r} 63 \\ -49 \\ \hline \end{array}$	$\begin{array}{r} 75 \\ -29 \\ \hline \end{array}$

Two-Digit Subtraction

Name ________________________

1. 2	5		2.		
		3.			
	4.			5.	
			6.		

ACROSS

1. $\begin{array}{r} 50 \\ -25 \\ \hline 25 \end{array}$

2. $\begin{array}{r} 78 \\ -9 \\ \hline \end{array}$

3. $\begin{array}{r} 62 \\ -25 \\ \hline \end{array}$

4. $\begin{array}{r} 62 \\ -16 \\ \hline \end{array}$

5. $\begin{array}{r} 85 \\ -28 \\ \hline \end{array}$

6. $\begin{array}{r} 42 \\ 19 \\ \hline \end{array}$

DOWN

1. $\begin{array}{r} 67 \\ -38 \\ \hline \end{array}$

2. $\begin{array}{r} 94 \\ -27 \\ \hline \end{array}$

3. $\begin{array}{r} 75 \\ -39 \\ \hline \end{array}$

4. $\begin{array}{r} 78 \\ -29 \\ \hline \end{array}$

5. $\begin{array}{r} 81 \\ -28 \\ \hline \end{array}$

6. $\begin{array}{r} 76 \\ -48 \\ \hline \end{array}$

Two-Digit Subtraction

Name________________________

Work problems. Color picture by color chart.

Red	Blue	Yellow	Green
67 − 29	51 − 38	96 − 28	94 − 48
72 − 48	44 − 15	71 − 19	60 − 39
94 − 59	31 − 14	46 − 27	65 − 16

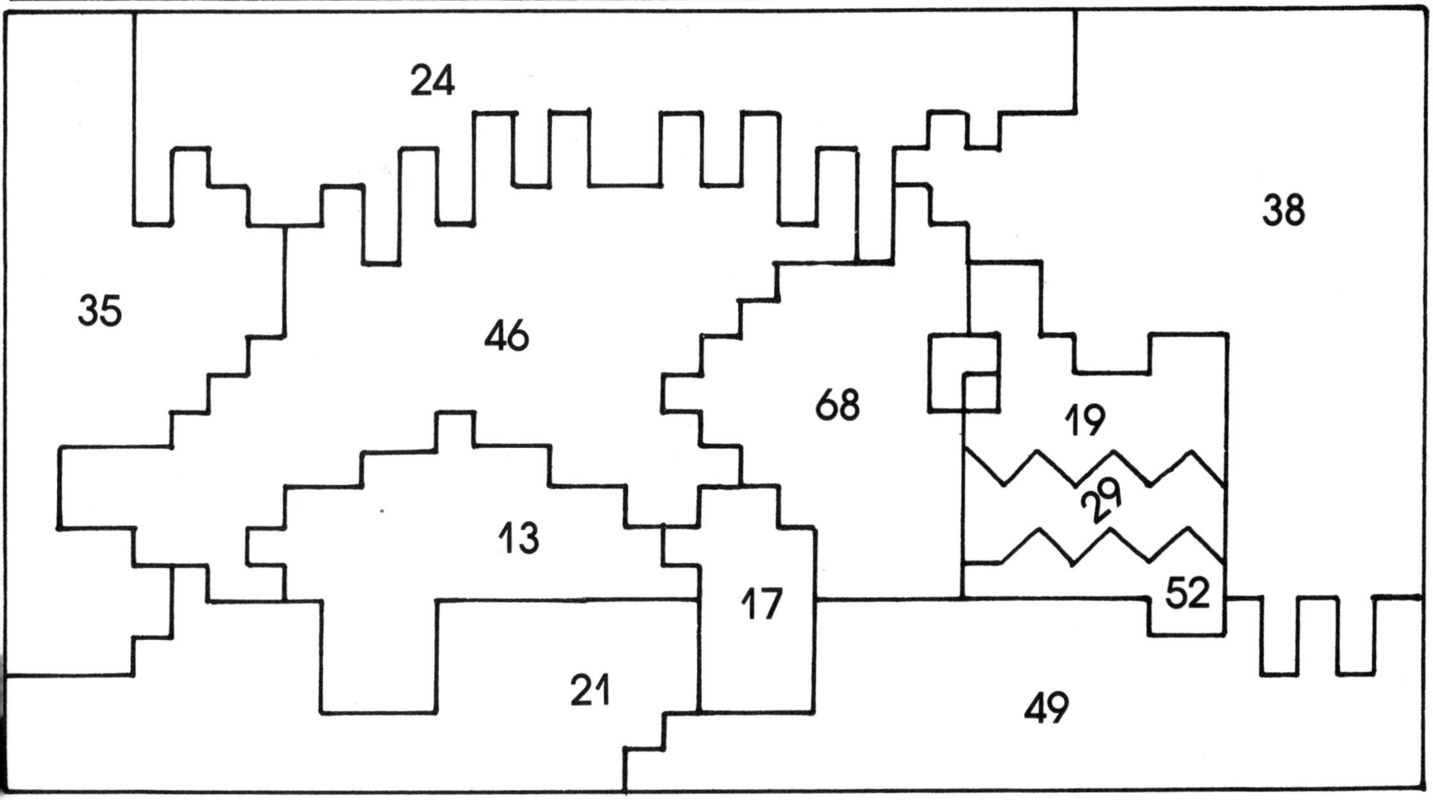

Name_____

What happens when ducks fly upside down?

19	36	53	48	34	16	67	47	75	28
T	Q	C	H	U	K	E	P	A	Y

$$\begin{array}{r} 47 \\ -\ 28 \\ \hline \end{array}$$
19
T

$$\begin{array}{r} 62 \\ -\ 14 \\ \hline \end{array}$$
☐

$$\begin{array}{r} 95 \\ -\ 28 \\ \hline \end{array}$$
☐

$$\begin{array}{r} 76 \\ -\ 48 \\ \hline \end{array}$$
☐

$$\begin{array}{r} 83 \\ -\ 47 \\ \hline \end{array}$$
☐

$$\begin{array}{r} 53 \\ -\ 19 \\ \hline \end{array}$$
☐

$$\begin{array}{r} 94 \\ -\ 19 \\ \hline \end{array}$$
☐

$$\begin{array}{r} 92 \\ -\ 39 \\ \hline \end{array}$$
☐

$$\begin{array}{r} 65 \\ -\ 49 \\ \hline \end{array}$$
☐

$$\begin{array}{r} 61 \\ -\ 27 \\ \hline \end{array}$$
☐

$$\begin{array}{r} 73 \\ -\ 26 \\ \hline \end{array}$$
☐ !

Name________________________

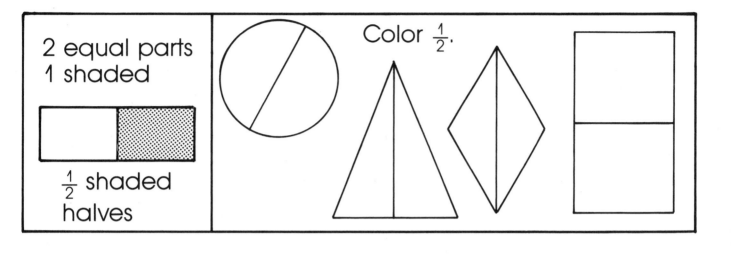

2 equal parts
1 shaded

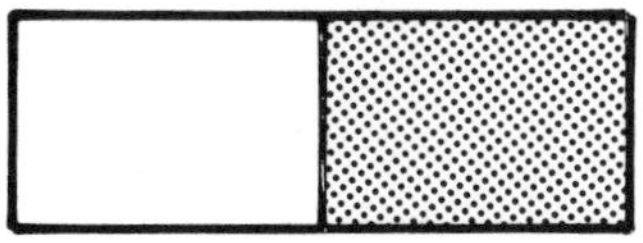

$\frac{1}{2}$ shaded
halves

Color $\frac{1}{2}$.

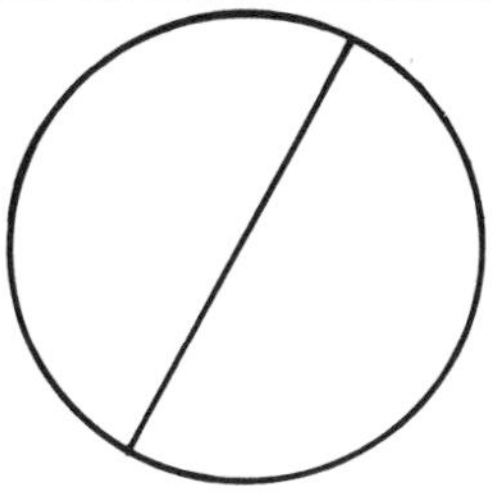
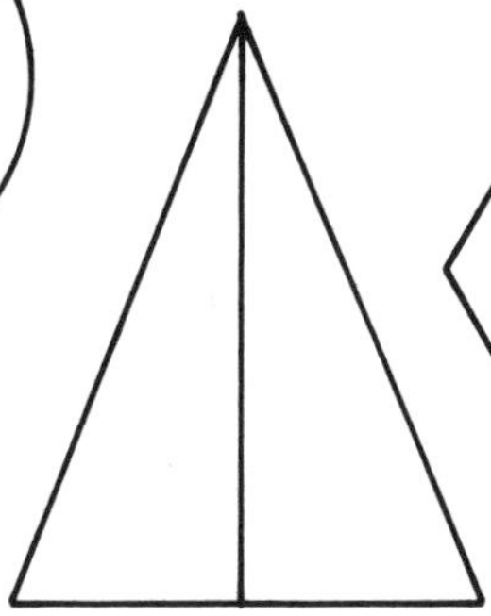
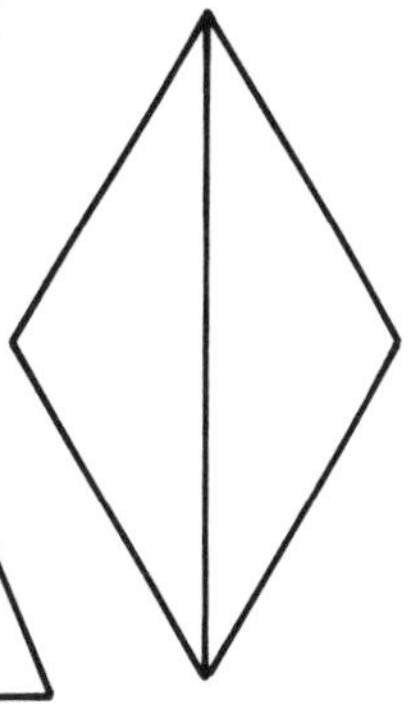

3 equal parts
1 shaded

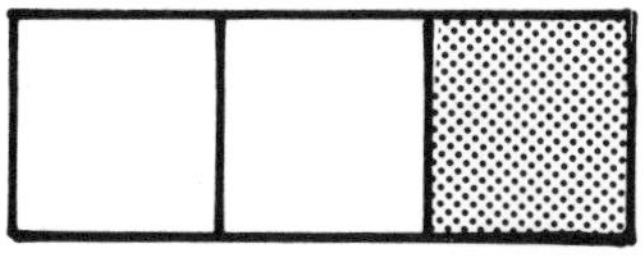

$\frac{1}{3}$ shaded
thirds

Color $\frac{1}{3}$.

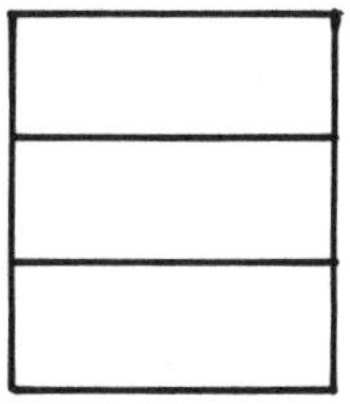
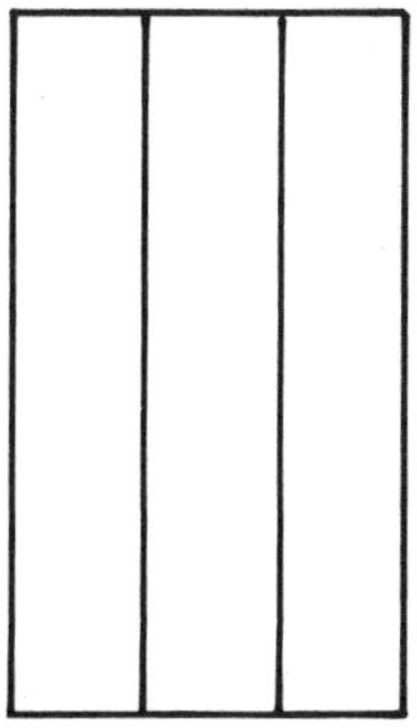

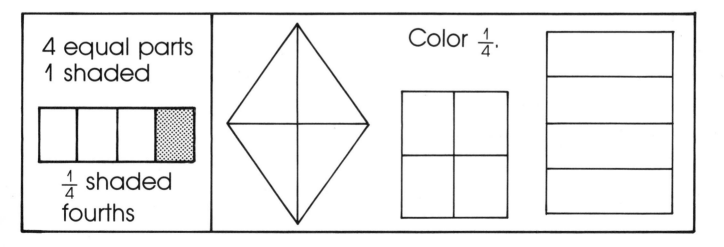

4 equal parts
1 shaded

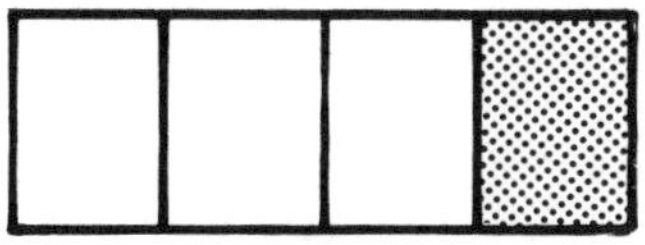

$\frac{1}{4}$ shaded
fourths

Color $\frac{1}{4}$.

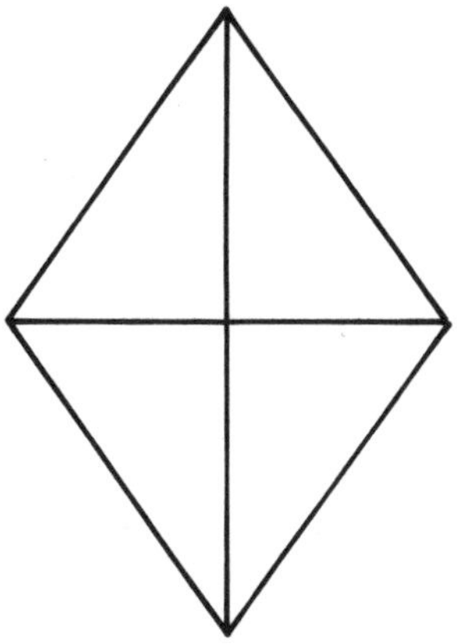
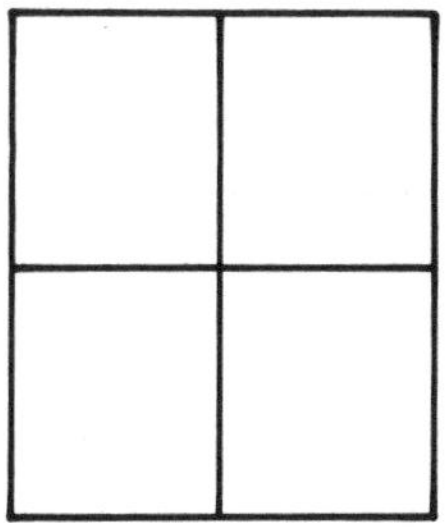

Name_____

____ equal parts
2 shaded

____ equal parts
3 shaded

____ equal parts
____ shaded

$\frac{2}{4}$ shaded
two fourths

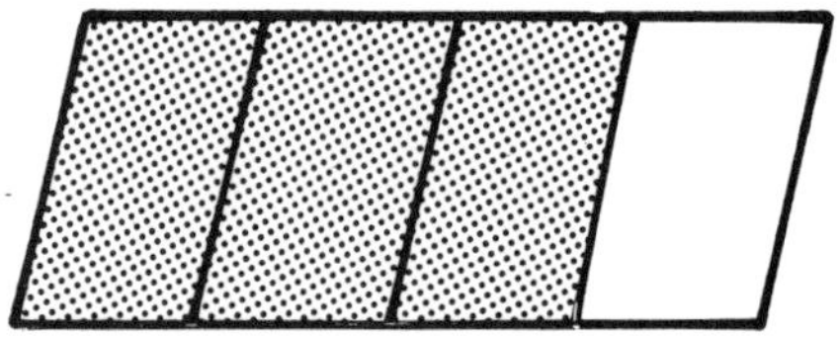

$\frac{3}{4}$ shaded
three fourths

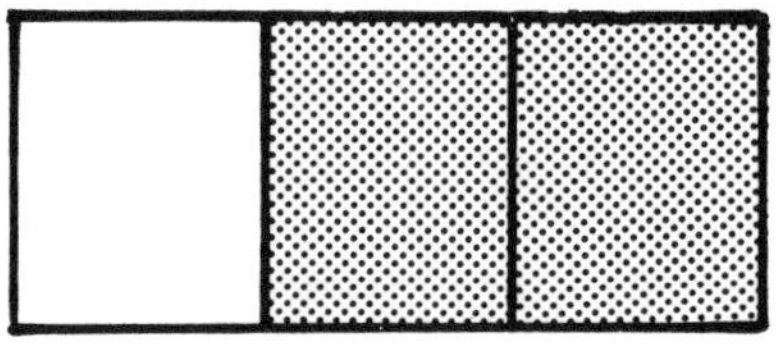

$\frac{2}{3}$ shaded
two thirds

---

white	shaded
$\frac{2}{4}$, $\frac{1}{4}$, $\frac{1}{3}$	$\frac{2}{3}$, $\frac{2}{4}$, $\frac{3}{4}$

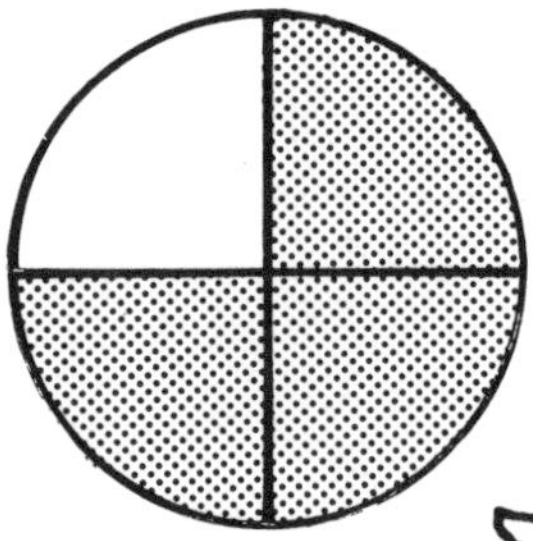

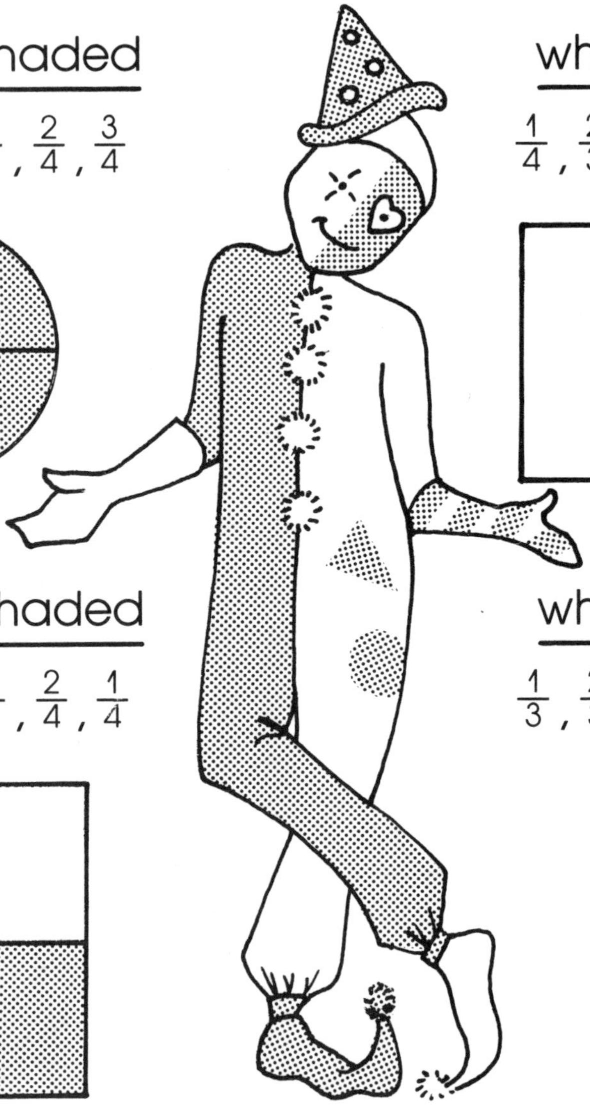

white	shaded
$\frac{1}{4}$, $\frac{2}{3}$, $\frac{1}{3}$	$\frac{2}{3}$, $\frac{1}{3}$, $\frac{1}{4}$

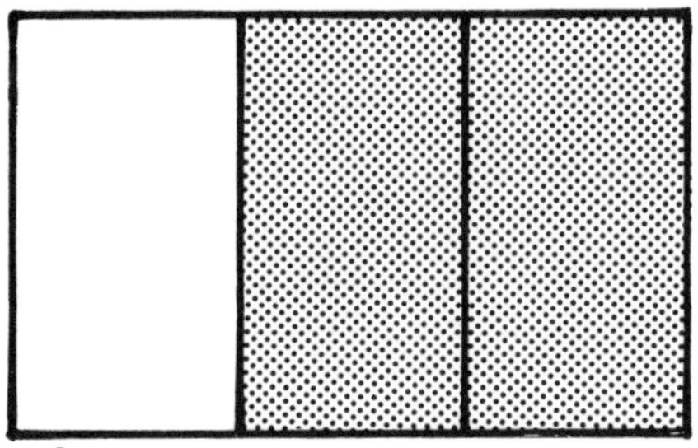

white	shaded
$\frac{2}{3}$, $\frac{2}{4}$, $\frac{3}{4}$	$\frac{2}{3}$, $\frac{2}{4}$, $\frac{1}{4}$

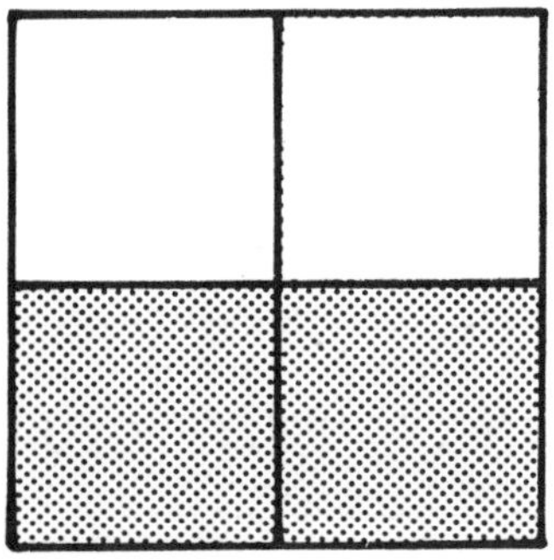

white	shaded
$\frac{1}{3}$, $\frac{2}{3}$, $\frac{1}{4}$	$\frac{1}{4}$, $\frac{2}{3}$, $\frac{1}{3}$

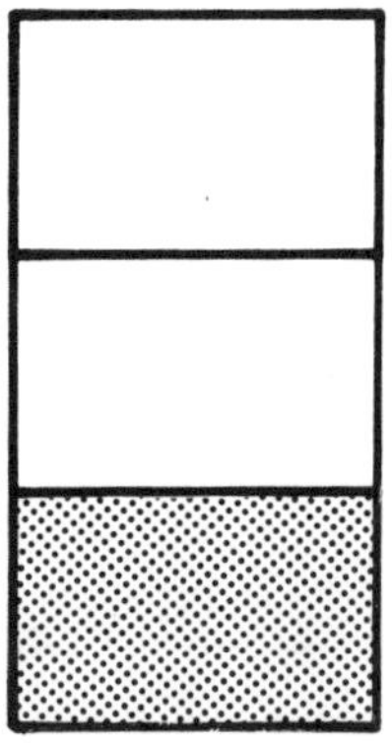

Name________________________

Draw line from fraction to correct shape.

$\frac{1}{3}$ shaded

$\frac{2}{4}$ shaded

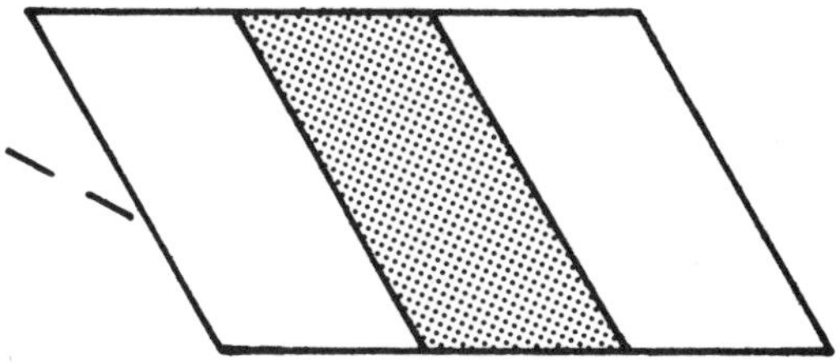

$\frac{1}{4}$ shaded

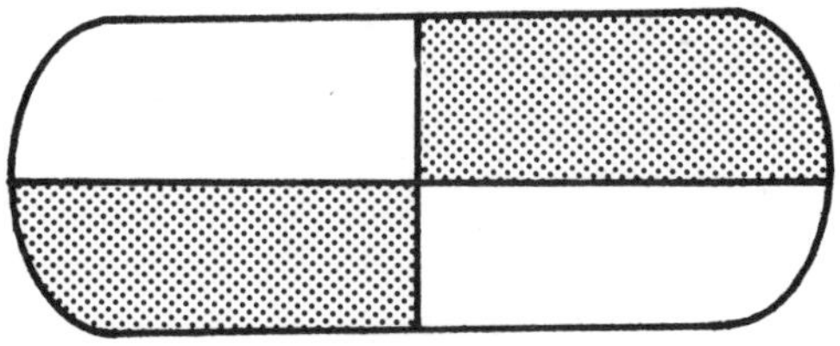

$\frac{1}{2}$ shaded

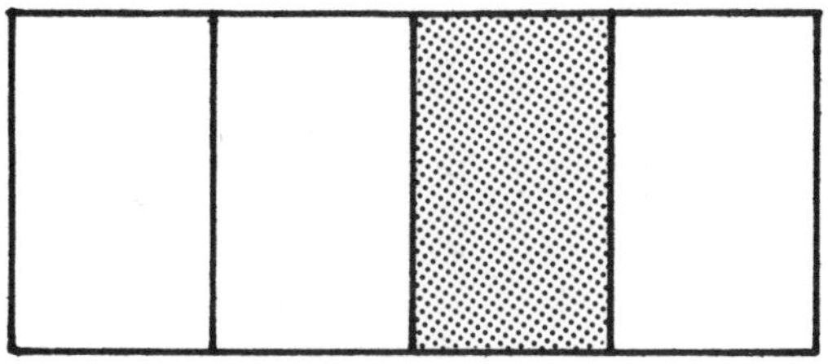

$\frac{3}{4}$ shaded

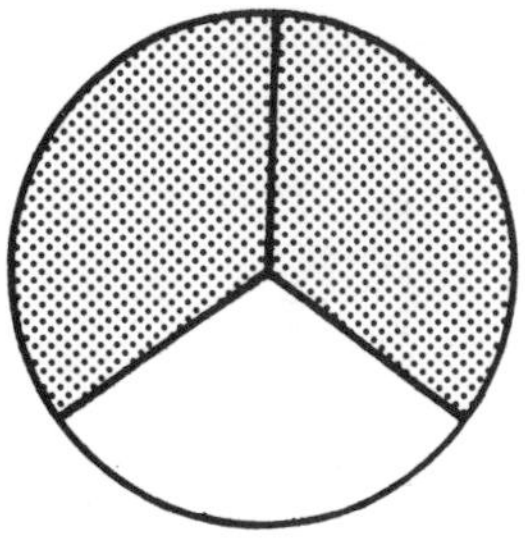

$\frac{2}{3}$ shaded

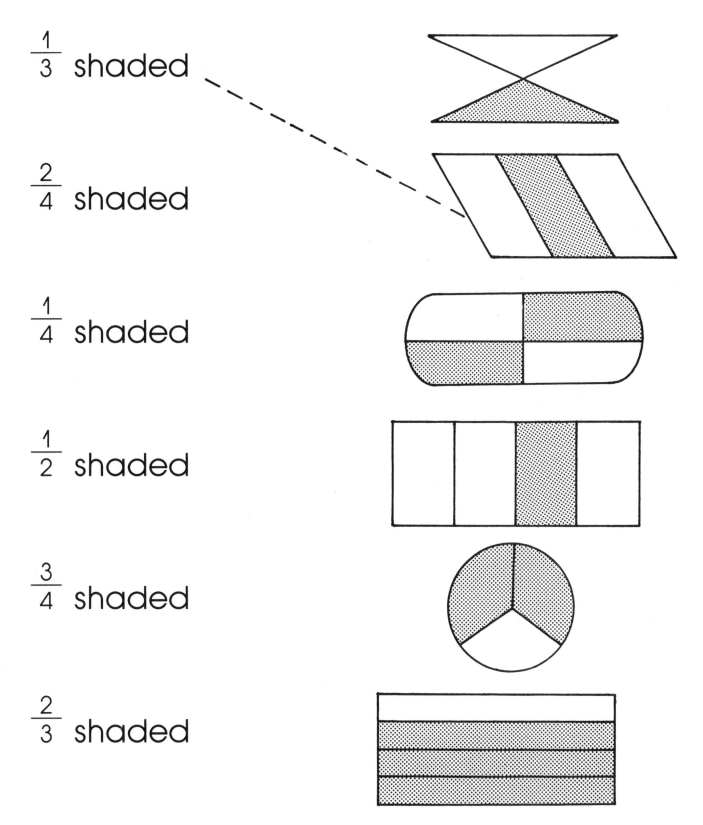

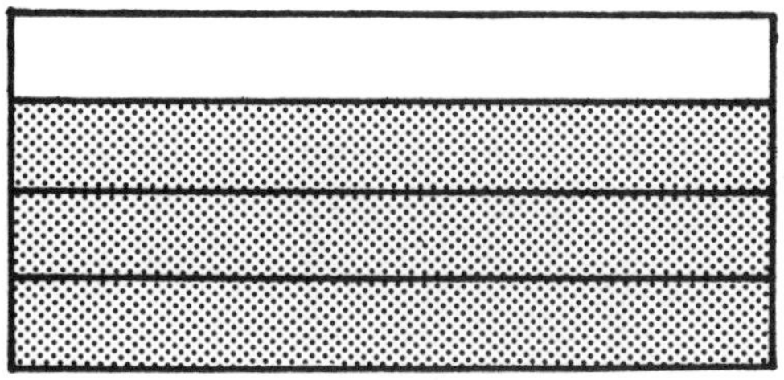

Name____________________

How much is shaded?

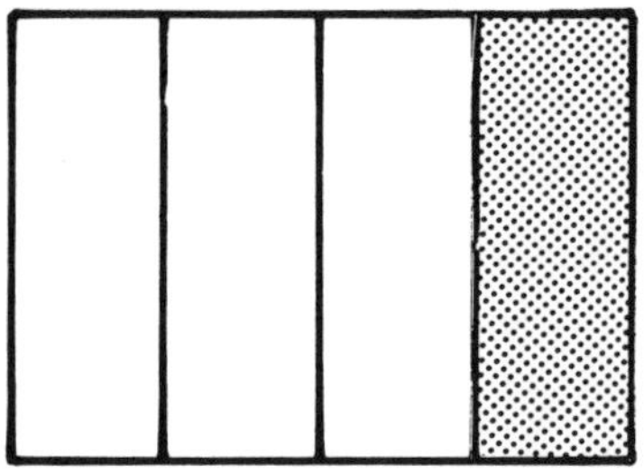

$\frac{1}{4}$ ______ A

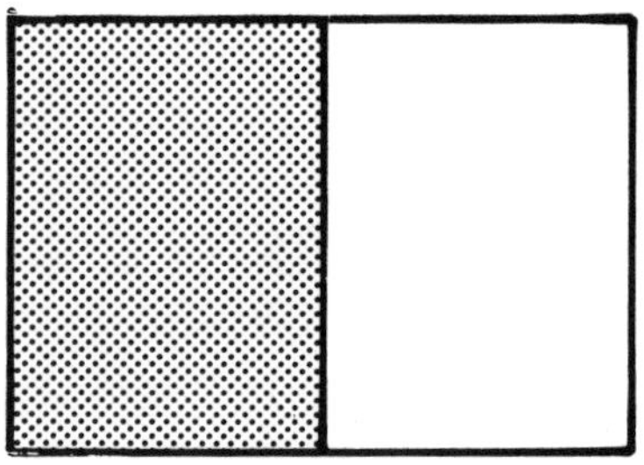

______ H

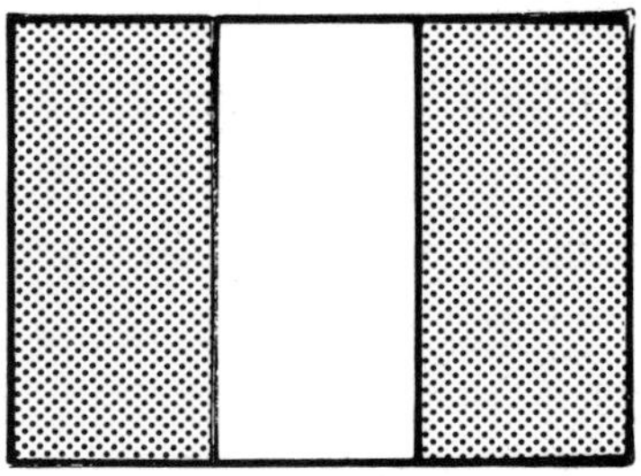

______ U

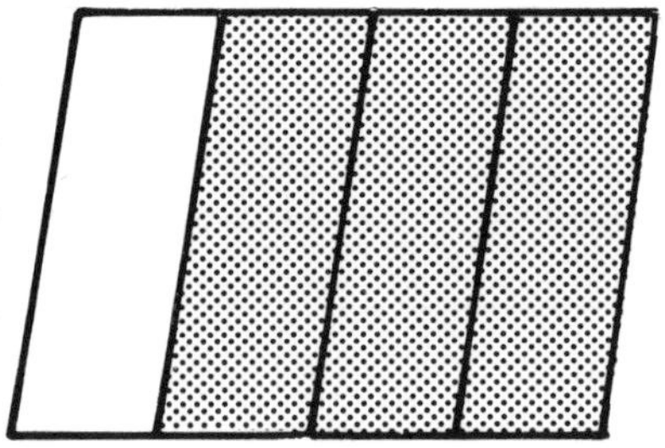

______ T

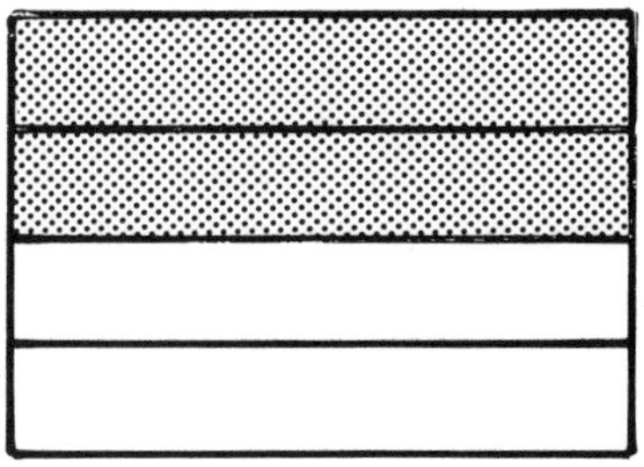

______ F

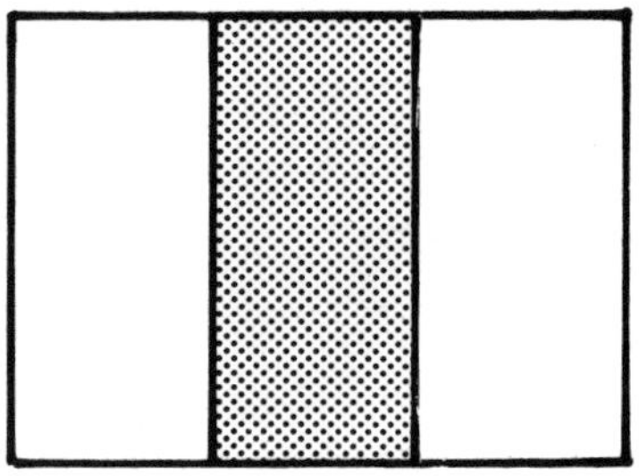

______ M

Complete secret message.

______	______	______	______	______	______	N!
$\frac{1}{3}$	$\frac{1}{4}$	$\frac{3}{4}$	$\frac{1}{2}$	$\frac{2}{4}$	$\frac{2}{3}$	

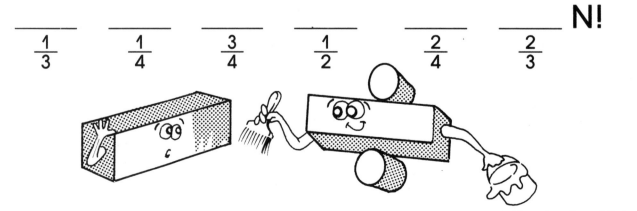

Fracti

Name____________________

Color $\frac{1}{2}$

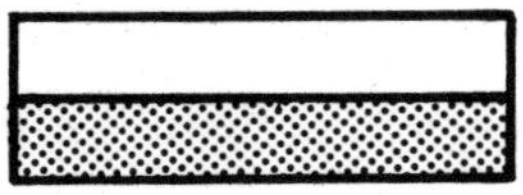

$\frac{1}{2}$

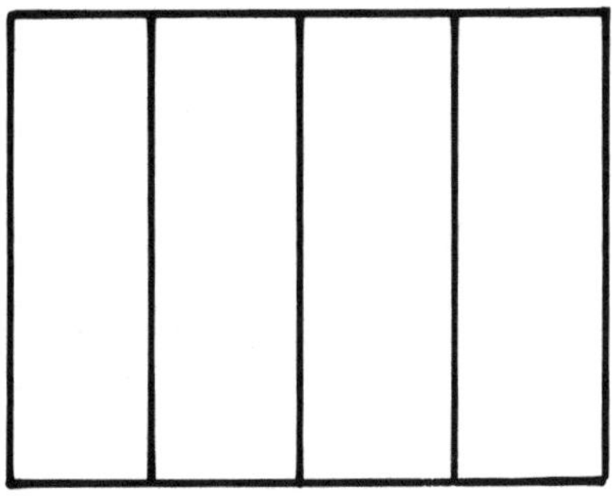

$\frac{3}{4}$

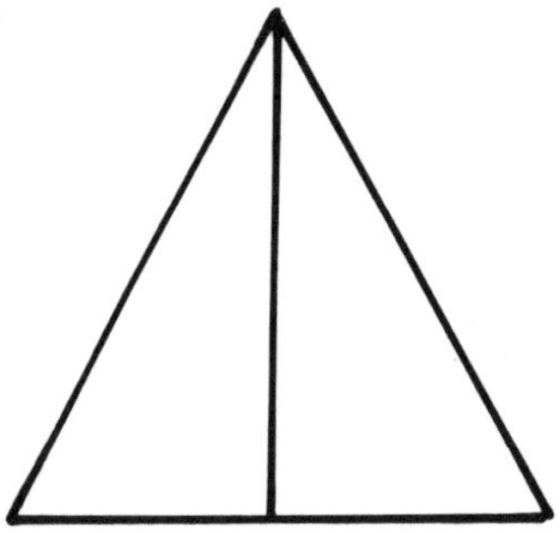

$\frac{1}{2}$

Color:

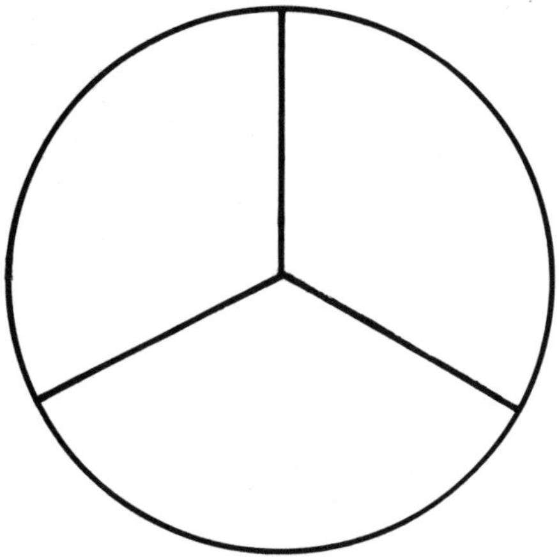

$\frac{1}{3}$

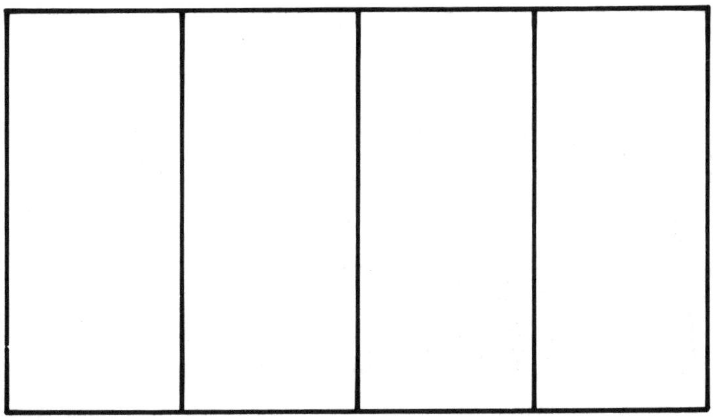

$\frac{2}{4}$

$\frac{2}{3}$

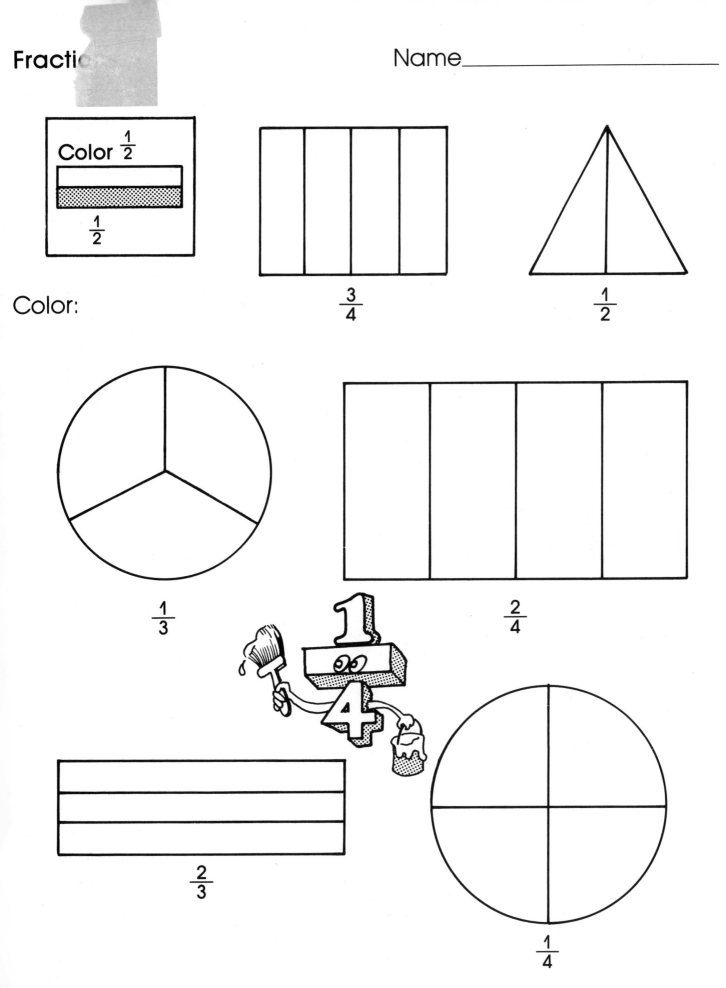

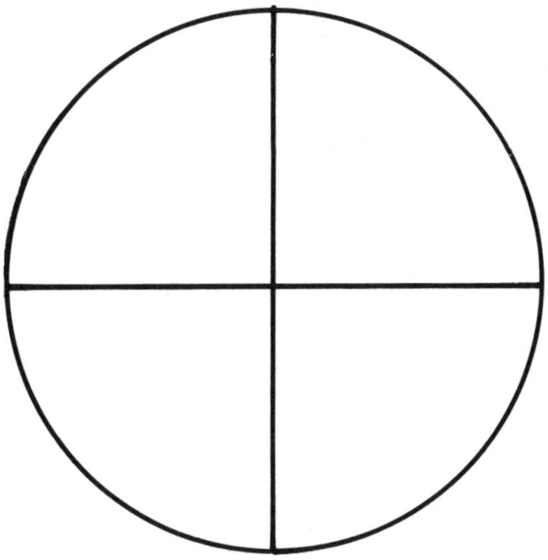

$\frac{1}{4}$

Matching Fractions

Name________________________

Put letter of drawing by matching white fractions. Do same for shaded fractions.

White		Shaded	
$\frac{1}{2}$	E	$\frac{1}{2}$	______
$\frac{1}{3}$	______	$\frac{1}{3}$	C
$\frac{2}{3}$	______	$\frac{2}{3}$	______
$\frac{1}{4}$	______	$\frac{1}{4}$	______
$\frac{2}{4}$	______	$\frac{2}{4}$	______
$\frac{3}{4}$	______	$\frac{3}{4}$	______

A

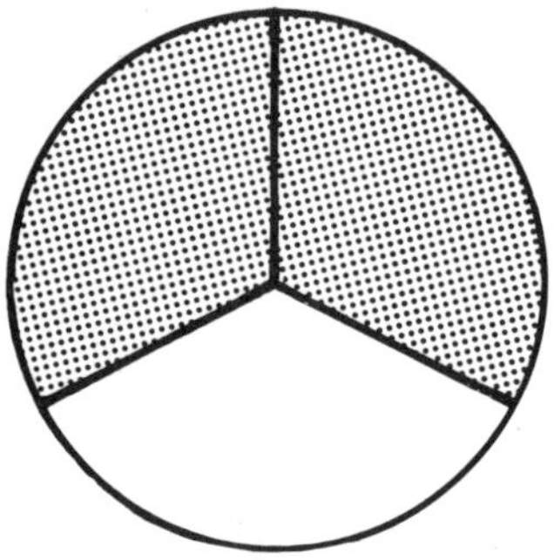

B

C

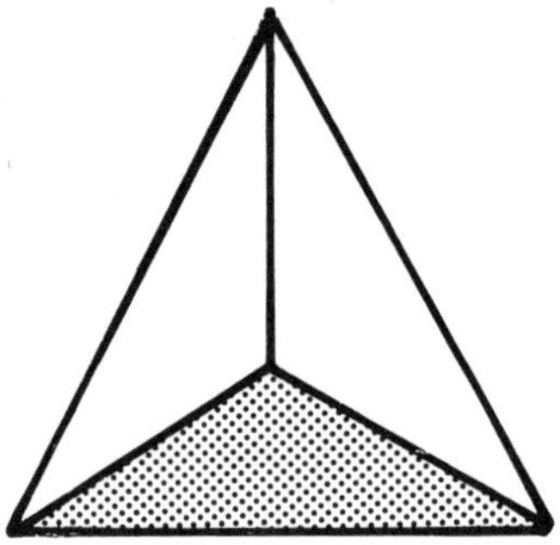

D

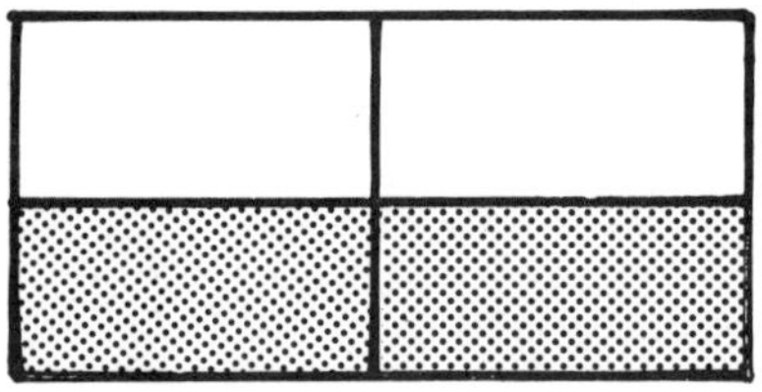

E

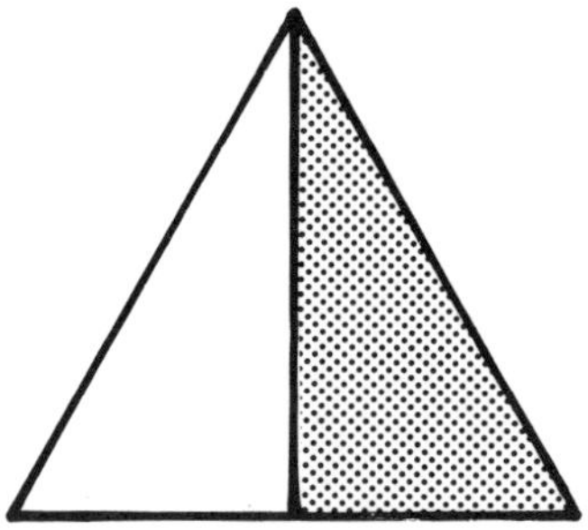

F

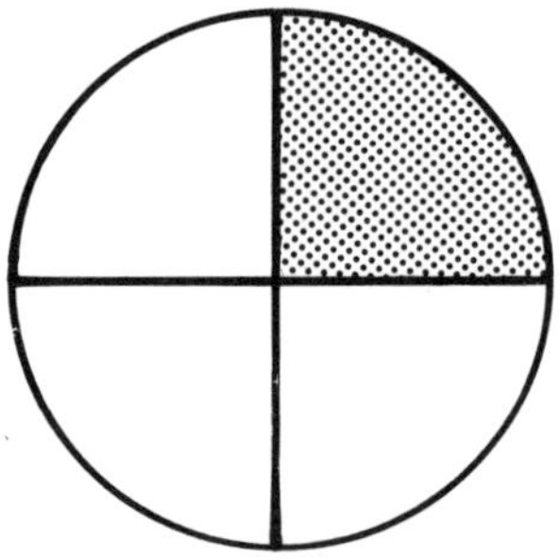

 Name________________________

Work problems. Color balloons with matching answers.

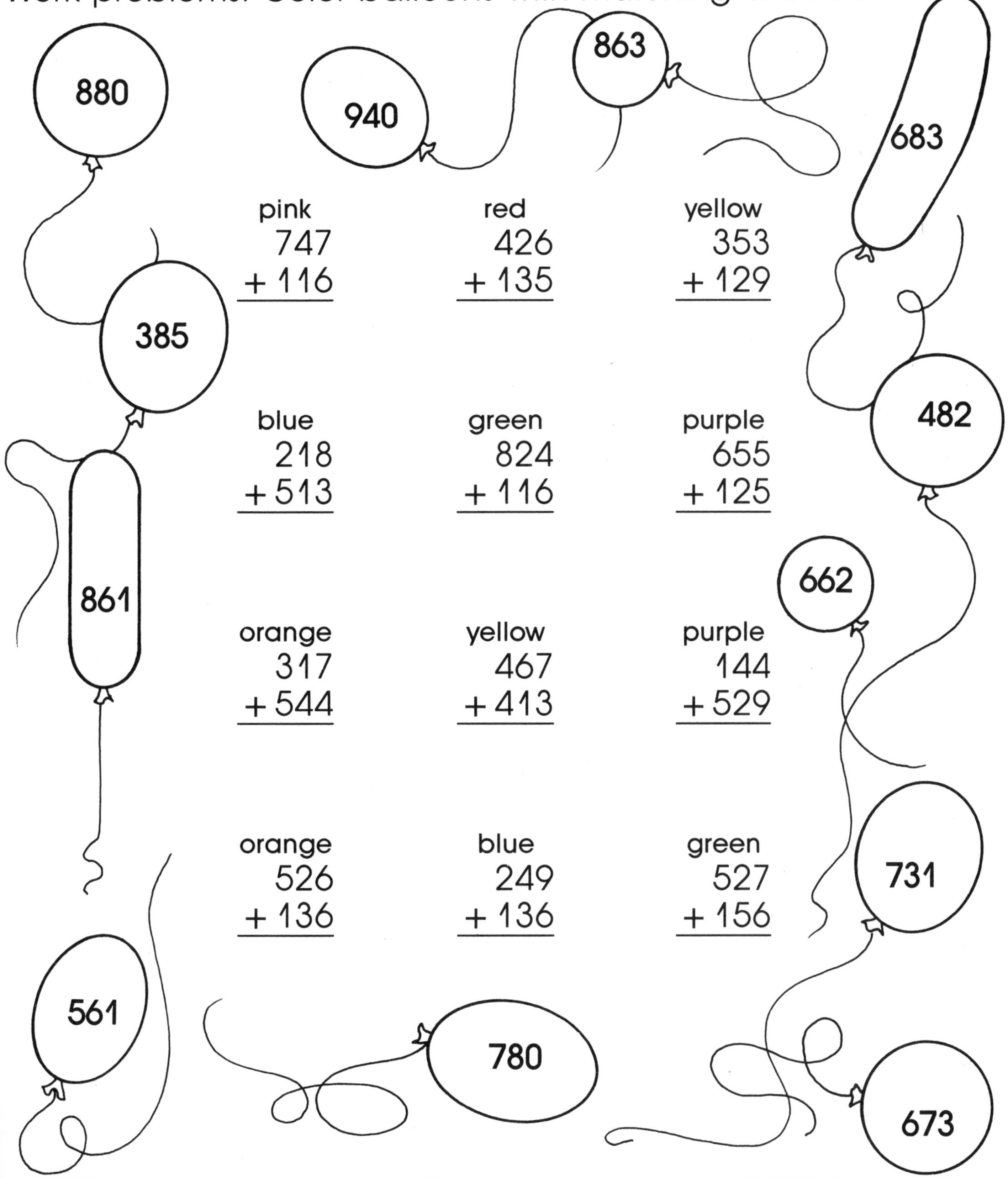

pink 747 + 116	red 426 + 135	yellow 353 + 129
blue 218 + 513	green 824 + 116	purple 655 + 125
orange 317 + 544	yellow 467 + 413	purple 144 + 529
orange 526 + 136	blue 249 + 136	green 527 + 156

Three-Digit Subtraction

Name_____

Math IF8742

REGROUP
Subtract ones.

$$
\begin{array}{r}
{}^{6}\cancel{5}{}^{1}\cancel{7}2 \\
-\ 136 \\
\hline
6
\end{array}
$$

Subtract tens.

$$
\begin{array}{r}
{}^{6}\cancel{5}{}^{1}\cancel{7}2 \\
-\ 136 \\
\hline
36
\end{array}
$$

Subtract hundreds.

$$
\begin{array}{r}
{}^{6}\cancel{5}{}^{1}\cancel{7}2 \\
-\ 136 \\
\hline
436
\end{array}
$$

436 /'s!

$$
\begin{array}{r}
675 \\
-\ 248 \\
\hline
\end{array}
\qquad
\begin{array}{r}
486 \\
-\ 377 \\
\hline
\end{array}
\qquad
\begin{array}{r}
368 \\
-\ 139 \\
\hline
\end{array}
\qquad
\begin{array}{r}
782 \\
-\ 565 \\
\hline
\end{array}
$$

$$
\begin{array}{r}
557 \\
-\ 438 \\
\hline
\end{array}
\qquad
\begin{array}{r}
844 \\
-\ 529 \\
\hline
\end{array}
\qquad
\begin{array}{r}
953 \\
-\ 628 \\
\hline
\end{array}
\qquad
\begin{array}{r}
342 \\
-\ 328 \\
\hline
\end{array}
$$

$$
\begin{array}{r}
890 \\
-\ 536 \\
\hline
\end{array}
\qquad
\begin{array}{r}
787 \\
-\ 438 \\
\hline
\end{array}
\qquad
\begin{array}{r}
666 \\
-\ 437 \\
\hline
\end{array}
\qquad
\begin{array}{r}
591 \\
-\ 257 \\
\hline
\end{array}
$$

$$
\begin{array}{r}
361 \\
-\ 122 \\
\hline
\end{array}
\qquad
\begin{array}{r}
956 \\
-\ 248 \\
\hline
\end{array}
\qquad
\begin{array}{r}
527 \\
-\ 319 \\
\hline
\end{array}
\qquad
\begin{array}{r}
463 \\
-\ 236 \\
\hline
\end{array}
$$

Circle answers with 2 in tens place.

Three-Digit Subtraction

Remember: Regroup,
subtract ones, next tens,
then hundreds.

$$\begin{array}{r} 6\ 18 \\ 4\cancel{7}\cancel{8} \\ -\ 259 \\ \hline 219 \end{array}$$

$$\begin{array}{r} 428 \\ -\ 119 \\ \hline \end{array} \qquad \begin{array}{r} 546 \\ -\ 137 \\ \hline \end{array} \qquad \begin{array}{r} 867 \\ -\ 448 \\ \hline \end{array} \qquad \begin{array}{r} 991 \\ -\ 157 \\ \hline \end{array}$$

$$\begin{array}{r} 655 \\ -\ 128 \\ \hline \end{array} \qquad \begin{array}{r} 768 \\ -\ 539 \\ \hline \end{array} \qquad \begin{array}{r} 527 \\ -\ 319 \\ \hline \end{array} \qquad \begin{array}{r} 666 \\ -\ 218 \\ \hline \end{array}$$

$$\begin{array}{r} 437 \\ -\ 118 \\ \hline \end{array} \qquad \begin{array}{r} 916 \\ -\ 108 \\ \hline \end{array} \qquad \begin{array}{r} 653 \\ -\ 218 \\ \hline \end{array} \qquad \begin{array}{r} 538 \\ -\ 319 \\ \hline \end{array}$$

$$\begin{array}{r} 528 \\ -\ 419 \\ \hline \end{array} \qquad \begin{array}{r} 745 \\ -\ 429 \\ \hline \end{array} \qquad \begin{array}{r} 691 \\ -\ 135 \\ \hline \end{array} \qquad \begin{array}{r} 836 \\ -\ 517 \\ \hline \end{array}$$

Circle answers with 9 in ones place.

Three-Digit Subtraction

Name________________________

Work problems. Connect dot-to-dot in order of problems.

1.	396 − 158	2.	677 − 129
3.	992 − 777	4.	836 − 218
5.	971 − 259	6.	932 − 118
7.	585 − 117	8.	656 − 227
9.	681 − 368	10.	284 − 138
11.	762 − 319	12.	533 − 214

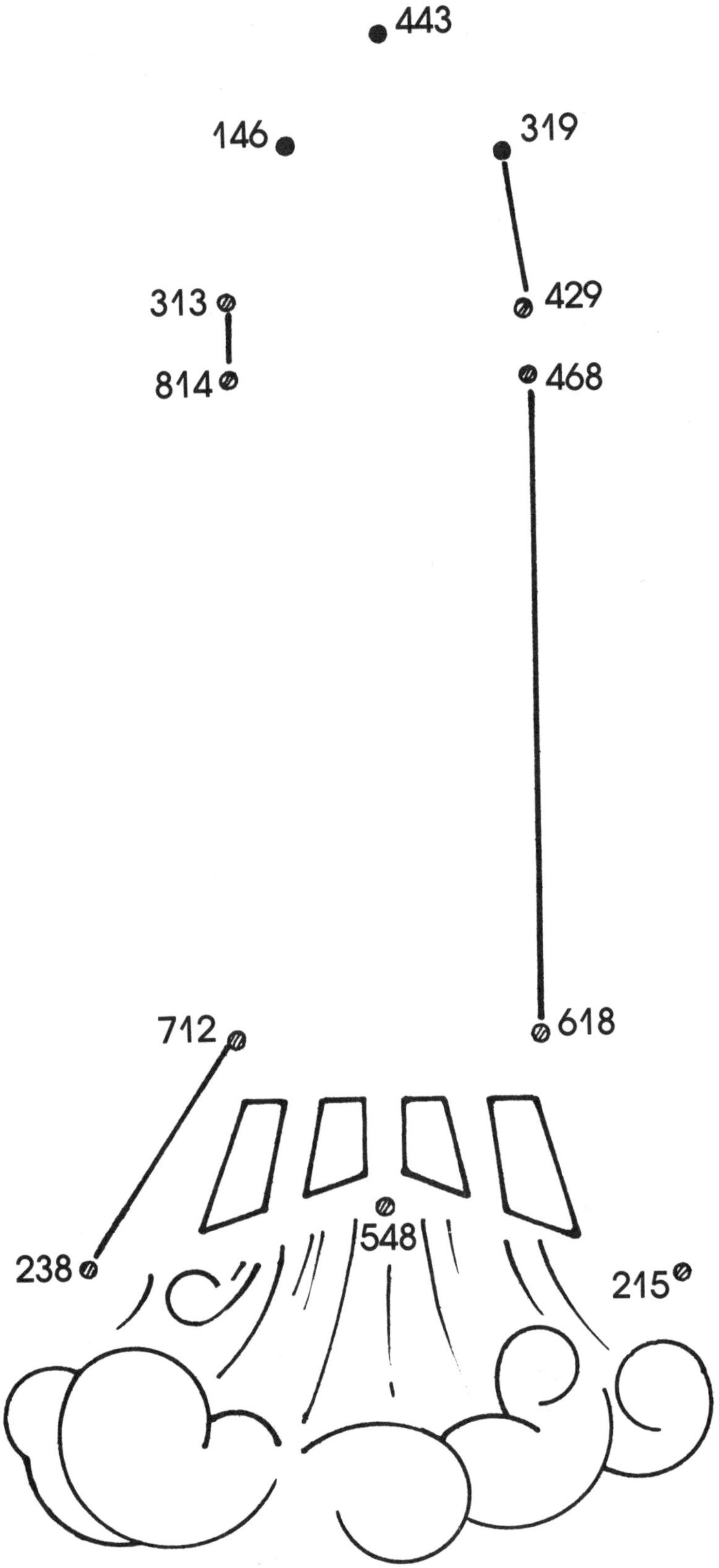

Greater Than; Less Than

Name________________________

Use 8 and 2.

82 > 28   28 < 82

Use 6 and 4. _____ > _____

Use 5 and 6. _____ < _____

Use 3 and 9. _____ > _____

Use 1 and 7. _____ < _____

Use 2 and 9. _____ < _____

Use 1 and 3. 3 52 > 1 76

Use 5 and 7. 4__3 < 4__6

Use 6 and 2. 55__ < 55__

Use 4 and 8. __61 > __33

Use 9 and 8. __98 > __98

Multiplication

Name________________________

$3 + 3 + 3 + 3 =$ 12

4 threes = 12

$4 \times 3 =$ 12

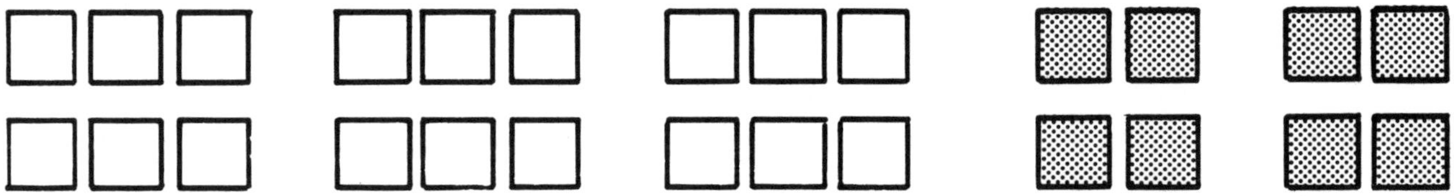

$6 + 6 + 6 =$ _____

3 sixes = _____

$3 \times$ = _____

$4 + 4 =$ _____

2 fours = _____

$2 \times$ ___ = _____

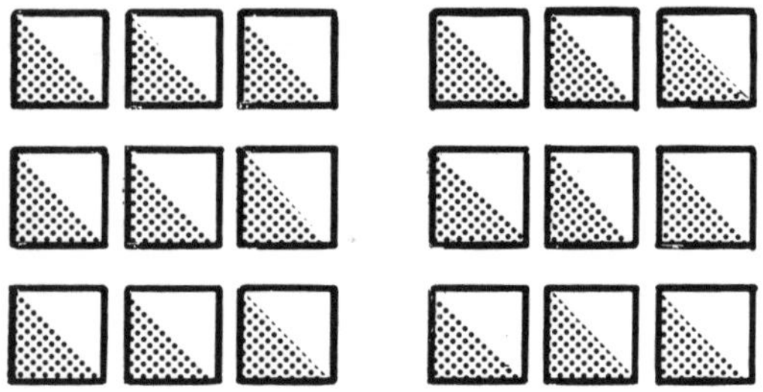

$9 + 9 =$ _____

2 nines = _____

$2 \times$ ___ = _____

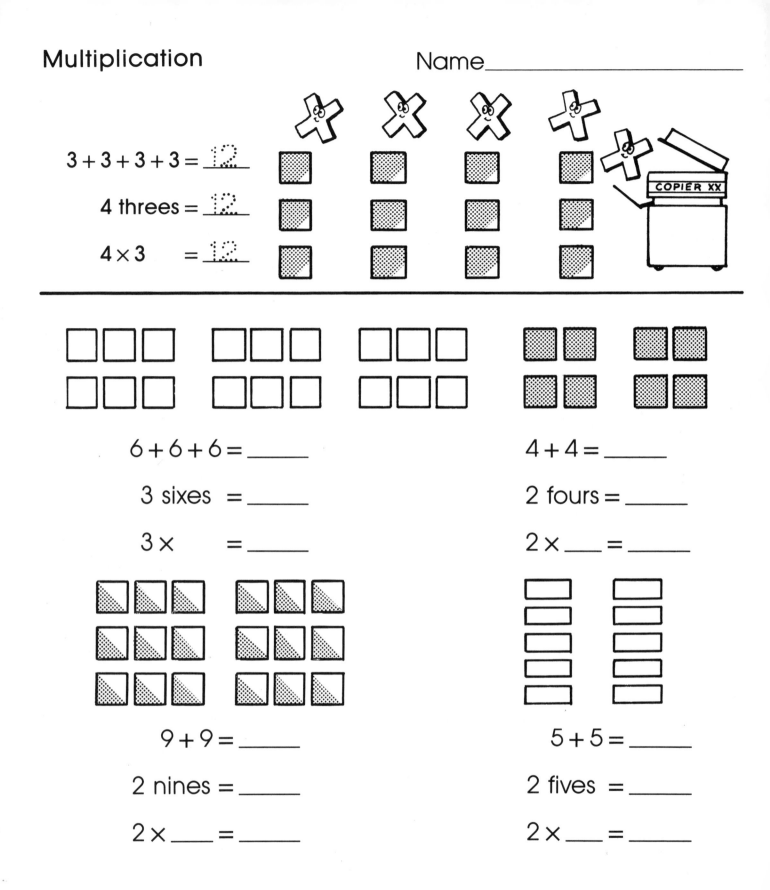

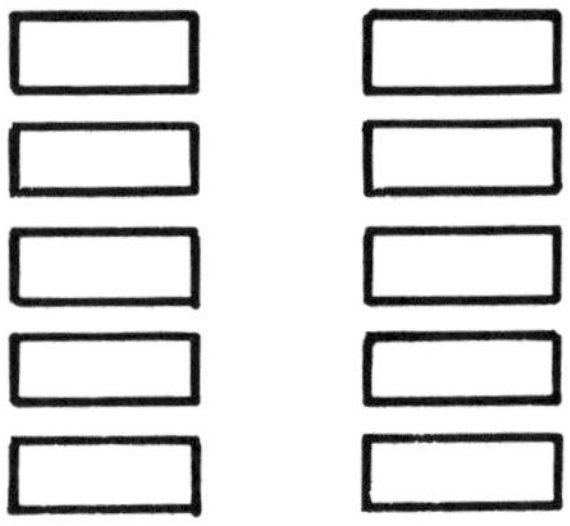

$5 + 5 =$ _____

2 fives = _____

$2 \times$ ___ = _____

Draw 3 twos.

 Name____________________

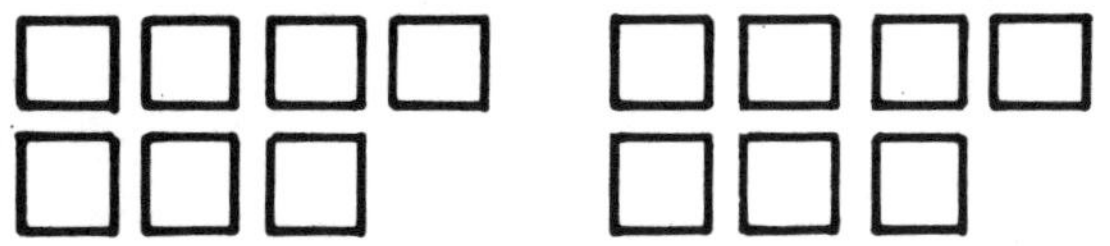

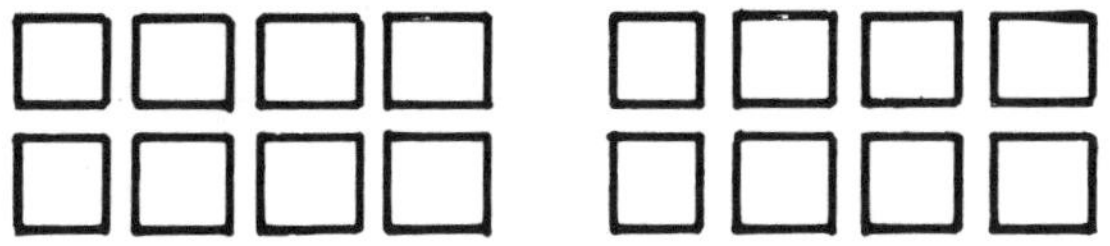

7 + 7 = __14__
2 sevens = _____
2 × 7 = _____

__8__ + __8__ = __16__
2 eights = _____
2 × __8__ = _____

---

2 + 2 + 2 + 2 = _____
_____ twos = _____
_____ × 2 = _____

3 + 3 + 3 + 3 + 3 = _____
_____ threes = _____
_____ × 3 = _____

4 + 4 + 4 = _____
_____ fours = _____
_____ × 4 = _____

9 + 9 = _____
2 nines = _____
_____ × 9 = _____

5 + 5 + 5 = _____
_____ fives = _____
_____ × 5 = _____

6 + 6 = _____
_____ sixes = _____
_____ × 6 = _____

3 + 3 + 3 + 3 = _____
_____ threes = _____
_____ × 3 = _____

4 + 4 = _____
_____ fours = _____
_____ × 4 = _____

Name____________________

Draw line from pictures to matching problem.

$4 \times 3 = 12$

$3 \times 3 = 9$

$2 \times 9 = 18$

$4 \times 4 = 16$

$3 \times 6 = 18$

$3 \times 5 = 15$

$5 \times 2 = 10$

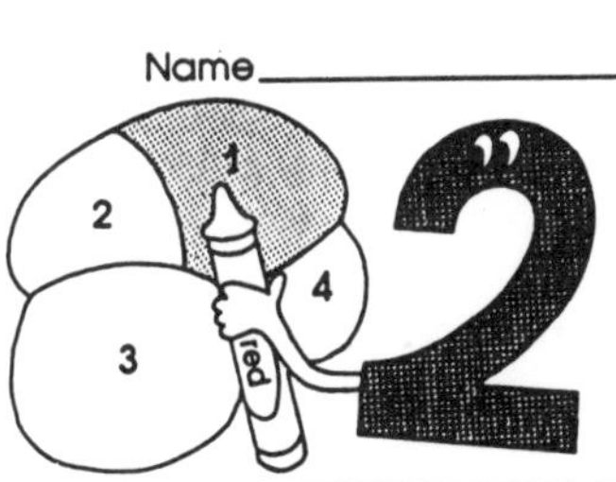

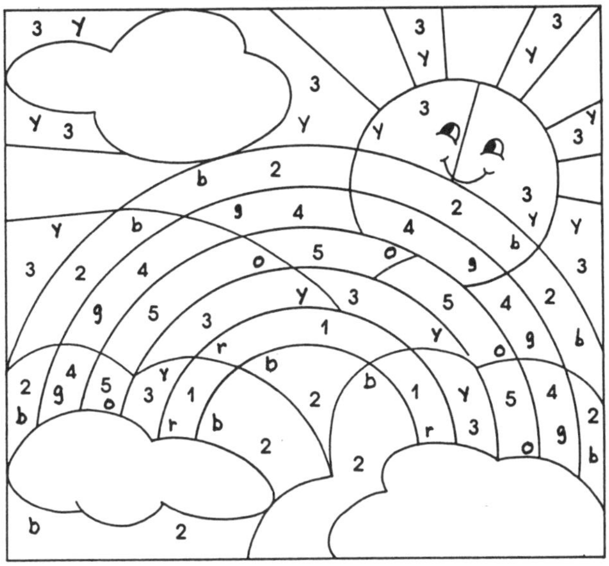

Page 1

Number Recognition — Name _____

Color: 1's—red
2's—blue
3's—yellow
4's—green
5's—orange

Page 2

Number Recognition — Name _____

Color: 6's—purple
7's—yellow
8's—black
9's—orange
10's—brown

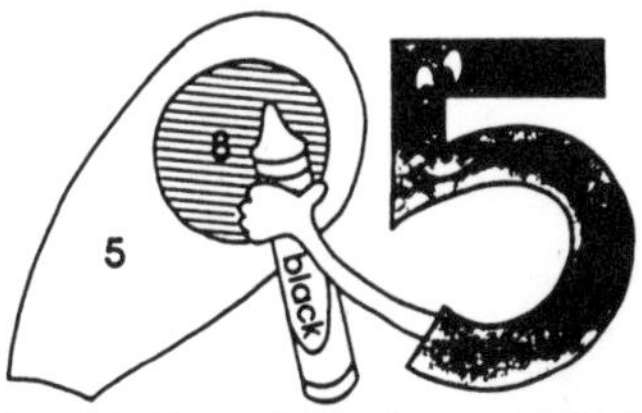

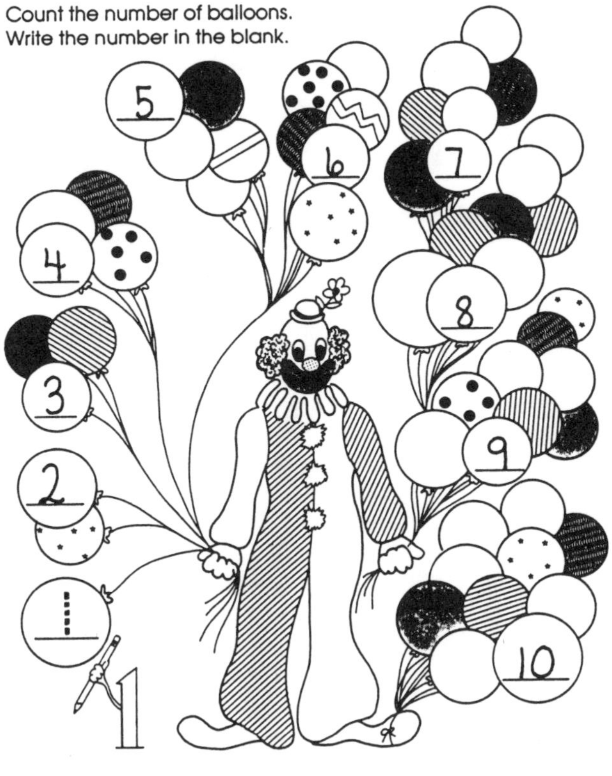

Page 3

Sequencing Numbers — Name _____

Count the number of balloons.
Write the number in the blank.

Balloons labeled: 5, 6, 7, 4, 8, 3, 9, 2, 1, 10

Page 4

Sequencing Numbers — Name _____

Write the missing numbers.

6, 7, __8__

6, __7__, 8   8, __9__, 10   7, __8__, 9

5, __6__, 7   __1__, 2, 3   __4__, 5, 6

1, 2, __3__   __6__, 7, 8   __2__, 3, 4

__7__, 8, 9   __5__, 6, 7   2, __3__, 4

4, 5, __6__   2, 3, __4__   7, 8, __9__

3, __4__, 5   __7__, 8, 9   4, __5__, 6

5, 6, __7__   3, 4, __5__   1, __2__, 3

8, 9, __10__   __3__, 4, 5   __8__, 9, 10

Answer Key

Page 5

Counting to 9   Name_____

How many?

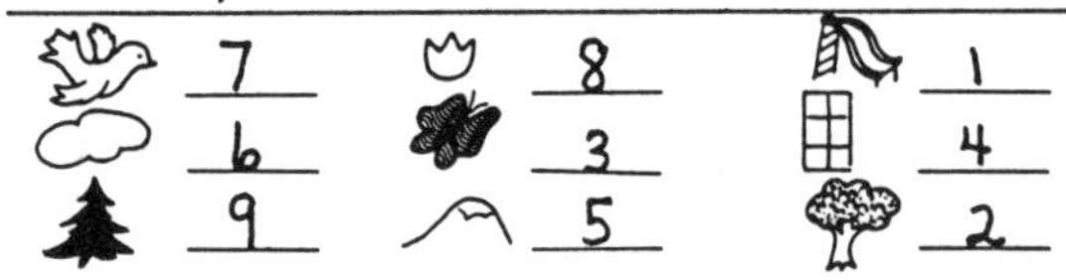

🕊	7	🌷	8	🪁	1
☁	6	🦋	3	▦	4
🌲	9	⌢	5	🌳	2

Page 5

Page 6

Counting   Name_____

Count. Use code to color answers.

1—blue   4—red   7—purple
2—yellow   5—orange   8—gray
3—green   6—brown   9—black

Page 6

Page 7

Counting to 20   Name_____

Join the dots in order.
Color the surprise.

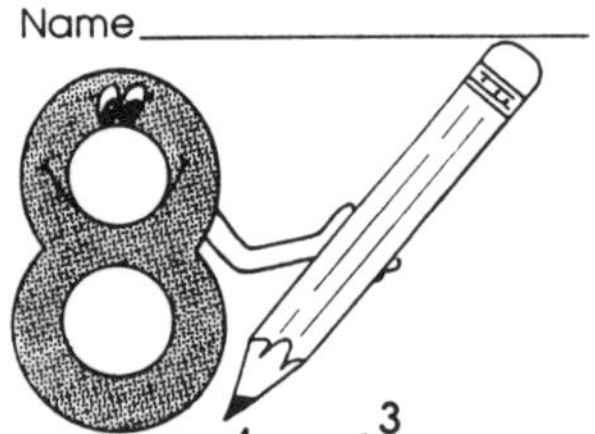

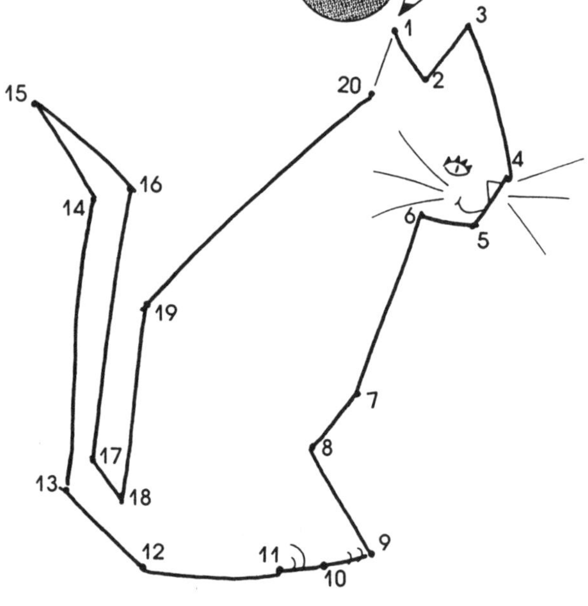

Page 7

Page 8

Number Word Recognition   Name_____

Number the train.

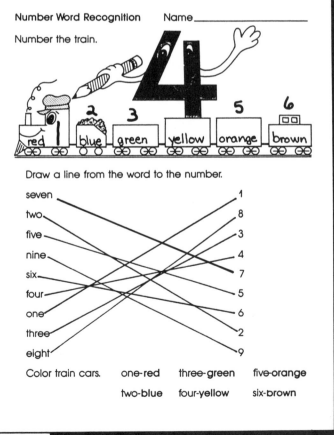

Draw a line from the word to the number.

seven   1
two   8
five   3
nine   4
six   7
four   5
one   6
three   2
eight   9

Color train cars.   one-red   three-green   five-orange

two-blue   four-yellow   six-brown

Page 8

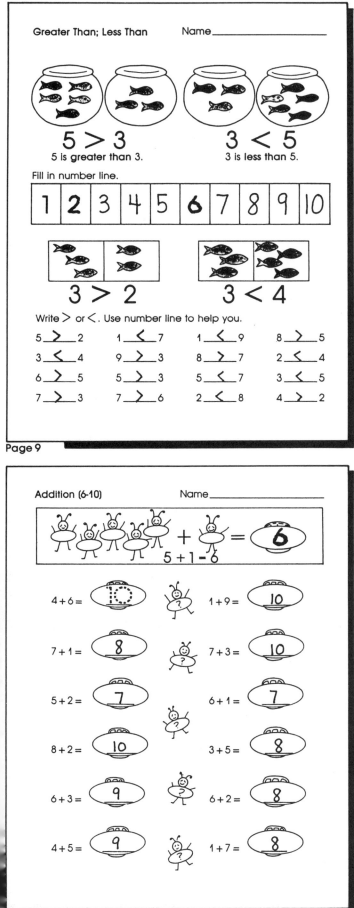

Greater Than; Less Than   Name_____

$$5 > 3$$
5 is greater than 3.

$$3 < 5$$
3 is less than 5.

Fill in number line.

| 1 | 2 | 3 | 4 | 5 | 6 | 7 | 8 | 9 | 10 |

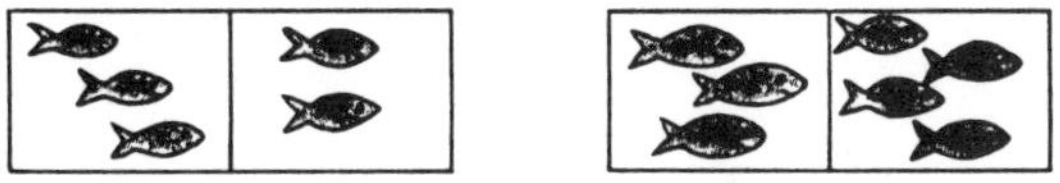

$$3 > 2$$

$$3 < 4$$

Write > or <. Use number line to help you.

5 > 2	1 < 7	1 < 9	8 > 5
3 < 4	9 > 3	8 > 7	2 < 4
6 > 5	5 > 3	5 < 7	3 < 5
7 > 3	7 > 6	2 < 8	4 > 2

Page 9

Addition (1-5)   Name_____

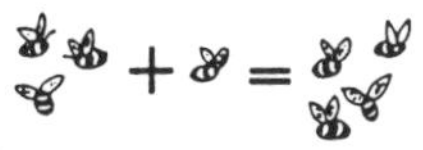

3 + 1 = 4

Add. Use code to color each bee.   2—red   4—blue
3—yellow   5—green

1 + 2 = 3   yellow
2 + 3 = 5   green
3 + 2 = 5   green
3 + 1 = 4   blue
1 + 1 = 2   red
2 + 2 = 4   blue
2 + 1 = 3   yellow
1 + 3 = 4   blue

Page 10

Addition (6-10)   Name_____

5 + 1 = 6

4 + 6 = 10		1 + 9 = 10
7 + 1 = 8		7 + 3 = 10
5 + 2 = 7		6 + 1 = 7
8 + 2 = 10		3 + 5 = 8
6 + 3 = 9		6 + 2 = 8
4 + 5 = 9		1 + 7 = 8

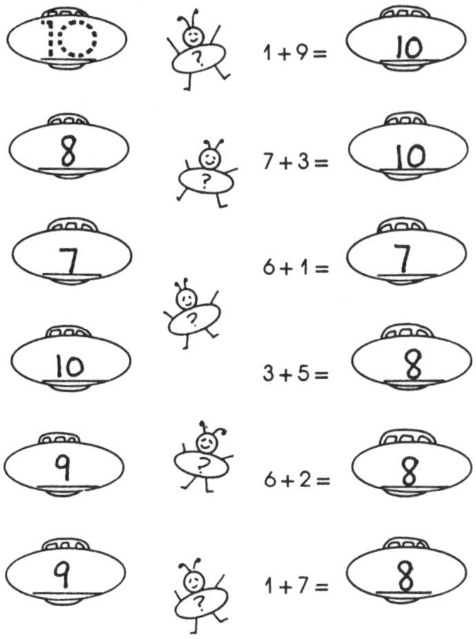

Page 11

ADDITION REVIEW   Name_____

Work all problems. Connect dots from smallest to largest answer.

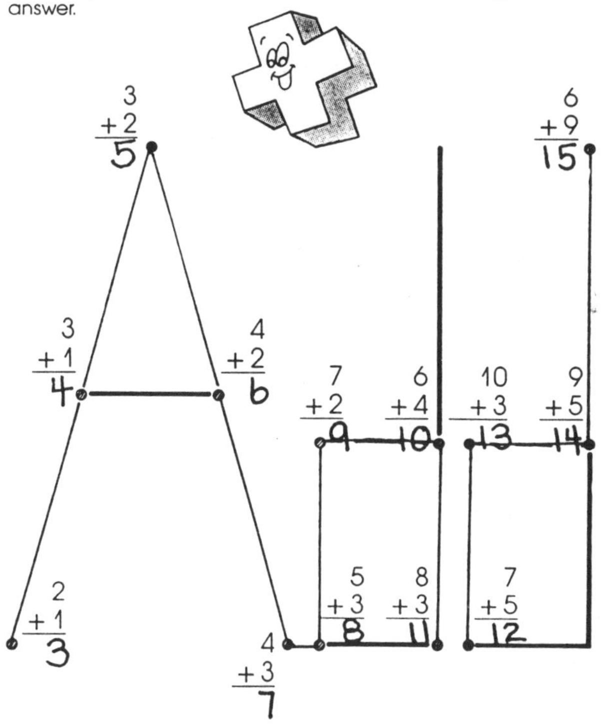

$$\begin{array}{r} 3 \\ +2 \\ \hline 5 \end{array}$$
$$\begin{array}{r} 3 \\ +1 \\ \hline 4 \end{array}$$
$$\begin{array}{r} 4 \\ +2 \\ \hline 6 \end{array}$$
$$\begin{array}{r} 2 \\ +1 \\ \hline 3 \end{array}$$
$$\begin{array}{r} 4 \\ +3 \\ \hline 7 \end{array}$$
$$\begin{array}{r} 7 \\ +2 \\ \hline 9 \end{array}$$
$$\begin{array}{r} 6 \\ +4 \\ \hline 10 \end{array}$$
$$\begin{array}{r} 10 \\ +3 \\ \hline 13 \end{array}$$
$$\begin{array}{r} 9 \\ +5 \\ \hline 14 \end{array}$$
$$\begin{array}{r} 6 \\ +9 \\ \hline 15 \end{array}$$
$$\begin{array}{r} 5 \\ +3 \\ \hline 8 \end{array}$$
$$\begin{array}{r} 8 \\ +3 \\ \hline 11 \end{array}$$
$$\begin{array}{r} 7 \\ +5 \\ \hline 12 \end{array}$$

Page 12

Answer Key

Commutative Property   Name_____

4 + 1 = 5 | 1 + 4 = 5

3 + 1 = __4__   4 + 1 = __5__
1 + 3 = __4__   1 + 4 = __5__
2 + 1 = __3__   3 + 2 = __5__
1 + 2 = __3__   2 + 3 = __5__

Add. Use code to color frogs.

2 green   3 purple   4 yellow   5 red

1 + 1 = __2__   green
3 + 2 = __5__   red
2 + 1 = __3__   purple
1 + 3 = __4__   yellow

2 + 1 = __3__   purple
2 + 2 = __4__   yellow
2 + 3 = __5__   red
3 + 1 = __4__   yellow

Page 13

Subtraction (1-5)   Name_____

3 − 2 = 1   3
                −2
                ‾1‾

5 − 1 = __4__   3 − 1 = __2__   5 − 2 = __3__
4 − 1 = __3__   2 − 1 = __1__   4 − 2 = __2__
3 − 2 = __1__   4 − 3 = __1__   5 − 3 = __2__

Subtract. Use code to color worms.   1—red   3—yellow
                                       2—orange   4—brown

5 − 1 = (4)   4 − 2 = (2)   5 − 2 = (3)
brown 5   orange 4   yellow 5
      −1   −2   −2
      ‾4‾   ‾2‾   ‾3‾

3 − 1 = (2)   4 − 3 = (1)   5 − 3 = (2)
orange 3   red 4   orange 5
      −1   −3   −3
      ‾2‾   ‾1‾   ‾2‾

2 − 1 = (1)   4 − 1 = (3)   3 − 2 = (1)
red 2   yellow 4   red 3
    −1   −1   −2
    ‾1‾   ‾3‾   ‾1‾

Page 14

Subtraction (1-5)   Name_____

Count the nuts.
Write answer on blank.
Circle problems with same answer.

1

__3__   2   5 − 4   5
          −1   −2
          5 − 4
          3 − 2

    2   (4 − 1)
   −2   5
            −1
  (5 − 2)

                4

          5 − 1
              5 − 4
              5
             −2
          (4 − 0)

__2__
 4 − 2   5
   4   −3
  −1
 3 − 1

                5

          5 − 0
          5   4   2
         −1 −3 −2

Page 15

SUBTRACTION REVIEW   Name_____

2—green   9—purple
3—blue   10—pink
4—yellow   11—red
7—orange   12—purple
8—red

Work problems.
Use code to color.

Page 16

Math IF8742   106   © 1990 Instructional Fair, Inc.

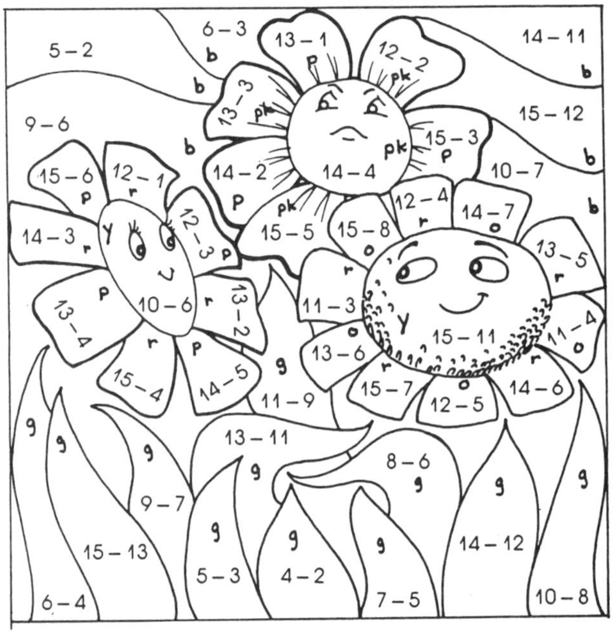

Answer Key

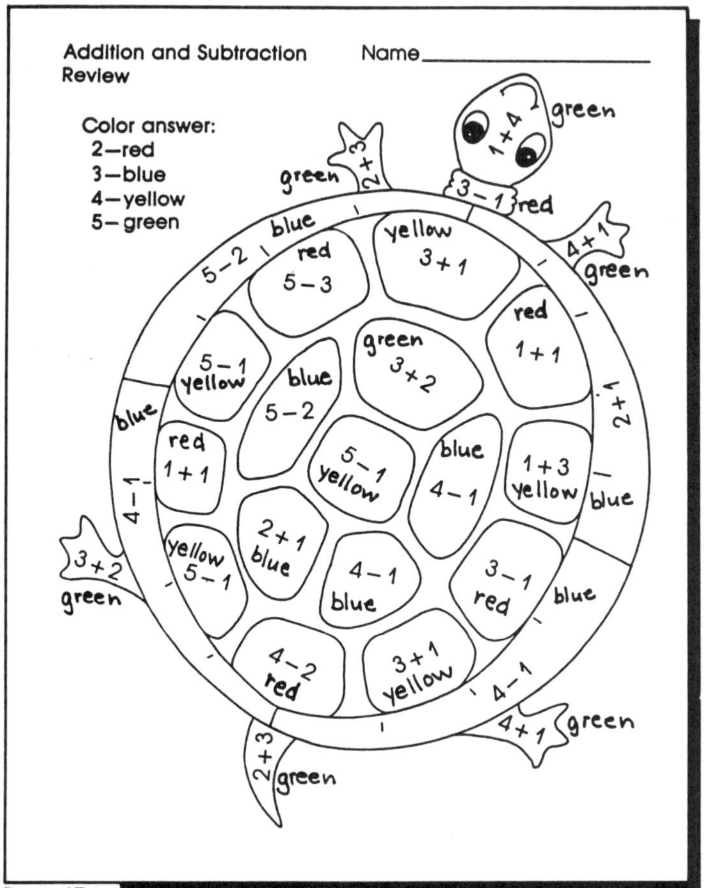

Page 17 — Addition and Subtraction Review

Color answer:
2—red
3—blue
4—yellow
5—green

green $1+4$
$3+2$ green
$3-1$ red
$5-2$ blue
$5-3$ red
yellow $3+1$
$4+1$ green
red $1+1$
green $3+2$
$5-1$ yellow
blue $5-2$
$1+2$
$4-1$ blue
red $1+1$
$5-1$ yellow
blue $4-1$
$1+3$ yellow
blue
$4-1$ blue
yellow $5-1$
$2+1$ blue
$4-1$ blue
$3-1$ red
blue
$3+2$ green
$4-2$ red
$3+1$ yellow
$4-1$
$4+1$ green
$2+3$ $2+2$ green

Page 18 — Zero Concept

$3+0 = 3$ $3-0 = 3$

$4+0 = 4$ $4-0 = 4$

$2+0 = 2$ $2-0 = 2$

$1+0 = \underline{1}$ $1-0 = \underline{1}$
$9+0 = \underline{9}$ $5-0 = \underline{5}$
$7+0 = \underline{7}$ $8-0 = \underline{8}$
$10+0 = \underline{10}$ $2-0 = \underline{2}$
$3+0 = \underline{3}$ $9+0 = \underline{9}$
$5+0 = \underline{5}$ $4-0 = \underline{4}$

Page 19 — Subtraction (6-10)

$9 - 2 = 7$

$$\begin{array}{r} 7 \\ -1 \\ \hline 6 \end{array}$$

Subtract. Use code to color.
6—orange   9—green
7—red   10—purple
8—yellow

$11-1 = 10$
purple

$$\begin{array}{r} 9 \\ -1 \\ \hline 8 \end{array}$$
yellow

$8-1 = 7$
red

$10-4 = 6$
orange

$$\begin{array}{r} 9 \\ -2 \\ \hline 7 \end{array}$$
red

$$\begin{array}{r} 10 \\ -1 \\ \hline 9 \end{array}$$
green

$10-2 = 8$
yellow

$11-2 = 9$
green

$$\begin{array}{r} 10 \\ -3 \\ \hline 7 \end{array}$$
red

Page 20 — Subtraction (6-10)

Count the candy.
Write number on blank.
Circle problems with same answer.

6
$9-3$ $7-1$
$8-2$ $9-2$

9
$10-1$ $10-4$
$11-2$ $9-1$

7
$9-2$ $8-1$ $10-3$
$10-4$

6
$10-4$ $7-2$ $8-2$
$8-2$

8
$9-4$ $10-2$ $10-1$ $9-1$

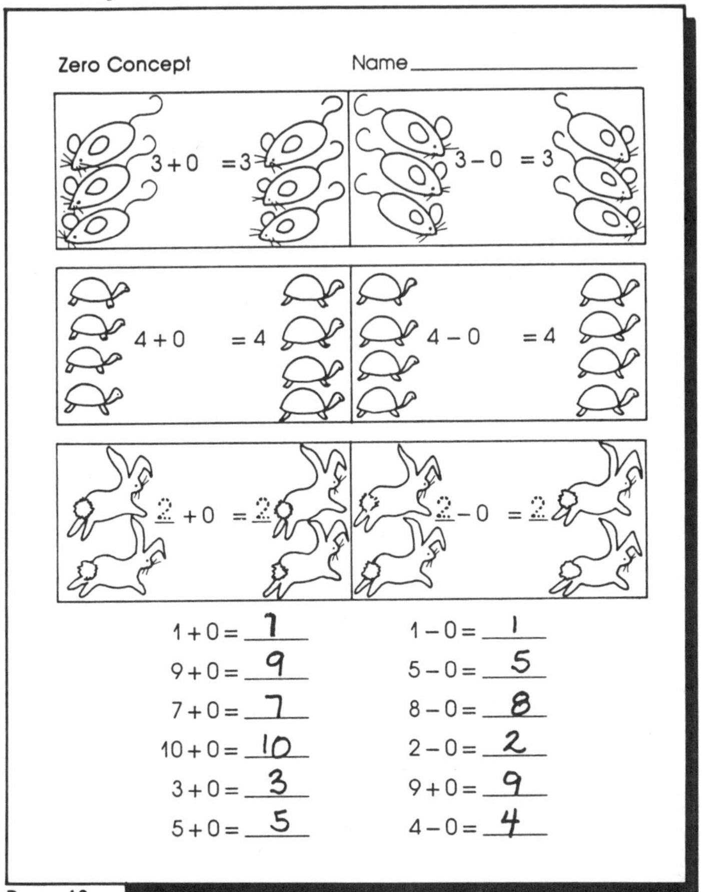

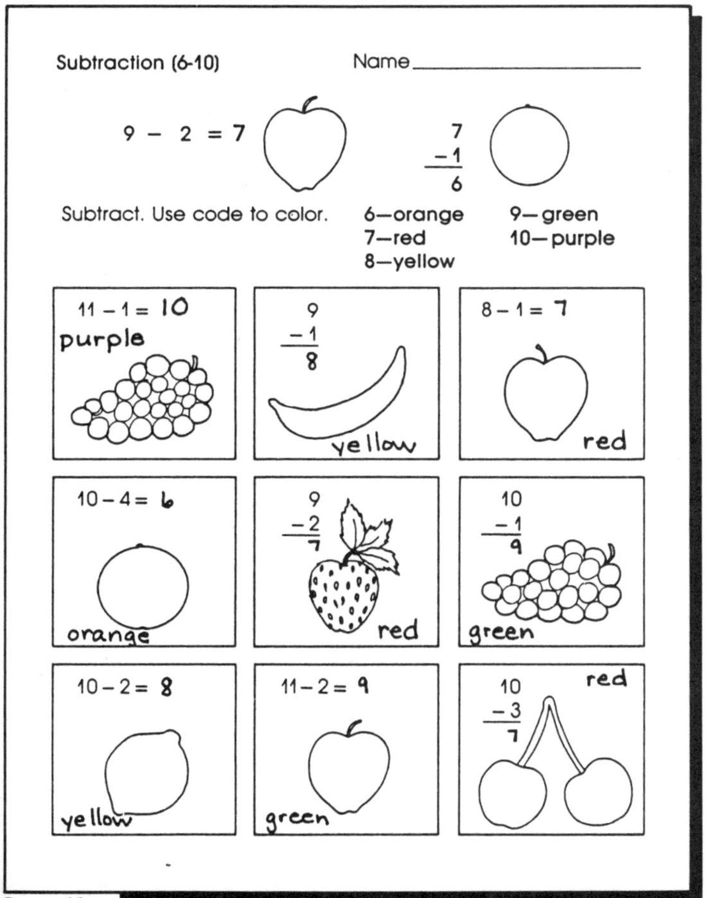

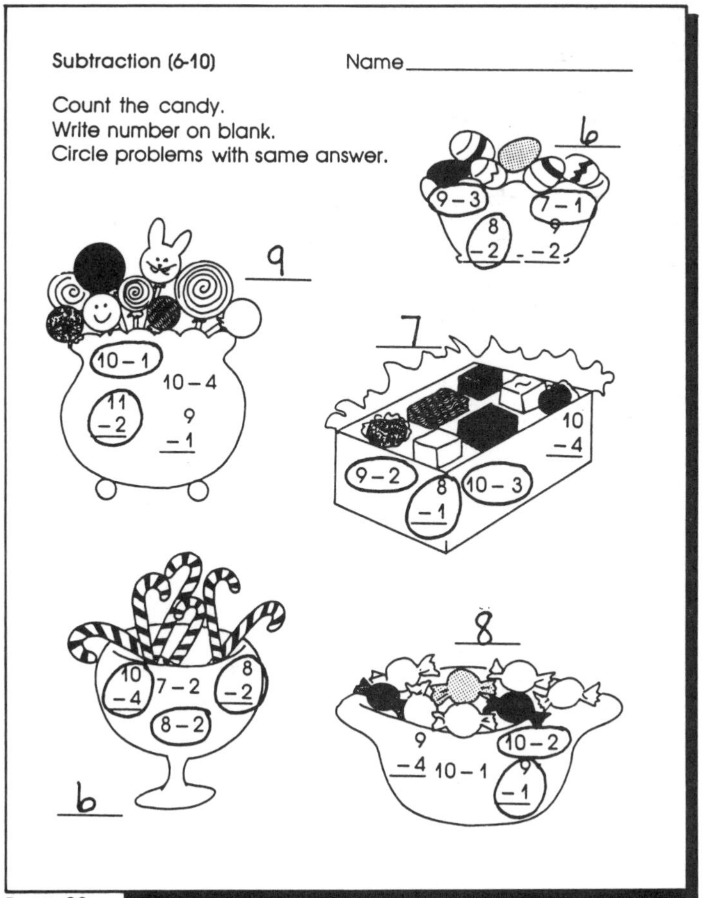

Answer Key

Page 21

Review
Addition and Subtraction

Name _____

Add or subtract.
Use code to color each part of picture.

6—yellow   9—blue
7—red   10—orange
8—green

orange   6+4   11−1
9+1
blue 5+4   9+0 blue   9−1   green
green   6+3   7+2   blue
blue   11−3   12−3 blue
red 3+4   4+4   6+1 green   7+1 green
9−2
orange 8+2   green 10−2   6+2
7−1
8−2   green   10−4 yellow
yellow

Page 22

Review
Addition and Subtraction

Name _____

Add or subtract.
Use code to color picture.

1—yellow   4—brown   7—black
2—blue   5—green   8—purple
3—red   6—orange

yellow 5−4   9−6 red   yellow 3−2
brown 2+2
black   6+1   orange 5+1
4+4 purple 9−1   10−6 brown
brown 1+3   3+2 green   7−2 green
orange 9−3   5−3
5+2 black   brown 3+1   blue   5−1 brown   black 9−2

Page 23

MAGIC SQUARES

Name _____

+ | 6 | 2 | **8**
3 | 4 | **7**
9 | **6** | **15**

− | 11 | 2 | **9**
6 | 1 | **5**
5 | **1** | **4**

+ | 5 | 2 | **7**
3 | 4 | **7**
8 | **6** | **14**

+ | 9 | 3 | **12**
2 | 1 | **3**
11 | **4** | **15**

+ | 8 | 1 | **9**
2 | 3 | **5**
10 | **4** | **14**

+ | 2 | 1 | **3**
3 | 6 | **9**
5 | **7** | **12**

− | 13 | 6 | **7**
3 | 2 | **1**
10 | **4** | **6**

− | 15 | 6 | **9**
9 | 3 | **6**
6 | **3** | **3**

− | 12 | 5 | **7**
3 | 2 | **1**
9 · | **3** | **6**

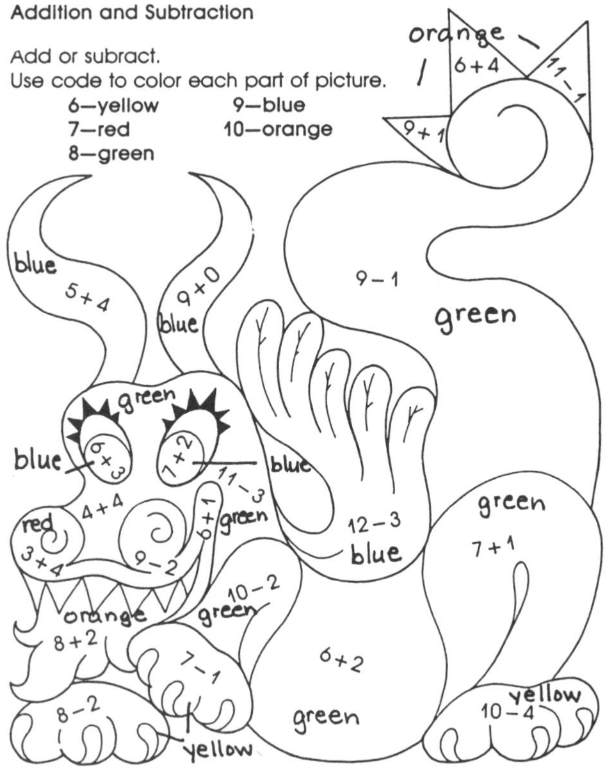

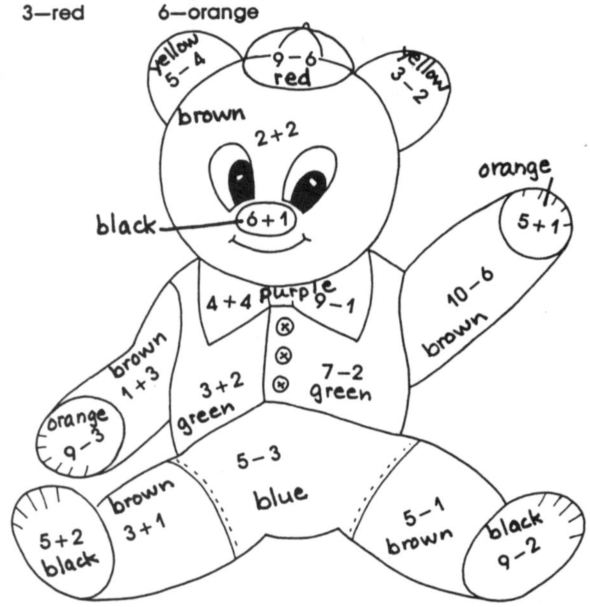

Page 24

ADDITION and SUBTRACTION REVIEW

Name _____

Work problems. Use color code to find the Secret Word!

15—yellow   12—green
14—orange   11—blue
13—red

13 − 9 | 15 − 9 | 8 + 1 | 14 − 12 | 13 − 8
2 + 8 | 11 − 8
5 − 1 | 3 − 1
15 − 6 | 9 − 8
9 − 6 | 4 + 6
13 − 6 | 15 − 8 | 13 − 8 | 10 − 2
6 − 2 | 7 − 1
14 − 5 | 15 − 10
15 − 7
6 − 3 | 10 − 1 | 8 − 1
15 − 5 | 3 + 7
4 − 1 | 3 − 2

GREAT

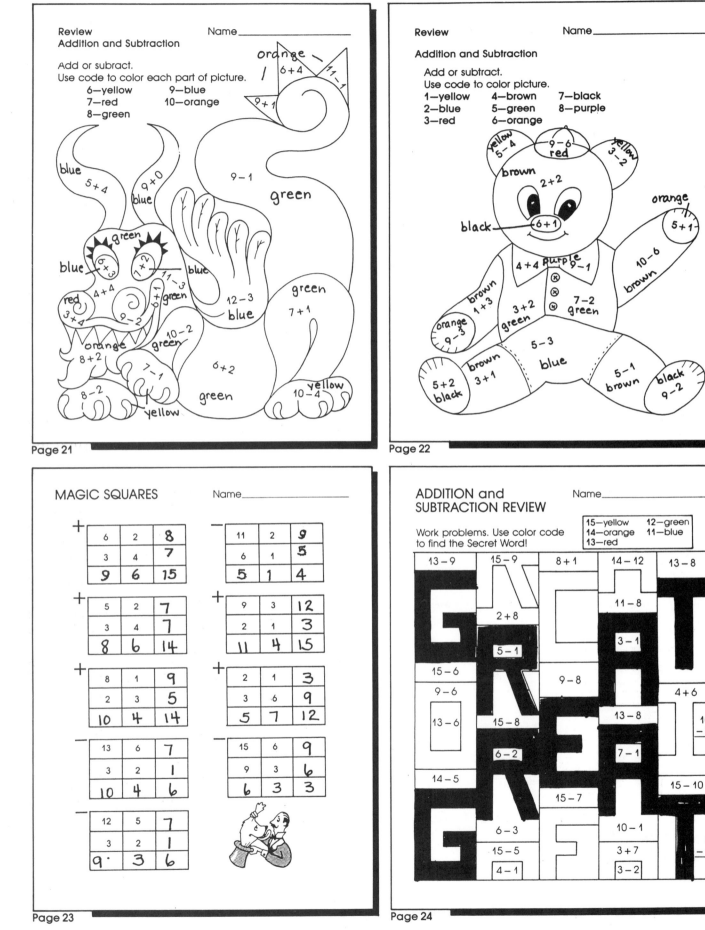

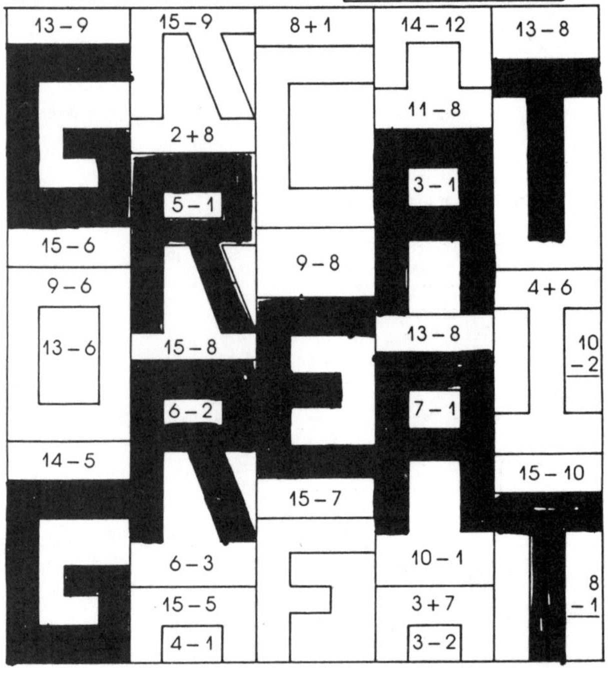

Answer Key

Page 25

ORDINAL NUMBERS   Name_____

Circle the ordinal number word for each treat.

- third, sixteenth, (fifth)
- fifteenth, (fourth) first
- (twelfth) second, seventh
- third, eleventh, (fifteenth)
- eighth, first, (tenth)
- (sixteenth) thirteenth, third
- ninth, second, (thirteenth)
- sixth, (seventh) ninth,

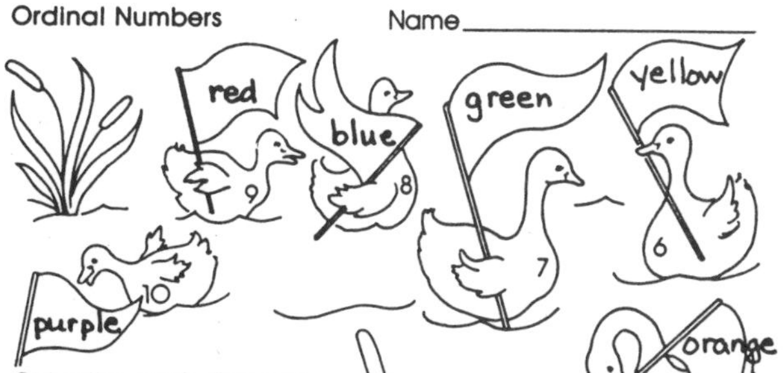

Page 26

Ordinal Numbers   Name_____

Color the ninth flag red.
Write O on the second flag.
Color the eighth flag blue.
Write D on the fourth flag.
Color the sixth flag yellow.
Write G on the first flag.
Color the tenth flag purple.
Write O on the third flag.
Color the seventh flag green.
Color the fifth flag orange.

Page 27

ORDINAL NUMBERS   Name_____

Number the circles in order, beginning at START.

Follow these directions:
Color the ninth blue.
Draw a ☐ on the eleventh.
Put a red X on the third.
Color the sixteenth purple.
Put a green ◯ on the fifth.
Color the thirteenth orange.
Put 3 lines in the sixth.
Color the tenth red striped.
Color the first green.
Put 6 black dots on the fourth.
Color the eighth 3 colors.
Put 2 green lines on the twelfth.
Put an orange △ on the fifteenth.
Color the second the same as the ninth.
Draw ☺ on the fourteenth.
Put 2 brown X 's on the seventh.

Page 28

Place Value: Tens and Ones   Name_____

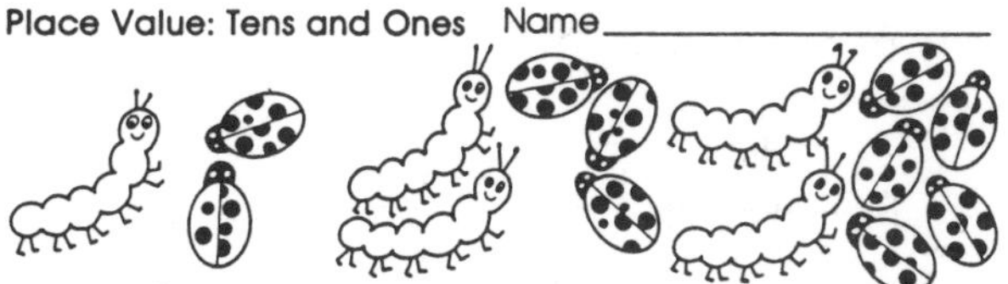

1 tens	2 ones
12	

2 tens	3 ones
23	

2 tens	5 ones
25	

4 tens	3 ones
43	

5 tens	1 ones
51	

3 tens	4 ones
34	

2 tens	2 ones
22	

3 tens	5 ones
35	

1 tens	4 ones
14	

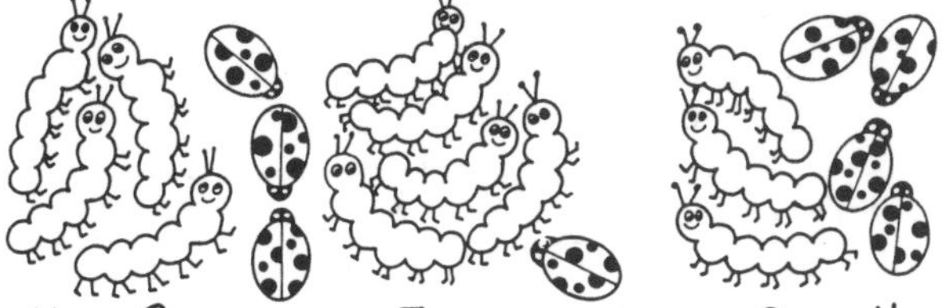

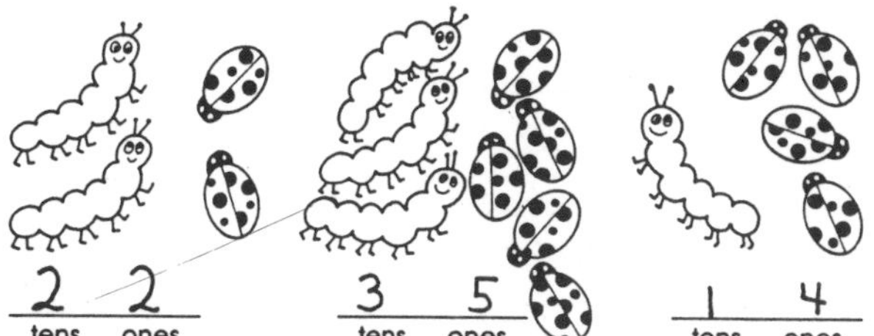

Answer Key

Page 29

Place Value: Tens and Ones   Name_____

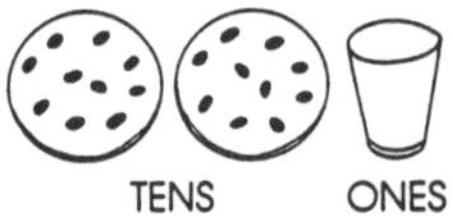

TENS   ONES

2 tens 1 ones **2 1** = **21**

tens ones
2 tens 8 ones **2 8** = **28**   8 tens 3 ones **8 3** = **83**
4 tens 6 ones **4 6** = **46**   7 tens 4 ones **7 4** = **74**
5 tens 7 ones **5 7** = **57**   1 ten 7 ones **1 7** = **17**
3 tens 8 ones **3 8** = **38**   6 tens 3 ones **6 3** = **63**
9 tens 1 one **9 1** = **91**   5 tens 3 ones **5 3** = **53**
1 ten 4 ones **1 4** = **14**   2 tens 6 ones **2 6** = **26**
6 tens 2 ones **6 2** = **62**   9 tens 5 ones **9 5** = **95**
8 tens 5 ones **8 5** = **85**   3 tens 6 ones **3 6** = **36**
7 tens 9 ones **7 9** = **79**   4 tens 2 ones **4 2** = **42**

38 = **3** tens **8** ones   46 = **4** tens **6** ones
57 = **5** tens **7** ones   29 = **2** tens **9** ones
15 = **1** tens **5** ones   71 = **7** tens **1** ones
65 = **6** tens **5** ones   21 = **2** tens **1** ones
88 = **8** tens **8** ones   13 = **1** tens **3** ones

Page 30

Place Value Review   Name_____

Color one of the two balloons. Here's how.

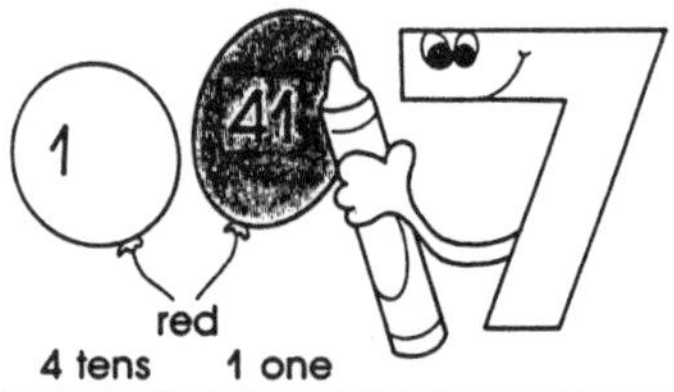

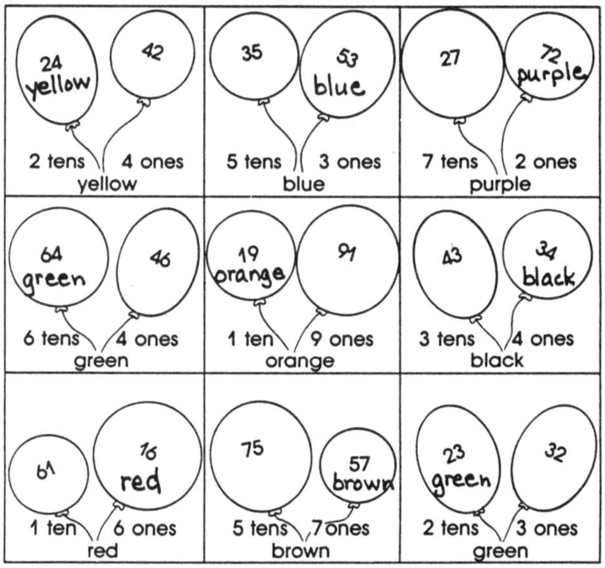

red

4 tens   1 one

24 yellow / 42	35 / 53 blue	27 / 72 purple
2 tens \ 4 ones yellow	5 tens \ 3 ones blue	7 tens \ 2 ones purple
64 green / 46	19 orange / 91	43 / 34 black
6 tens \ 4 ones green	1 ten \ 9 ones orange	3 tens \ 4 ones black
61 / 16 red	75 / 57 brown	23 green / 32
1 ten \ 6 ones red	5 tens \ 7 ones brown	2 tens \ 3 ones green

Page 31

Sequencing Numbers   Name_____

Put the numbers on each house in order.

28, 25, 27, 26   36, 38, 37   15, 17, 16, 18
25, 26, 27, 28   **36, 37, 38**   **15, 16, 17, 18**

32, 34, 33, 35, 36   17, 19, 18   66, 68, 67
32, 33, 34, 35, 36 **17, 18, 19**   **66, 67, 68**

65, 61, 63, 64, 62   41, 43, 42   75, 78, 77, 76
61, 62, 63, 64, 65 **41, 42, 43**   **75, 76, 77, 78**

Page 32

Greater Than; Less Than   Name_____

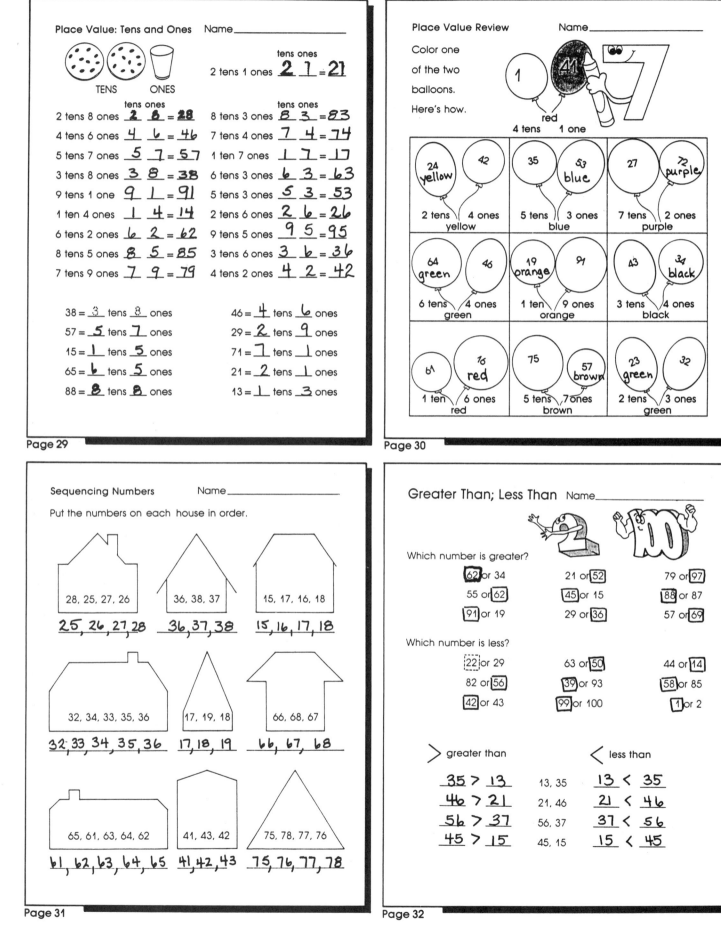

Which number is greater?

62 or 34   21 or **52**   79 or **97**
55 or **62**   **45** or 15   **88** or 87
91 or 19   29 or **36**   57 or **69**

Which number is less?

22 or 29   63 or **50**   44 or **14**
82 or **56**   **39** or 93   **58** or 85
42 or 43   **99** or 100   **1** or 2

> greater than   < less than

35 > **13**   13, 35   **13** < **35**
46 > **21**   21, 46   **21** < **46**
56 > **37**   56, 37   **37** < **56**
45 > **15**   45, 15   **15** < **45**

Answer Key

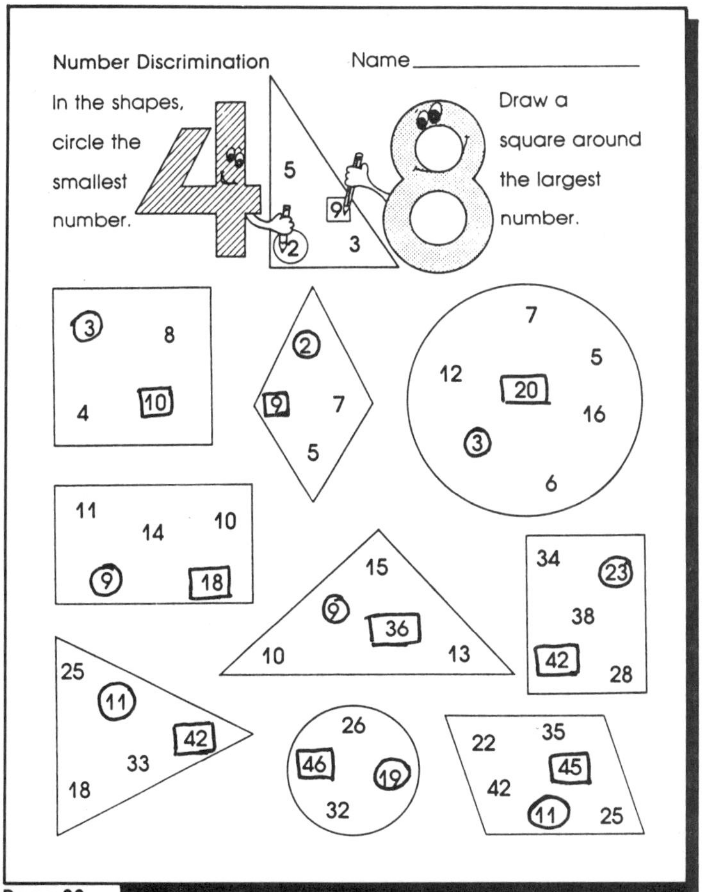

Page 33

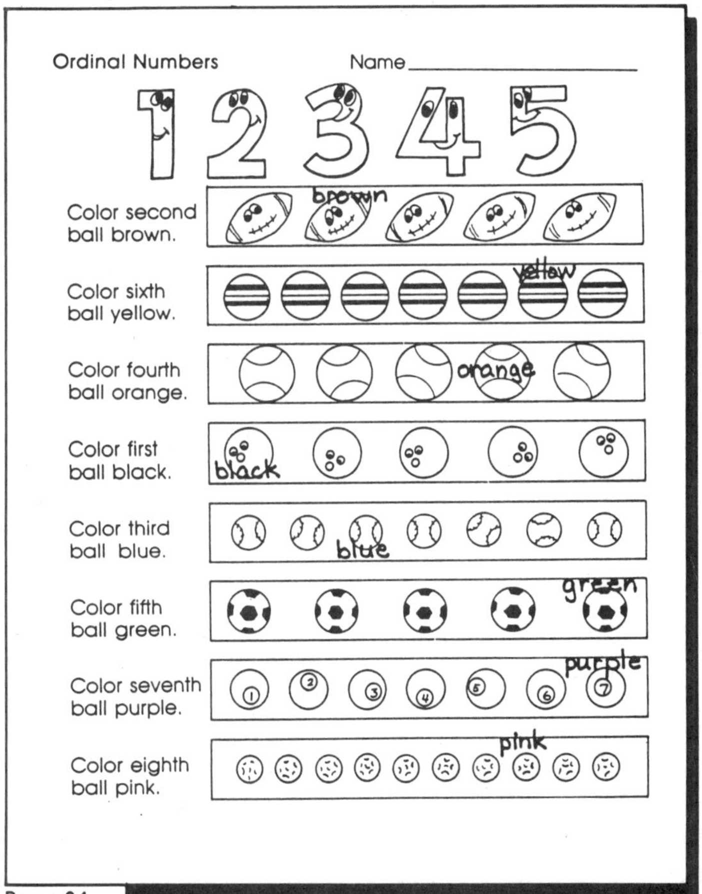

Page 34

Page 35

Page 36

Answer Key

Counting by 2's and 5's Name ____________

Write and count by 2's.

2	4	6	8	10	12	14	16	18	20

Write and count by 5's.

5	10	15	20	25	30	35	40	45	50

Connect the dots by 2's.

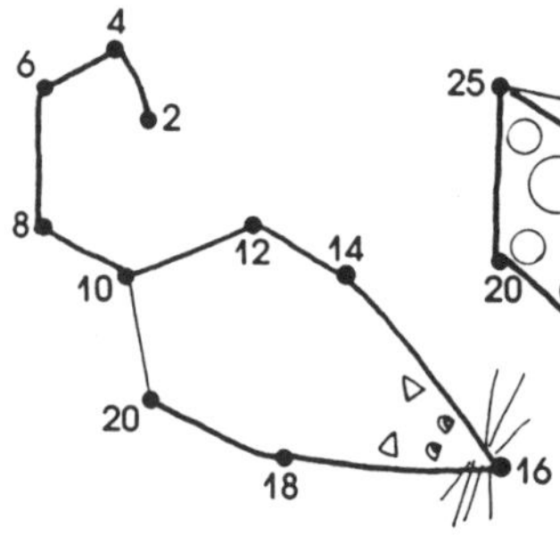

Connect the dots by 5's.

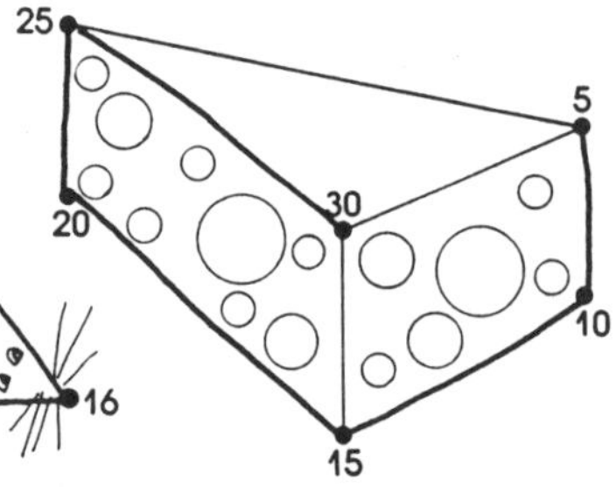

Page 37

Shape Recognition Name ____________

Color: brown yellow green red

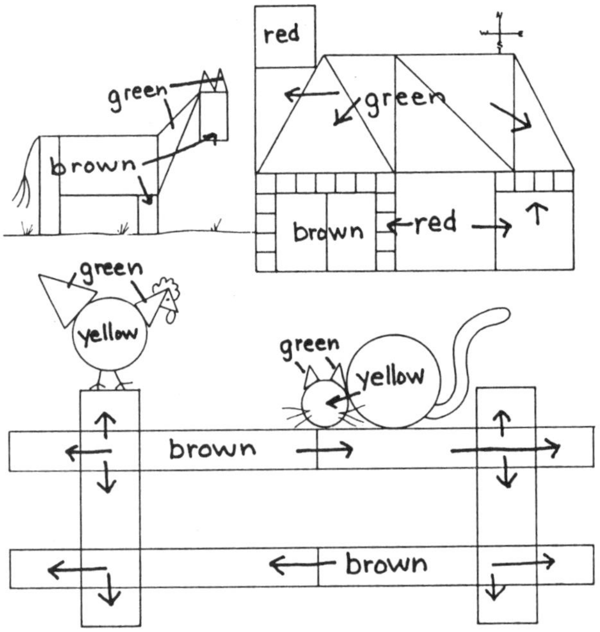

Page 38

Shape Recognition Name ____________

Color:
squares — green
rectangles — yellow
circles — red
triangles — blue

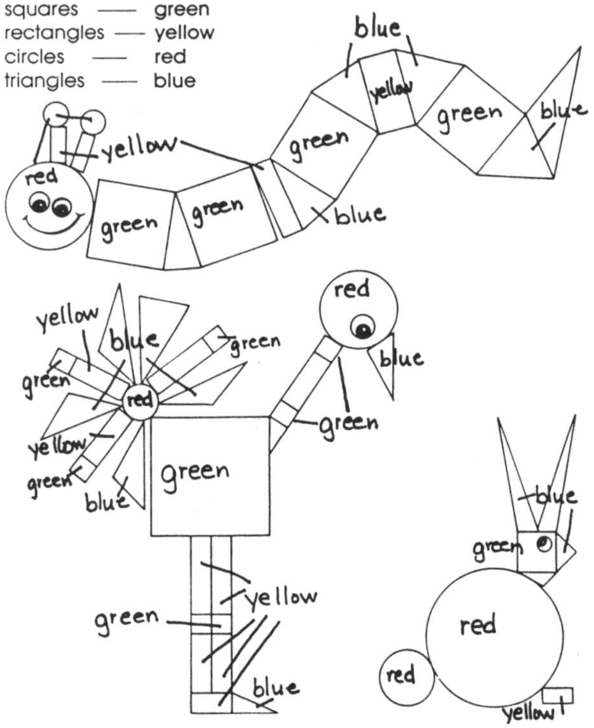

Page 39

Shape Discrimination Name ____________

How many circles? ○ 8 How many triangles? △ 11

How many rectangles? ▯ 6 How many squares? □ 4

Color toys.

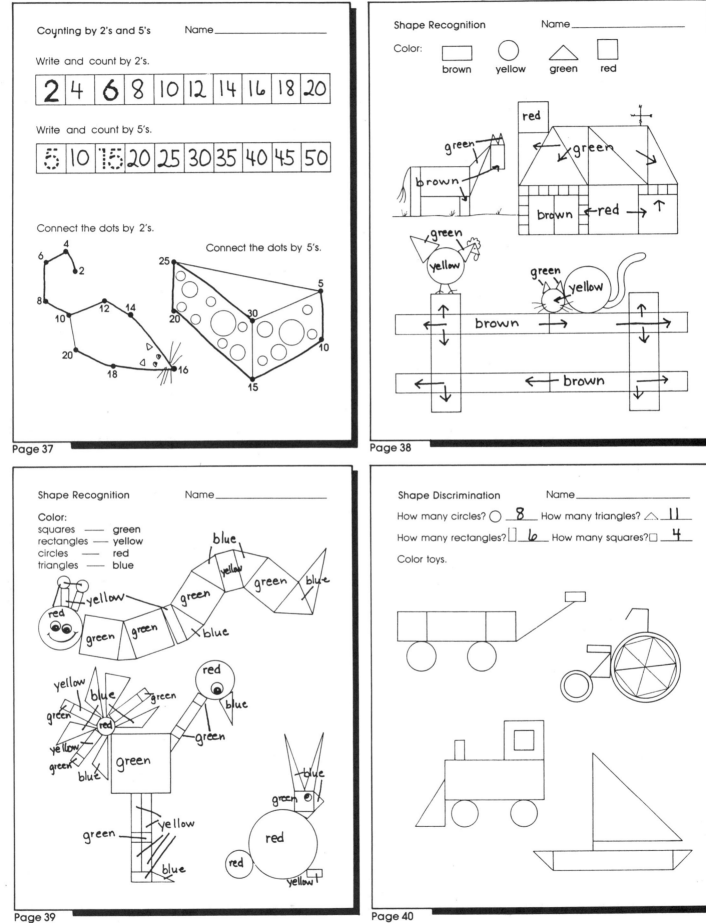

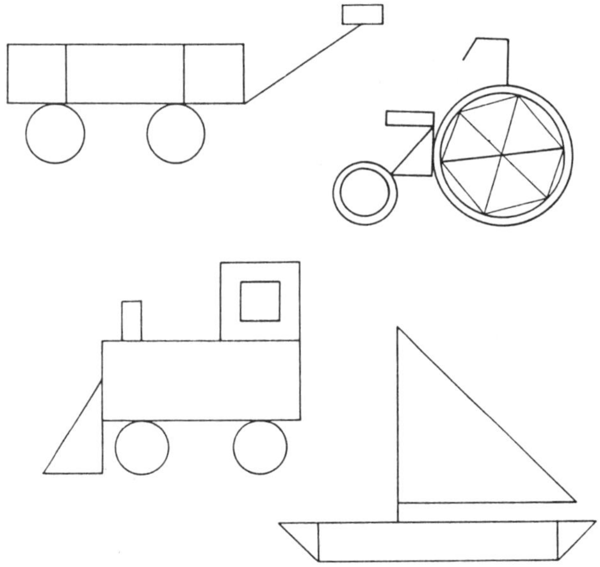

Page 40

Answer Key

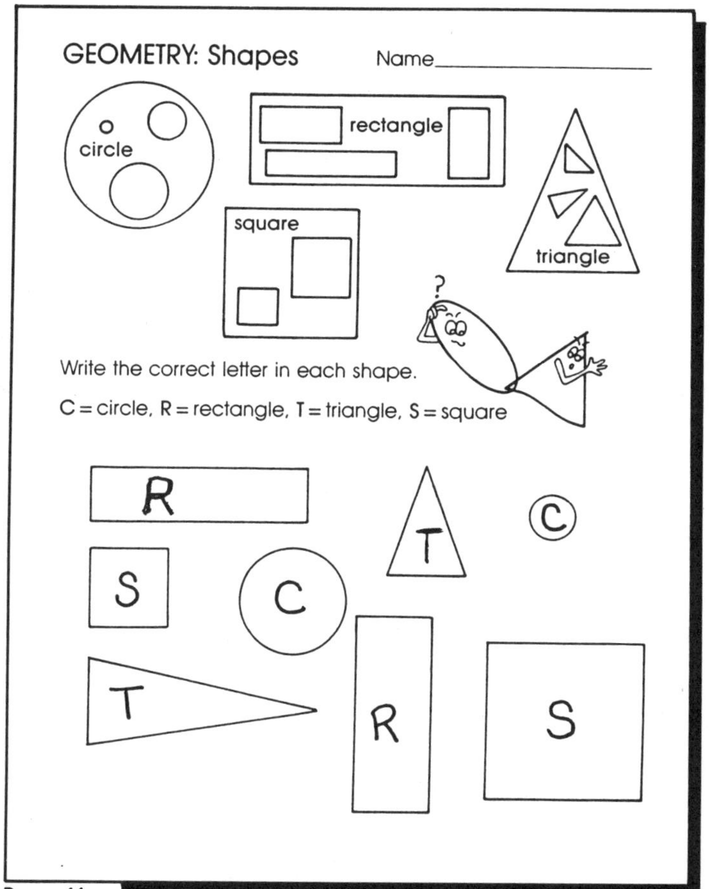
GEOMETRY: Shapes
Name
circle
rectangle
square
triangle
Write the correct letter in each shape.
C = circle, R = rectangle, T = triangle, S = square
R
T
C
S
C
T
R
S

Page 41

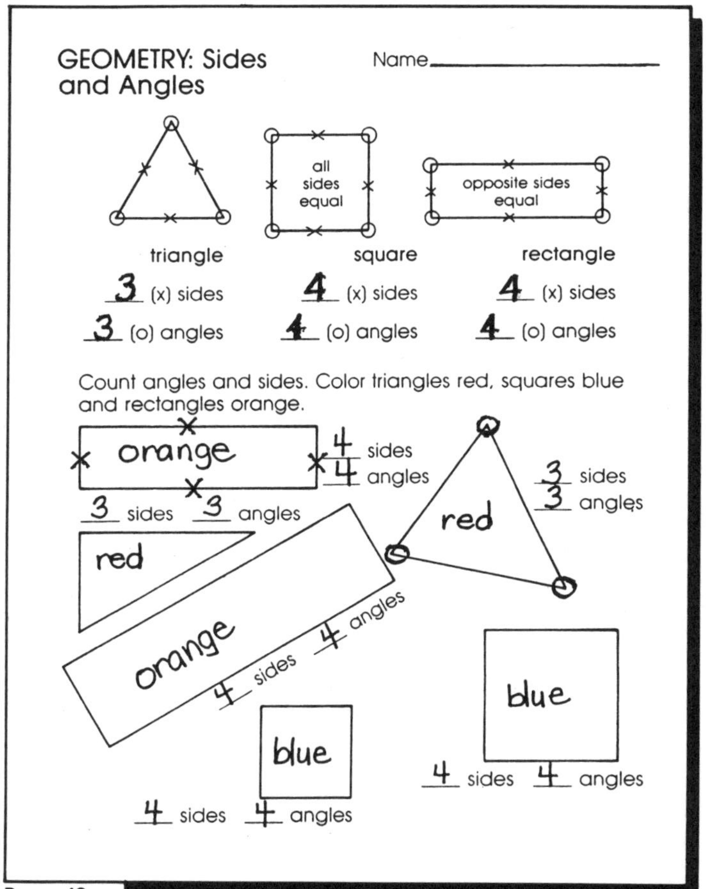
GEOMETRY: Sides and Angles
Name
all sides equal
opposite sides equal
triangle
square
rectangle
3 (x) sides
3 (o) angles
4 (x) sides
4 (o) angles
4 (x) sides
4 (o) angles
Count angles and sides. Color triangles red, squares blue and rectangles orange.
orange
4 sides
4 angles
3 sides
3 angles
red
3 sides
3 angles
red
orange
4 sides
4 angles
blue
4 sides
4 angles
blue
4 sides
4 angles

Page 42

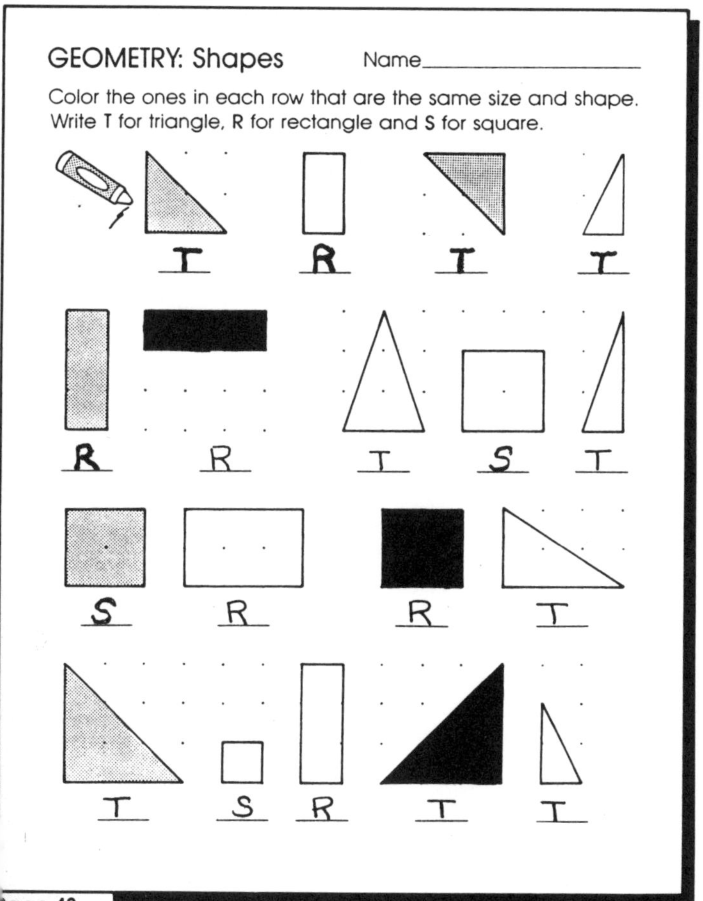
GEOMETRY: Shapes
Name
Color the ones in each row that are the same size and shape.
Write T for triangle, R for rectangle and S for square.
T
R
T
T
R
R
T
S
T
S
R
R
T
T
S
R
T
T

Page 43

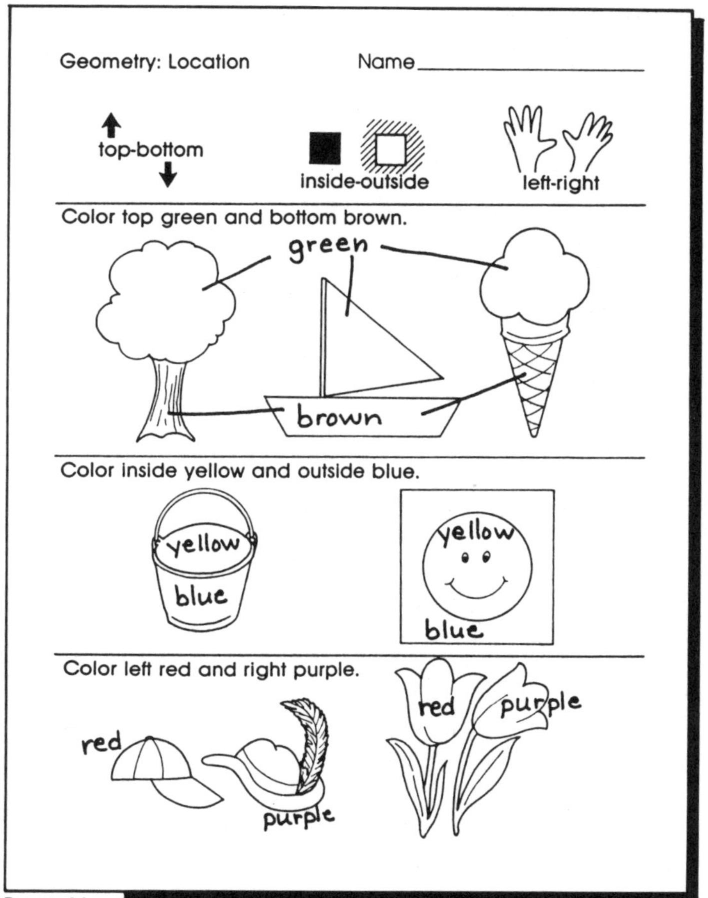
Geometry: Location
Name
top-bottom
inside-outside
left-right
Color top green and bottom brown.
green
brown
Color inside yellow and outside blue.
yellow
blue
yellow
blue
Color left red and right purple.
red
purple
red
purple

Page 44

Answer Key

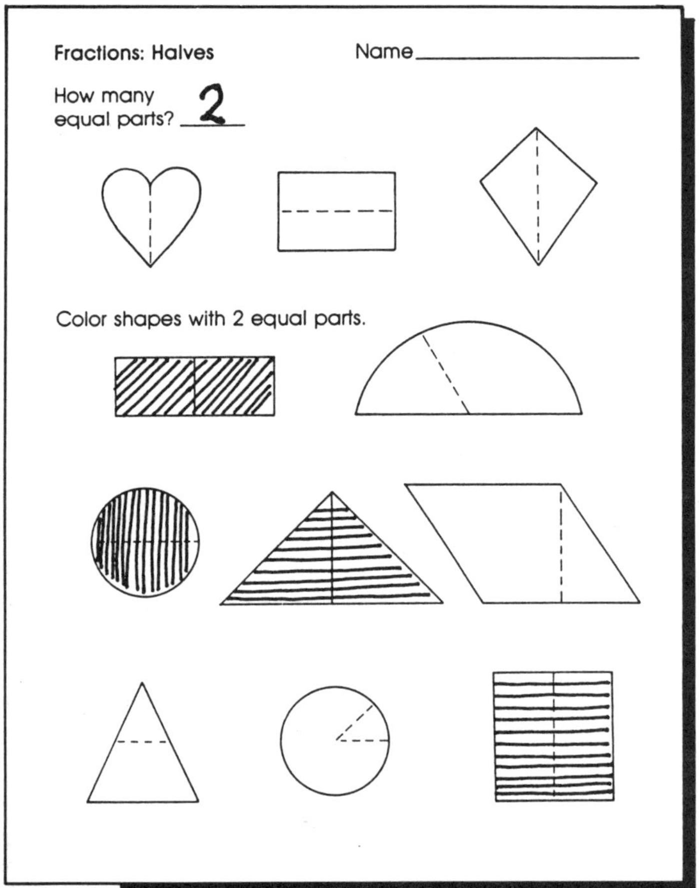
Fractions: Halves Name____________

How many equal parts? 2

Color shapes with 2 equal parts.

Page 45

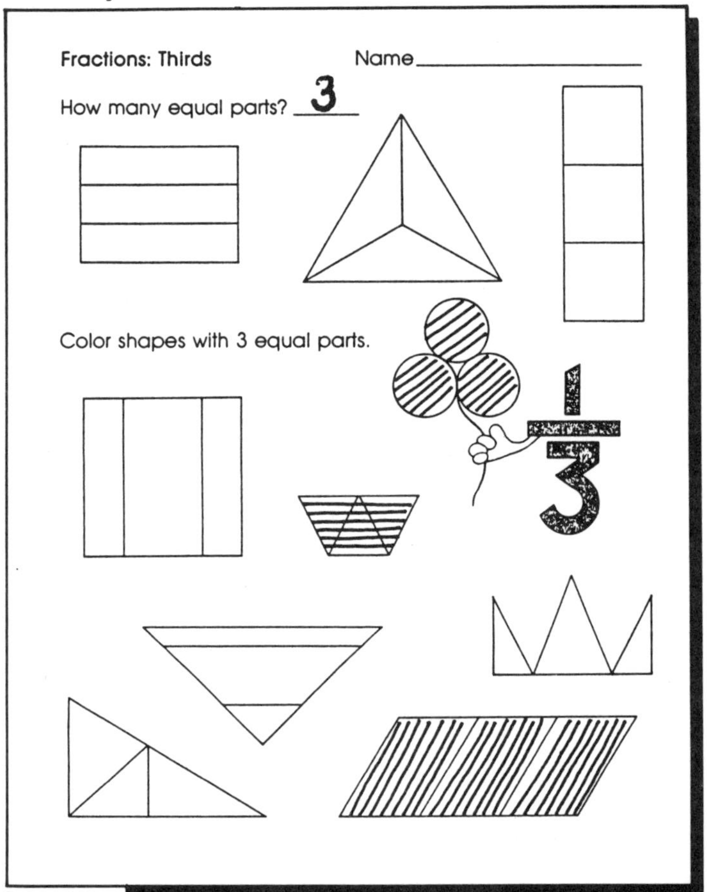
Fractions: Thirds Name____________

How many equal parts? 3

Color shapes with 3 equal parts.

Page 46

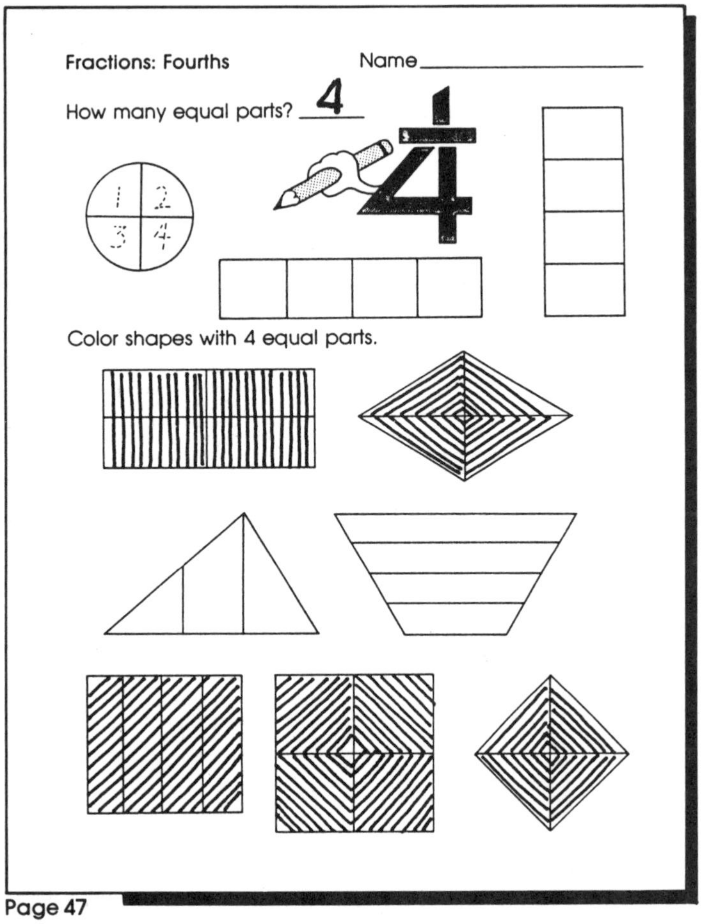
Fractions: Fourths Name____________

How many equal parts? 4

Color shapes with 4 equal parts.

Page 47

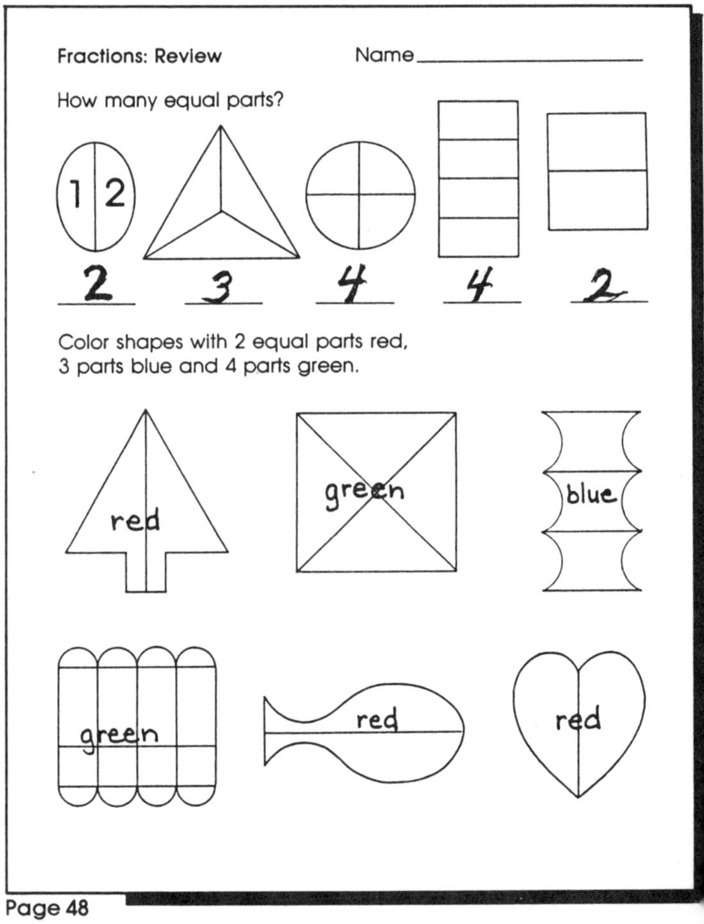
Fractions: Review Name____________

How many equal parts?

2 3 4 4 2

Color shapes with 2 equal parts red, 3 parts blue and 4 parts green.

Page 48

Answer Key

Page 49

Addition (11-15)   Name_____

4	+	7	=	11

Add.

3 + 9 = **12**

6 + 7 = **13**

6 + 5 = **11**

5 + 7 = **12**

4 + 9 = **13**

9 + 6 = **15**

7 + 7 = **14**

7 + 8 = **15**

6 + 8 = **14**

Page 50

Addition (2-15)   Name_____

Match.

8 + 2 — 15
9 + 6 — 4
2 + 2 — 10

1 + 2 — 11
6 + 7 — 3
5 + 6 — 13

6 + 2 — 8
1 + 1 — 6
1 + 5 — 2

3 + 2 — 10
6 + 8 — 14
5 + 5 — 5

6 + 6 — 12
6 + 3 — 9
3 + 4 — 7

7 + 2 — 15
6 + 9 — 9
12 + 1 — 13

10 + 1 — 14
9 + 5 — 8
7 + 1 — 11

Page 51

COLUMN ADDITION   Name_____

Work problem. Use color codes to find secret problem:

10 – pink	13 – green
11 – red	14 – blue
12 – yellow	15 – orange

7   3
   + 5
   9

red 2
     2
     1
   + 6
   11

6
2
+ 1
9

5   1
     6
   + 2
     9

3   8
     3
   + 4
    15
orange

6   4
     3
   + 2
     9

7 + 1 + 1 = **9**

1 + 4 + 1 + 1 = **7**

green 6
       1
       4
     + 2
      13

blue 4
      6
      3
    + 1
     14

7   1
     5
     2
   + 1
     9

6 + 5 + 1 = **12**
yellow

9   2
     6
   + 2
    10 pink

4
3
+ 2
9

Page 52

Addition (2-15)   Name_____

Add. ⬡2 and ▢7 = ⬭9

⬡2 and ▢4 = ⬭6

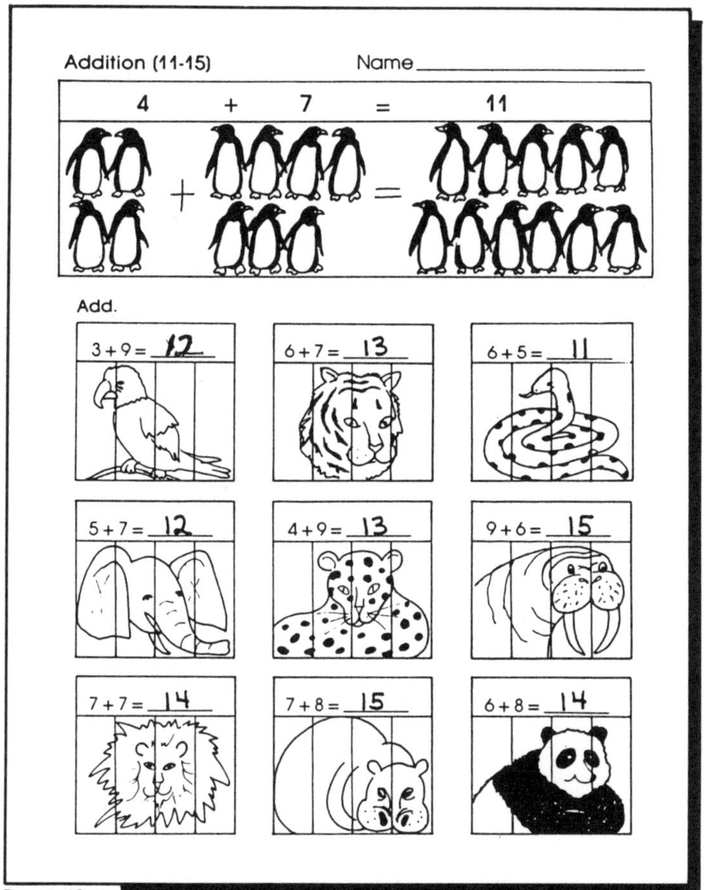

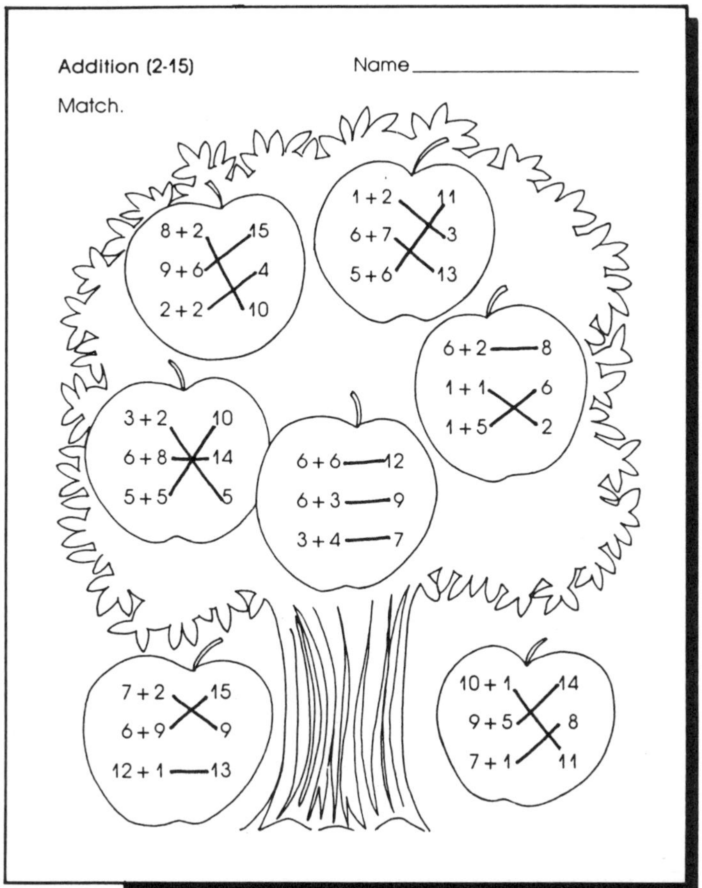

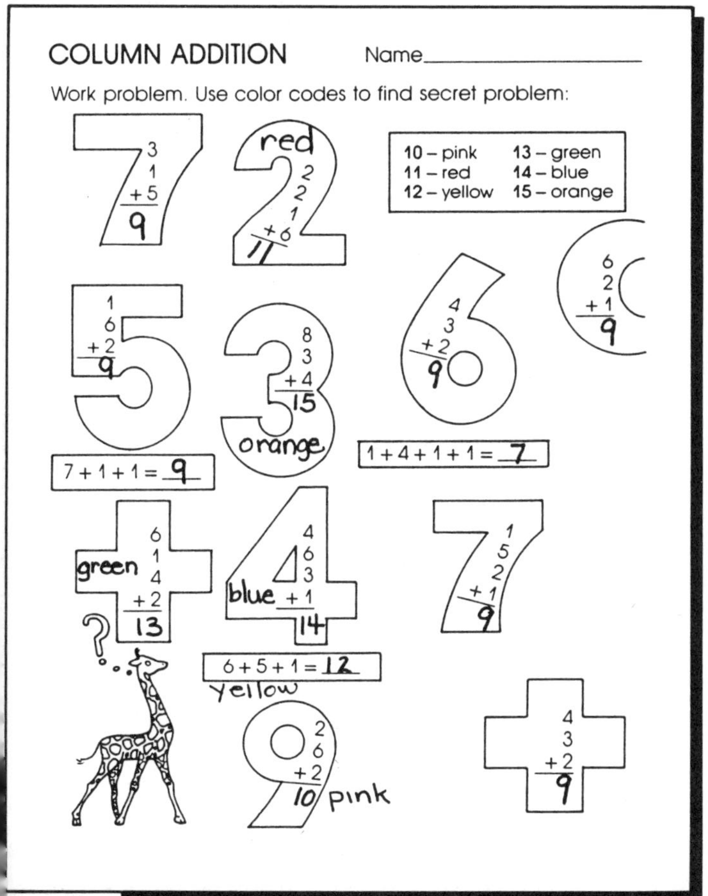

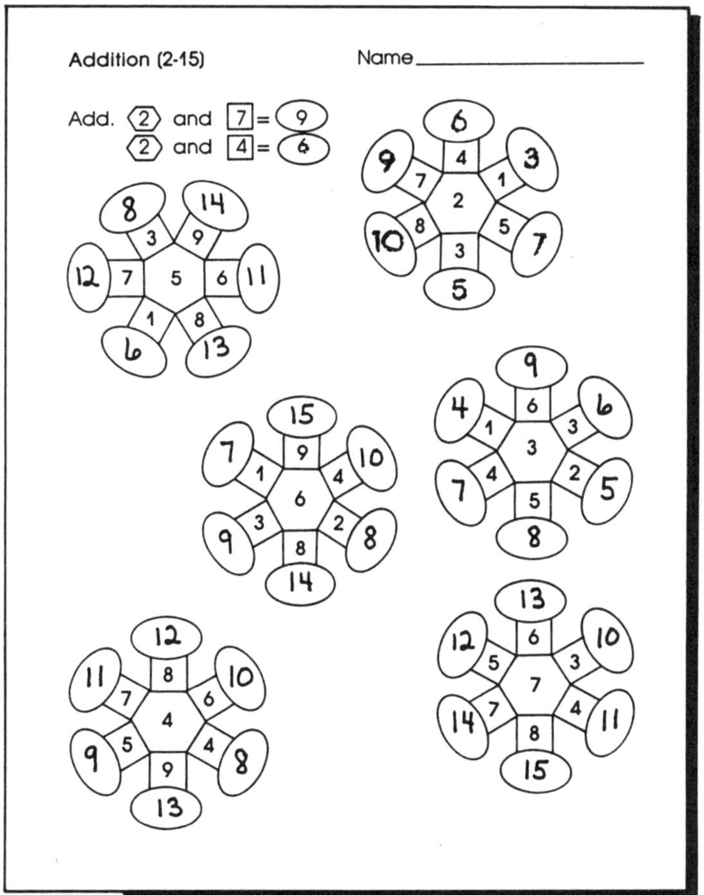

Answer Key

Subtraction (10-15)   Name_____

Count crayons. Write number on blank.
Circle problems that name answer.

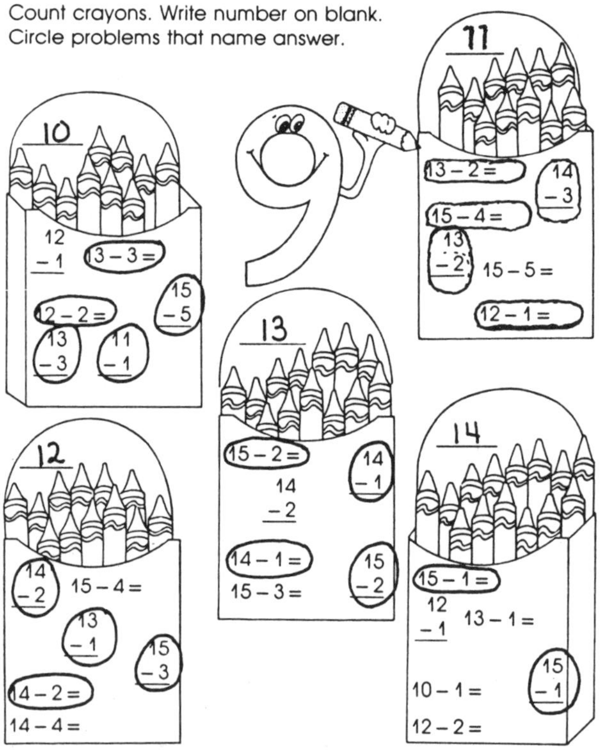

11

10

9

13 − 2 = __
$\begin{array}{r} 14 \\ -\ 3 \end{array}$

15 − 4 = __

$\begin{array}{r} 13 \\ -\ 2 \end{array}$

15 − 5 = __

12 − 1 = __

$\begin{array}{r} 12 \\ -\ 1 \end{array}$

13 − 3 =

$\begin{array}{r} 15 \\ -\ 5 \end{array}$

12 − 2 =

$\begin{array}{r} 13 \\ -\ 3 \end{array}$ $\begin{array}{r} 11 \\ -\ 1 \end{array}$

13

15 − 2 =

$\begin{array}{r} 14 \\ -\ 2 \end{array}$

14 − 1 = $\begin{array}{r} 15 \\ -\ 2 \end{array}$

15 − 3 =

12

$\begin{array}{r} 14 \\ -\ 2 \end{array}$ 15 − 4 =

$\begin{array}{r} 13 \\ -\ 1 \end{array}$ $\begin{array}{r} 15 \\ -\ 3 \end{array}$

14 − 2 =

14 − 4 =

14

$\begin{array}{r} 14 \\ -\ 1 \end{array}$

$\begin{array}{r} 14 \\ -\ 2 \end{array}$

15 − 1 =

$\begin{array}{r} 12 \\ -\ 1 \end{array}$ 13 − 1 =

10 − 1 =

12 − 2 =

$\begin{array}{r} 15 \\ -\ 1 \end{array}$

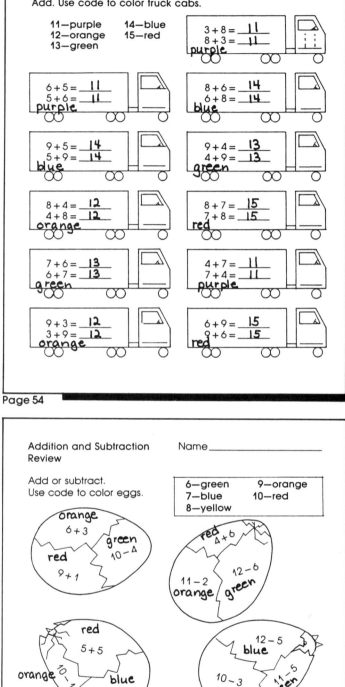

Commutative Property   Name_____

Add. Use code to color truck cabs.

11—purple   14—blue
12—orange   15—red
13—green

3 + 8 = **11**
8 + 3 = **11**
purple

6 + 5 = **11**
5 + 6 = **11**
purple

8 + 6 = **14**
6 + 8 = **14**
blue

9 + 5 = **14**
5 + 9 = **14**
blue

9 + 4 = **13**
4 + 9 = **13**
green

8 + 4 = **12**
4 + 8 = **12**
orange

8 + 7 = **15**
7 + 8 = **15**
red

7 + 6 = **13**
6 + 7 = **13**
green

4 + 7 = **11**
7 + 4 = **11**
purple

9 + 3 = **12**
3 + 9 = **12**
orange

6 + 9 = **15**
9 + 6 = **15**
red

Subtraction (10-15)   Name_____

11 − 1 = 10

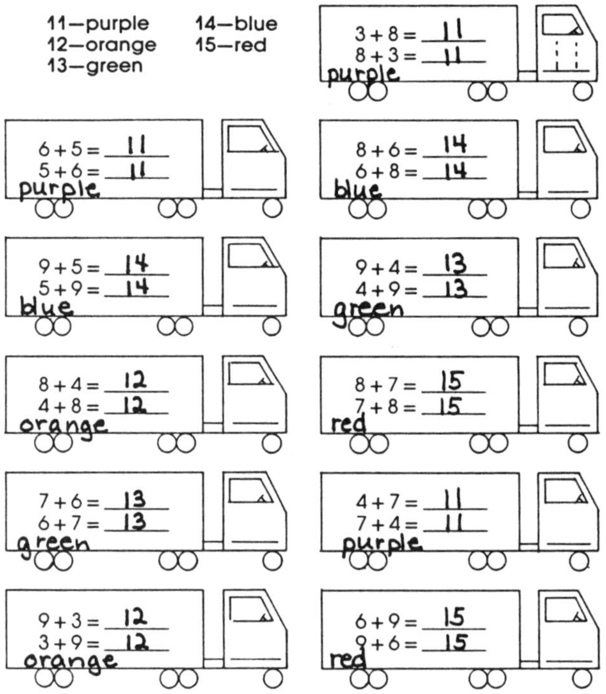

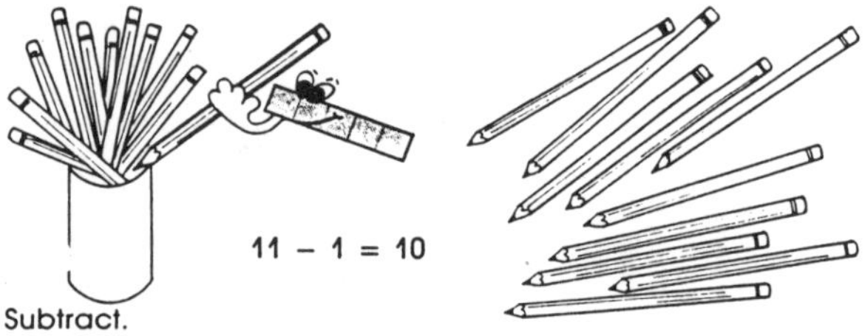

Subtract.

Use code to color crayons.

10—red   13—yellow
11—blue   14—orange
12—green   15—purple

red
11 − 1 = **10**

$\begin{array}{r} 11 \\ -\ 1 \\ \hline 10 \end{array}$

yellow
14 − 1 = **13**

$\begin{array}{r} 14 \\ -\ 1 \\ \hline 13 \end{array}$

purple
15 − 0 = **15**

$\begin{array}{r} 15 \\ -\ 0 \\ \hline 15 \end{array}$

orange
15 − 1 = **14**

$\begin{array}{r} 15 \\ -\ 1 \\ \hline 14 \end{array}$

blue
13 − 3 = **11**

green
14 − 2 = **12**

$\begin{array}{r} 14 \\ -\ 2 \\ \hline 12 \end{array}$

$\begin{array}{r} 13 \\ -\ 2 \\ \hline 11 \end{array}$

Addition and Subtraction Review   Name_____

Add or subtract.
Use code to color eggs.

6—green   9—orange
7—blue   10—red
8—yellow

orange
6 + 3
green
10 − 4
red
9 + 1

red
4 + 6
12 − 6
11 − 2
orange   green

red
5 + 5
orange
10 − 1
blue
3 + 4

12 − 5
blue
10 − 3
11 − 5
blue   green

blue
3 + 4
red
11 − 1
12 − 6
green

yellow
10 − 2
3 + 5
yellow
6 + 2
4 + 4
yellow

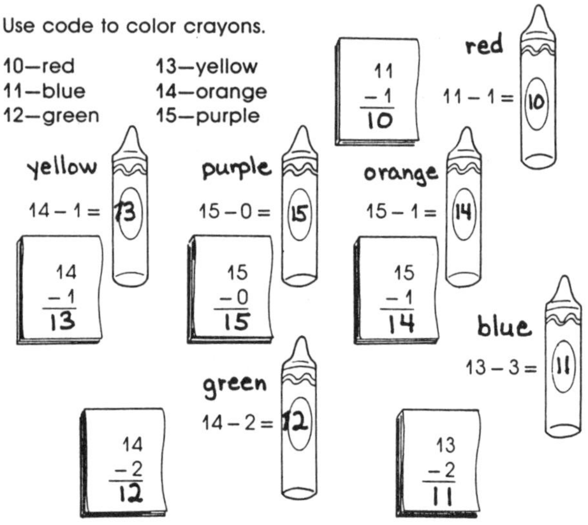

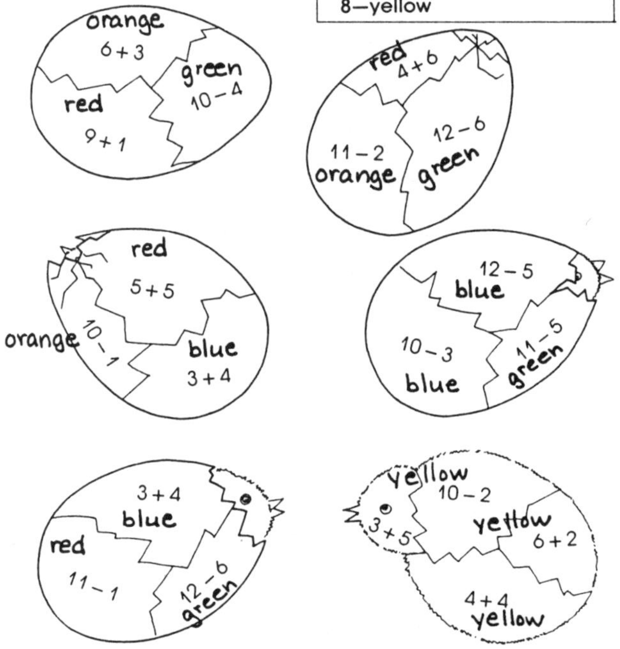

Answer Key

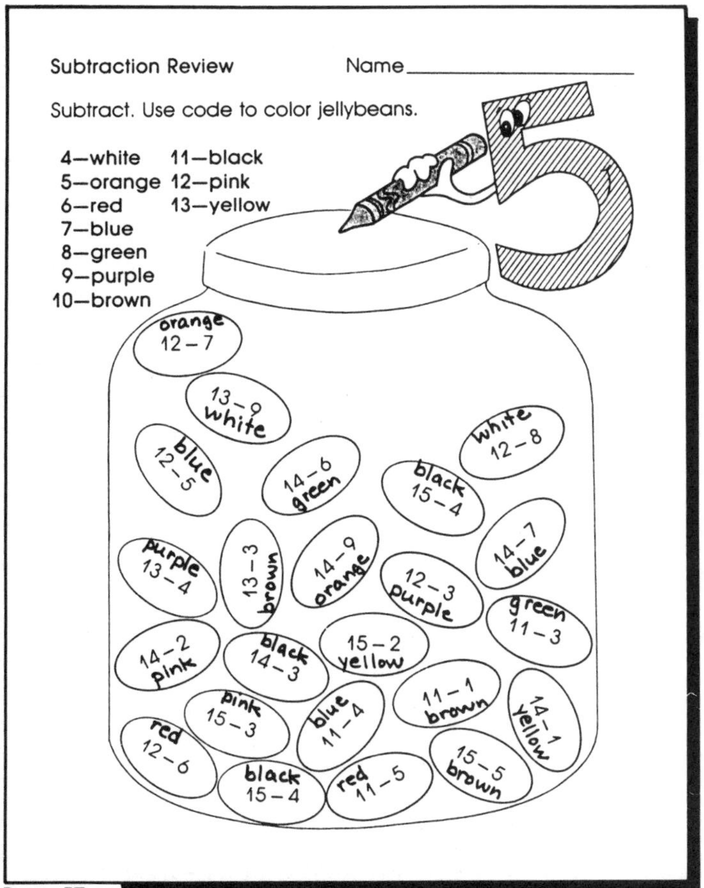

Page 57

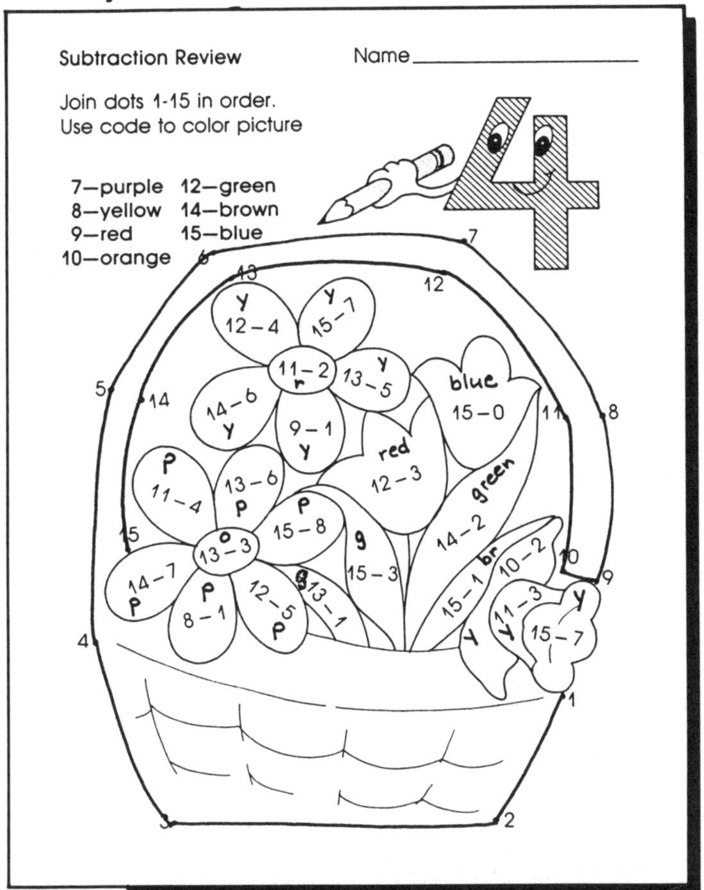

Page 58

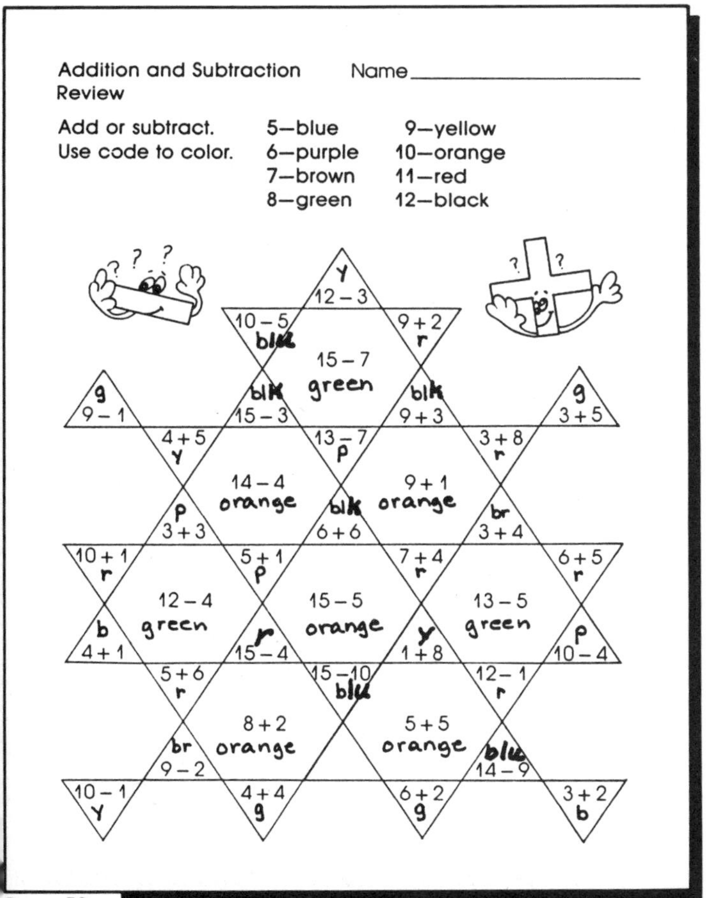

Page 59

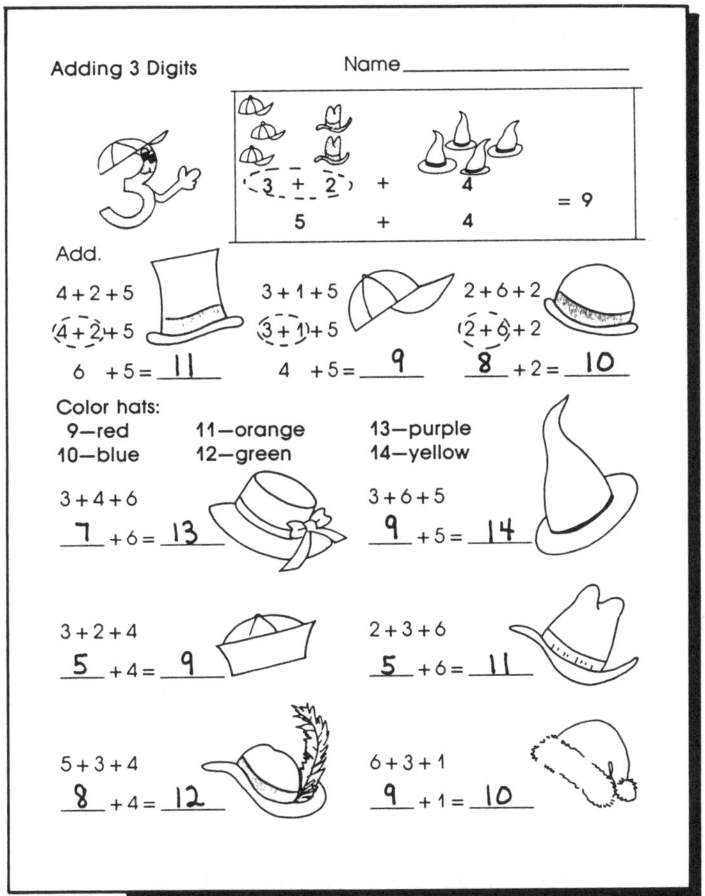

Page 60

Subtraction Review Name_____

Subtract. Use code to color jellybeans.

4—white 11—black
5—orange 12—pink
6—red 13—yellow
7—blue
8—green
9—purple
10—brown

Subtraction Review Name_____

Join dots 1-15 in order.
Use code to color picture

7—purple 12—green
8—yellow 14—brown
9—red 15—blue
10—orange

Addition and Subtraction Review Name_____

Add or subtract. 5—blue 9—yellow
Use code to color. 6—purple 10—orange
 7—brown 11—red
 8—green 12—black

Adding 3 Digits Name_____

$3 + 2 + 4 = 9$
$5 + 4 = 9$

Add.

$4+2+5$ $3+1+5$ $2+6+2$
$6 + 5 = 11$ $4 + 5 = 9$ $8 + 2 = 10$

Color hats:
9—red 11—orange 13—purple
10—blue 12—green 14—yellow

$3+4+6$ $3+6+5$
$7 + 6 = 13$ $9 + 5 = 14$

$3+2+4$ $2+3+6$
$5 + 4 = 9$ $5 + 6 = 11$

$5+3+4$ $6+3+1$
$8 + 4 = 12$ $9 + 1 = 10$

117

Answer Key

Page 61

$$4 + 3 = 7 \qquad 7 + 1 = 8$$

$4 + 3 + 1$
$\underline{7} + 1 = \underline{8}$

$\begin{array}{r} 4 \\ 3 \\ +1 \\ \hline 8 \end{array}$

$9 + 1 + 2$
$\underline{10} + 2 = \underline{12}$

$\begin{array}{r} 9 \\ 1 \\ +2 \\ \hline 12 \end{array}$

$5 + 1 + 2$
$\underline{6} + 2 = \underline{8}$

$\begin{array}{r} 5 \\ 1 \\ +2 \\ \hline 8 \end{array}$

$6 + 7 + 2$
$\underline{13} + 2 = \underline{15}$

$\begin{array}{r} 6 \\ 7 \\ +2 \\ \hline 15 \end{array}$

$1 + 3 + 9$
$\underline{4} + 9 = \underline{13}$

$\begin{array}{r} 1 \\ 3 \\ +9 \\ \hline 13 \end{array}$

$5 + 6 + 1$
$\underline{11} + 1 = \underline{12}$

$\begin{array}{r} 5 \\ 6 \\ +1 \\ \hline 12 \end{array}$

$1 + 3 + 4$
$\underline{4} + 4 = \underline{8}$

$\begin{array}{r} 1 \\ 3 \\ +4 \\ \hline 8 \end{array}$

$2 + 9 + 1$
$\underline{11} + 1 = \underline{12}$

$\begin{array}{r} 2 \\ 9 \\ +1 \\ \hline 12 \end{array}$

$\begin{array}{r} 3 \\ 4 \\ +7 \\ \hline 14 \end{array}$
$\begin{array}{r} 5 \\ 3 \\ +1 \\ \hline 9 \end{array}$
$\begin{array}{r} 4 \\ 4 \\ +1 \\ \hline 9 \end{array}$
$\begin{array}{r} 2 \\ 3 \\ +3 \\ \hline 8 \end{array}$
$\begin{array}{r} 3 \\ 5 \\ +1 \\ \hline 9 \end{array}$

$\begin{array}{r} 4 \\ 1 \\ +2 \\ \hline 7 \end{array}$
$\begin{array}{r} 6 \\ 1 \\ +3 \\ \hline 10 \end{array}$
$\begin{array}{r} 7 \\ 1 \\ +5 \\ \hline 13 \end{array}$
$\begin{array}{r} 8 \\ 1 \\ +2 \\ \hline 11 \end{array}$
$\begin{array}{r} 9 \\ 1 \\ +1 \\ \hline 11 \end{array}$

Page 62

Add the 3 numbers.

Page 63

1	2	3	4	5	6	7	8	9	10	11	12	13	14	15
H	I	C	A	N	T	S	O	B	D	M	G	Y	R	U

Work problems. Use code for secret message.

$\begin{array}{r} 1 \\ +1 \\ \hline 2 \end{array}$
$\begin{array}{r} 1 \\ +2 \\ \hline 3 \end{array}$
$\begin{array}{r} 6 \\ -2 \\ \hline 4 \end{array}$
$\begin{array}{r} 2 \\ +3 \\ \hline 5 \end{array}$
$\begin{array}{r} 14 \\ -10 \\ \hline 4 \end{array}$
$\begin{array}{r} 5 \\ +5 \\ \hline 10 \end{array}$
$\begin{array}{r} 15 \\ -5 \\ \hline 10 \end{array}$
$\begin{array}{r} 4 \\ -2 \\ \hline 2 \end{array}$

| I | | C | A | N | | A | D | D | . | | I |

$\begin{array}{r} 5 \\ -2 \\ \hline 3 \end{array}$
$\begin{array}{r} 2 \\ +2 \\ \hline 4 \end{array}$
$\begin{array}{r} 10 \\ -5 \\ \hline 5 \end{array}$
$\begin{array}{r} 14 \\ -7 \\ \hline 7 \end{array}$
$\begin{array}{r} 9 \\ +6 \\ \hline 15 \end{array}$
$\begin{array}{r} 6 \\ +3 \\ \hline 9 \end{array}$
$\begin{array}{r} 11 \\ -5 \\ \hline 6 \end{array}$
$\begin{array}{r} 15 \\ -1 \\ \hline 14 \end{array}$
$\begin{array}{r} 3 \\ +1 \\ \hline 4 \end{array}$
$\begin{array}{r} 14 \\ -11 \\ \hline 3 \end{array}$
$\begin{array}{r} 3 \\ +3 \\ \hline 6 \end{array}$

| C | A | N | | S | U | B | T | R | A | C | T | . |

$\begin{array}{r} 5 \\ -3 \\ \hline 2 \end{array}$
$\begin{array}{r} 10 \\ -7 \\ \hline 3 \end{array}$
$\begin{array}{r} 13 \\ -9 \\ \hline 4 \end{array}$
$\begin{array}{r} 4 \\ +1 \\ \hline 5 \end{array}$
$\begin{array}{r} 6 \\ +4 \\ \hline 10 \end{array}$
$\begin{array}{r} 14 \\ -6 \\ \hline 8 \end{array}$
$\begin{array}{r} 13 \\ -2 \\ \hline 11 \end{array}$
$\begin{array}{r} 6 \\ +2 \\ \hline 8 \end{array}$
$\begin{array}{r} 3 \\ +4 \\ \hline 7 \end{array}$
$\begin{array}{r} 9 \\ -3 \\ \hline 6 \end{array}$

| I | | C | A | N | | D | O | | M | O | S | T |

$\begin{array}{r} 11 \\ -7 \\ \hline 4 \end{array}$
$\begin{array}{r} 4 \\ +1 \\ \hline 5 \end{array}$
$\begin{array}{r} 10 \\ +3 \\ \hline 13 \end{array}$
$\begin{array}{r} 4 \\ +2 \\ \hline 6 \end{array}$
$\begin{array}{r} 15 \\ -14 \\ \hline 1 \end{array}$
$\begin{array}{r} 9 \\ -7 \\ \hline 2 \end{array}$
$\begin{array}{r} 6 \\ -1 \\ \hline 5 \end{array}$
$\begin{array}{r} 6 \\ +6 \\ \hline 12 \end{array}$

| A | N | Y | T | H | I | N | G | ! |

Page 64

Add or subtract.
Write number words of answers in puzzle.

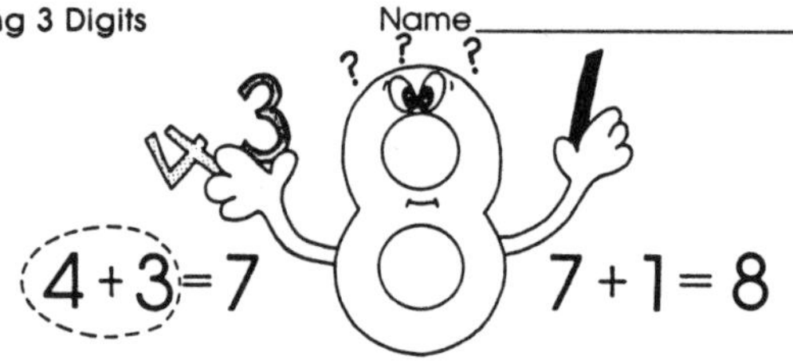

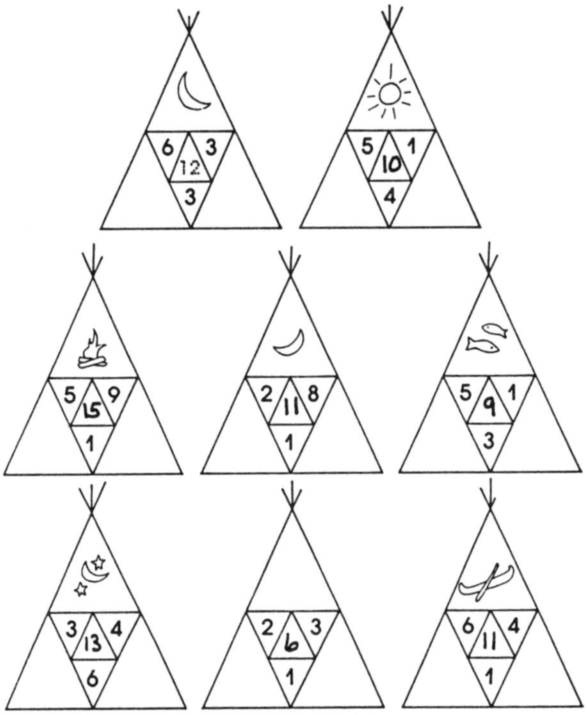

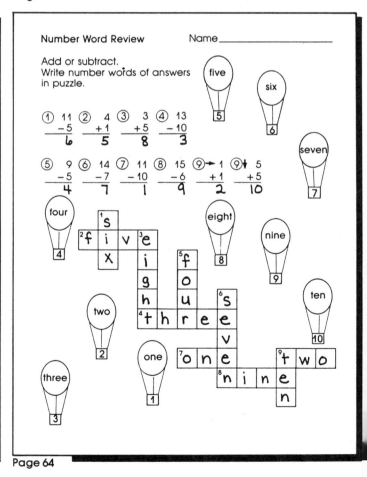

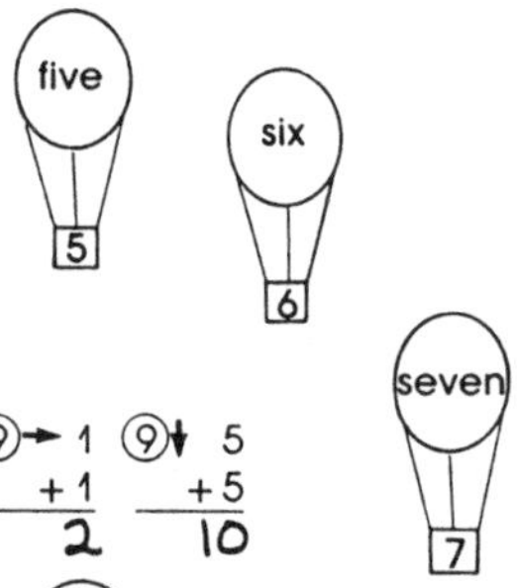

① $\begin{array}{r} 11 \\ -5 \\ \hline 6 \end{array}$
② $\begin{array}{r} 4 \\ +1 \\ \hline 5 \end{array}$
③ $\begin{array}{r} 3 \\ +5 \\ \hline 8 \end{array}$
④ $\begin{array}{r} 13 \\ -10 \\ \hline 3 \end{array}$

⑤ $\begin{array}{r} 9 \\ -5 \\ \hline 4 \end{array}$
⑥ $\begin{array}{r} 14 \\ -7 \\ \hline 7 \end{array}$
⑦ $\begin{array}{r} 11 \\ -10 \\ \hline 1 \end{array}$
⑧ $\begin{array}{r} 15 \\ -6 \\ \hline 9 \end{array}$
⑨→ $\begin{array}{r} 1 \\ +1 \\ \hline 2 \end{array}$
⑨↓ $\begin{array}{r} 5 \\ +5 \\ \hline 10 \end{array}$

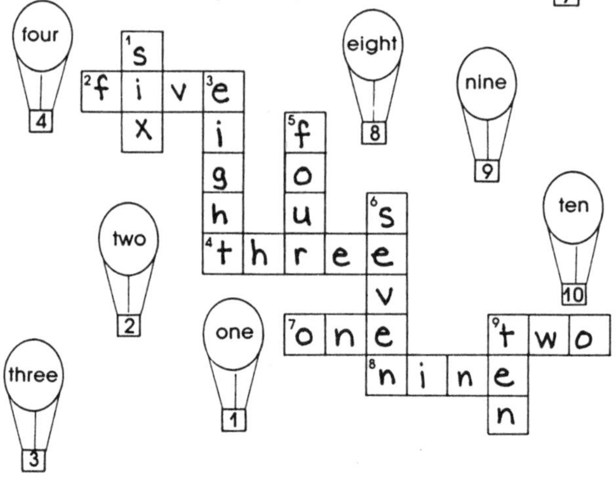

Answer Key

Page 65

Addition and Subtraction Review   Name_____

$8 \ominus 1 = 7$ $8 \oplus 1 = 9$

Write + or − in circle.
Color the correct symbol for each problem. The first one has been done for you.

$2 \oplus 3 = 5$

$12 \ominus 2 = 10$

$13 \ominus 9 = 4$

$6 \oplus 5 = 11$

$11 \oplus 3 = 14$

$7 \ominus 5 = 2$

$14 \ominus 10 = 4$

$15 \ominus 2 = 13$

$7 \oplus 7 = 14$

$13 \ominus 2 = 11$

$4 \oplus 5 = 9$

$6 \oplus 7 = 13$

Page 66

Ordinal Number Review   Name_____

Color the first animal orange.
Draw a blue X under the fourth animal.
Draw a black □ around the fifth animal.
Color the sixth animal red with blue spots.
Color the fourth animal green.
Draw a yellow hat on the first animal.
Color the fifth animal purple.
Draw brown tennis shoes on the second animal.
Draw a blue ○ around the sixth animal.
Color the second animal yellow.
Color the third animal blue.

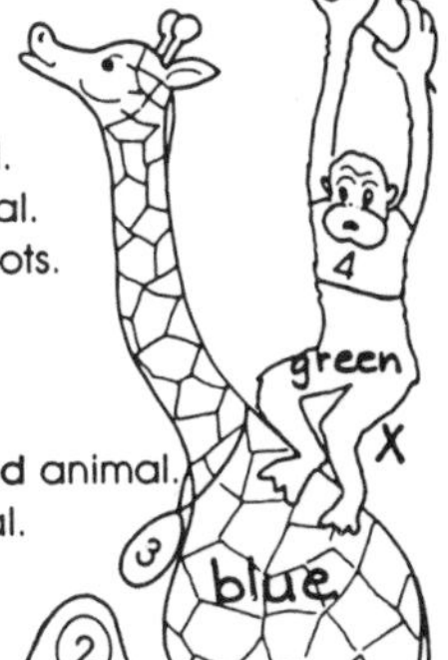

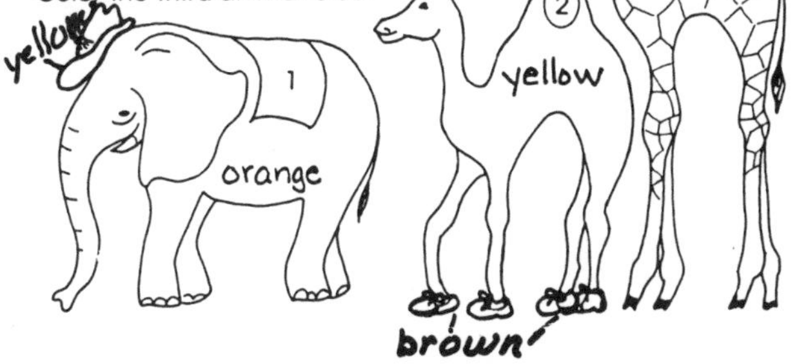

Page 67

Addition and Subtraction Review   Name_____

Work problems.
Join dots from smallest number to largest number.
Watch out! Some numbers are missing!

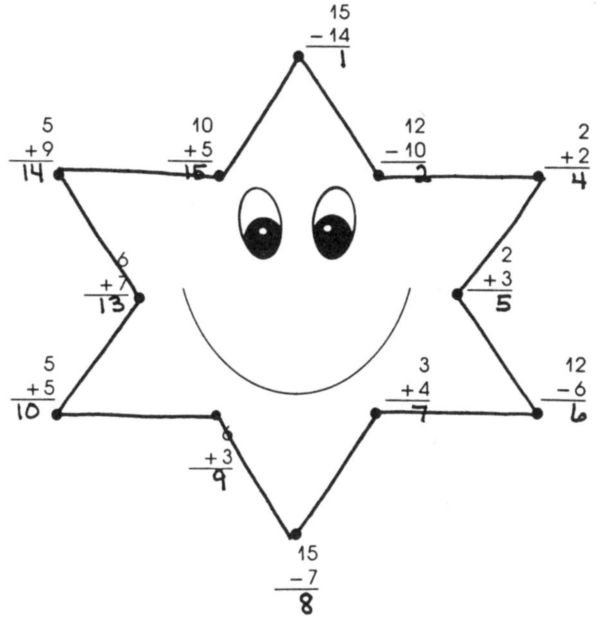

$\begin{array}{r} 15 \\ -14 \\ \hline 1 \end{array}$

$\begin{array}{r} 5 \\ +9 \\ \hline 14 \end{array}$
$\begin{array}{r} 10 \\ +5 \\ \hline 15 \end{array}$
$\begin{array}{r} 12 \\ -10 \\ \hline 2 \end{array}$
$\begin{array}{r} 2 \\ +2 \\ \hline 4 \end{array}$

$\begin{array}{r} 6 \\ +7 \\ \hline 13 \end{array}$
$\begin{array}{r} 2 \\ +3 \\ \hline 5 \end{array}$

$\begin{array}{r} 5 \\ +5 \\ \hline 10 \end{array}$
$\begin{array}{r} 3 \\ +4 \\ \hline 7 \end{array}$
$\begin{array}{r} 12 \\ -6 \\ \hline 6 \end{array}$

$\begin{array}{r} 6 \\ +3 \\ \hline 9 \end{array}$

$\begin{array}{r} 15 \\ -7 \\ \hline 8 \end{array}$

Page 68

Review
Greater Than; Less Than   Name_____

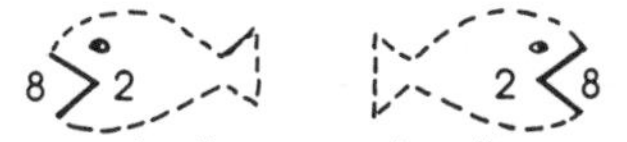

$8 > 2$ greater than $2 < 8$ less than

•Think of the signs always being open toward the larger number.

Write each problem.

$3 > 2$ $1 < 4$ $4 > 2$

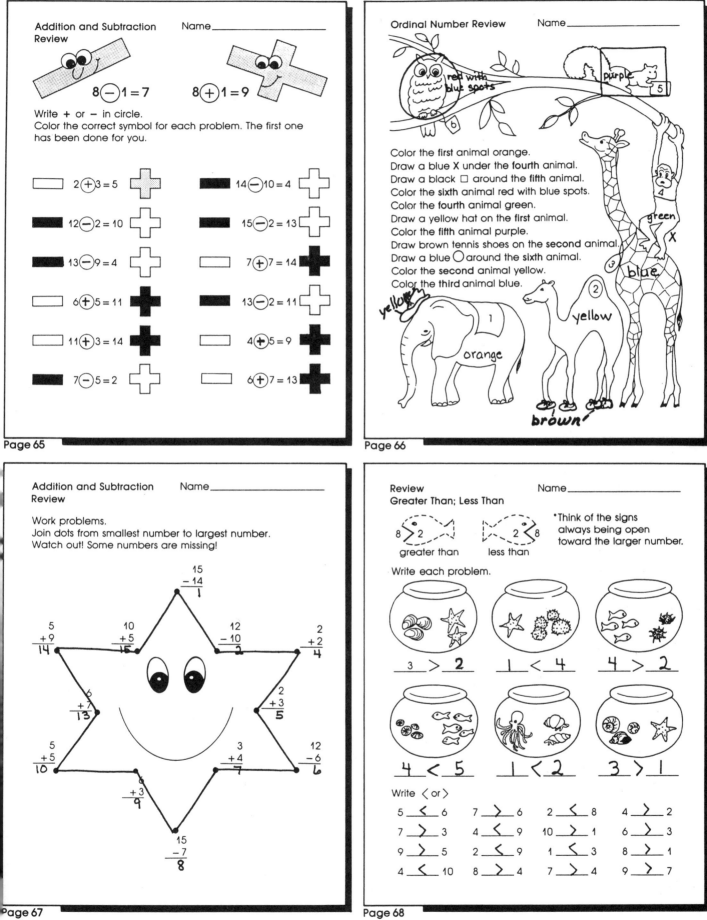

$4 < 5$ $1 < 2$ $3 > 1$

Write < or >

$5 < 6$ $7 > 6$ $2 < 8$ $4 > 2$
$7 > 3$ $4 < 9$ $10 > 1$ $6 > 3$
$9 > 5$ $2 < 9$ $1 < 3$ $8 > 1$
$4 < 10$ $8 > 4$ $7 > 4$ $9 > 7$

Answer Key

Addition and Subtraction Review Name____________________

Work problems to win the race.

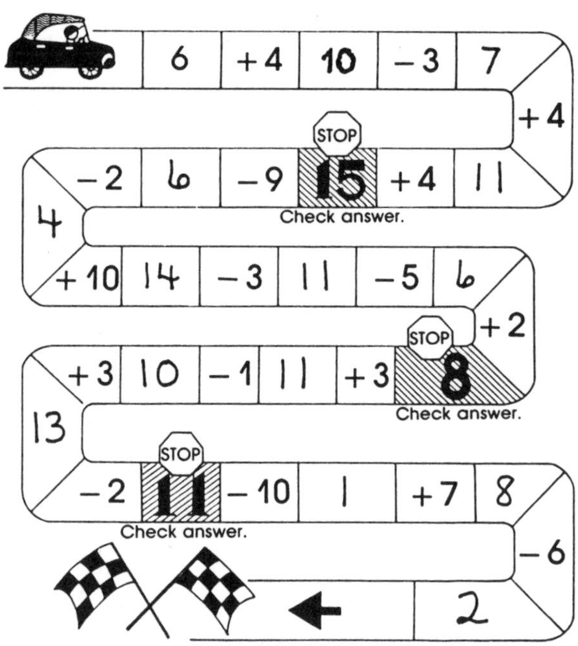

6
+4
10
−3
7
+4
11
+4
STOP
15
Check answer.
−9
6
−2
4
+10
14
−3
11
−5
6
+2
STOP
8
Check answer.
+3
11
−1
10
+3
13
−2
STOP
11
Check answer.
−10
1
+7
8
−6
2

Page 69

PLACE VALUE Name____________________

hundreds	tens	ones
3	4	5

345

hundred	tens	ones		
8	7	6	=	8 hundreds 7 tens 6 ones
3	2	9	=	3 hundreds 9 ones 2 tens
7	4	5	=	5 ones 7 hundreds 4 tens
1	9	2	=	9 tens 2 ones 1 hundred
3	8	4	=	3 hundreds 8 tens 4 ones
5	6	7	=	5 hundreds 6 tens 7 ones
2	1	3	=	2 hundreds 1 ten 3 ones
4	4	1	=	4 hundreds 4 tens 1 one
8	2	6	=	8 hundreds 2 tens 6 ones

Page 70

COUNTING Name____________________

Connect dots that number 201-205, 526-533, 791-798, 662-670.

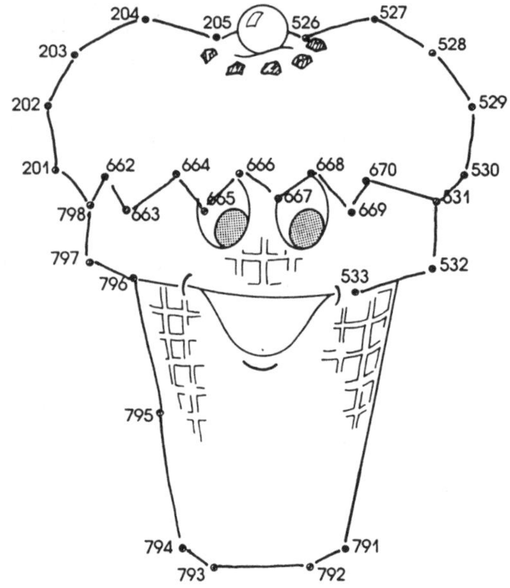

Page 71

COUNTING BY 2'S, 5'S, 10'S Name____________________

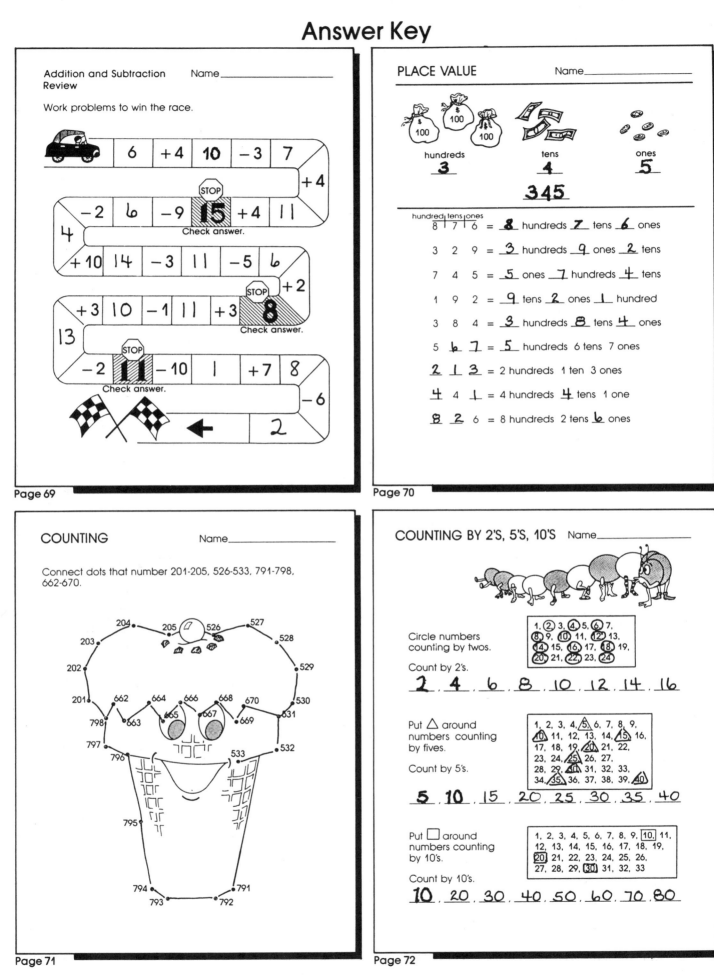

Circle numbers counting by twos.

1, (2), 3, (4), 5, (6), 7, (8), 9, (10), 11, (12), 13, (14), 15, (16), 17, (18), 19, (20), 21, (22), 23, (24)

Count by 2's.

2, 4, 6, 8, 10, 12, 14, 16

Put △ around numbers counting by fives.

1, 2, 3, 4, △5, 6, 7, 8, 9, △10, 11, 12, 13, 14, △15, 16, 17, 18, 19, △20, 21, 22, 23, 24, △25, 26, 27, 28, 29, △30, 31, 32, 33, 34, △35, 36, 37, 38, 39, △40

Count by 5's.

5, 10, 15, 20, 25, 30, 35, 40

Put □ around numbers counting by 10's.

1, 2, 3, 4, 5, 6, 7, 8, 9, [10], 11, 12, 13, 14, 15, 16, 17, 18, 19, [20], 21, 22, 23, 24, 25, 26, 27, 28, 29, [30], 31, 32, 33

Count by 10's.

10, 20, 30, 40, 50, 60, 70, 80

Page 72

Answer Key

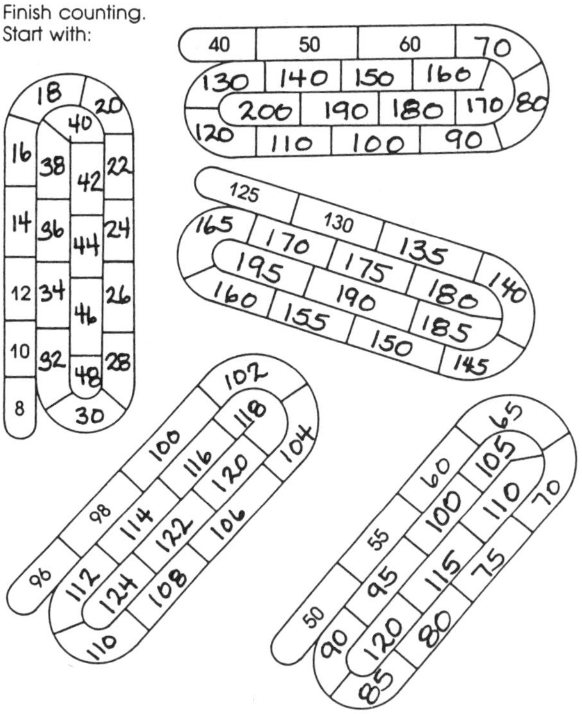

Page 73

COUNTING BY 2'S, 5'S, 10'S Name_____

Finish counting.
Start with:

40 50 60 70
130 140 150 160
200 190 180 170 80
120 110 100 90

18 20
40
16 38 42 22
14 36 44 24
12 34 46 26
10 32 48 28
8 30

125
165 170 130 135
195 175 135 140
160 155 190 180
150 185 145

102
100 116 118
98 114 122 120 104
96 112 124 108 110

65
60 105
55 100 110 70
50 95 115 75
90 120 80
85

Page 74

COUNTING BY 2'S, 5'S, 10'S Name_____

Number of 🐢's found. 🐢 = 5

🐢🐢🐢🐢 = **20**

🐢🐢🐢🐢🐢🐢🐢 = 35

🐢🐢🐢 = 15

Number of 🐌's found. 🐌 = 10

🐌🐌🐌🐌🐌 = 50

🐌🐌🐌🐌🐌🐌 = 60

🐌🐌🐌 = 30

Number of 🐛's found. 🐛 = 2

🐛🐛🐛🐛🐛🐛🐛🐛 = 16

🐛🐛🐛 = 6

🐛🐛🐛🐛🐛 = 10

Page 75

2-DIGIT ADDITION Name_____

Add ones first. Then, add tens.
4 + 2 = 6   2 + 3 = 5

tens	ones
2	4
+3	2
6	

tens	ones
2	4
+3	2
5	6

tens	ones
1	7
+2	1
3	**8**

tens	ones
3	4
+5	2
8	**6**

tens	ones
	5
+6	2
6	**7**

tens	ones
	6
+5	2
5	**8**

tens	ones
2	0
+4	0
6	**0**

tens	ones
5	1
+	8
5	**9**

tens	ones
7	2
+1	7
8	**9**

tens	ones
4	7
+2	1
6	**8**

tens	ones
2	5
+6	2
8	**7**

tens	ones
4	2
+2	4
6	**6**

tens	ones
8	3
+1	4
9	**7**

tens	ones
3	2
+2	5
5	**7**

tens	ones
4	4
+3	1
7	**5**

tens	ones
	8
+3	1
3	**9**

tens	ones
6	2
+1	7
7	**9**

tens	ones
8	2
+	7
8	**9**

Page 76

2-DIGIT ADDITION Name_____

Remember to add
ones first. Then, add tens.

tens	ones
3	1
+2	2

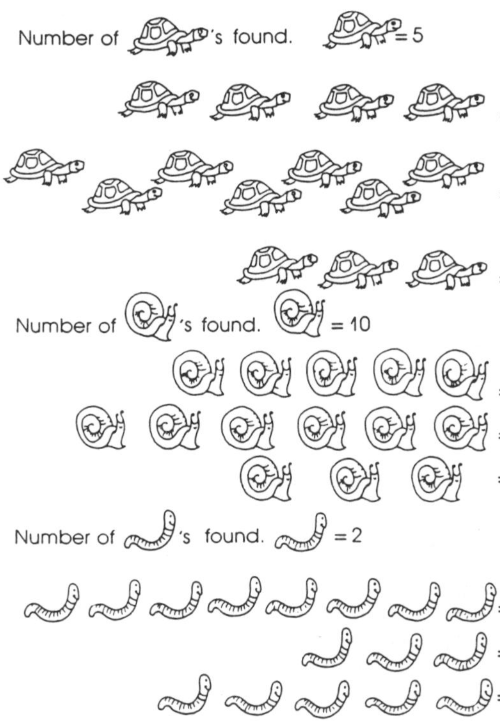

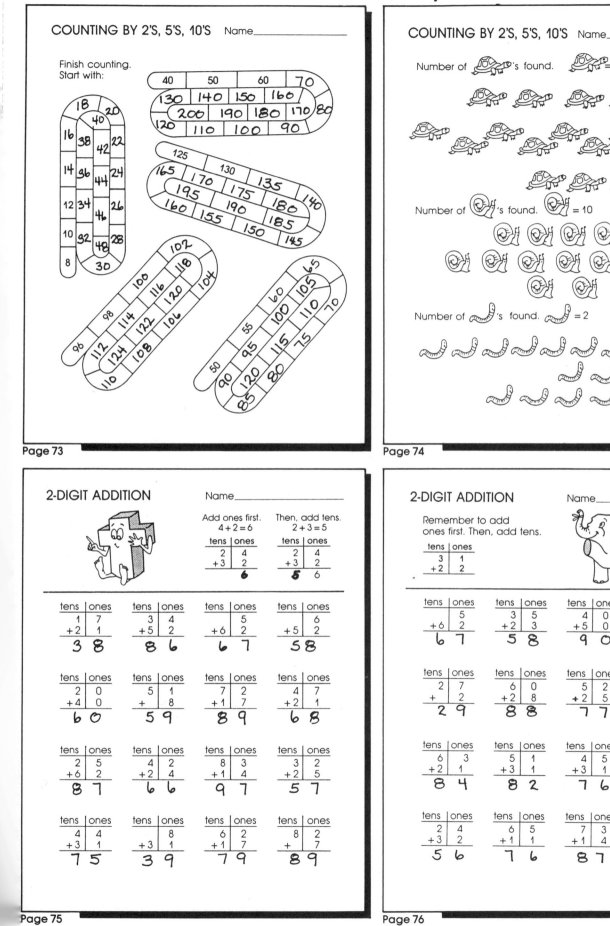

tens	ones
	5
+6	2
6	**7**

tens	ones
3	5
+2	3
5	**8**

tens	ones
4	0
+5	0
9	**0**

tens	ones
5	0
+1	9
6	**9**

tens	ones
2	7
+	2
2	**9**

tens	ones
6	0
+2	8
8	**8**

tens	ones
5	2
+2	5
7	**7**

tens	ones
2	7
+6	0
8	**7**

tens	ones
6	3
+2	1
8	**4**

tens	ones
5	1
+3	1
8	**2**

tens	ones
4	5
+3	1
7	**6**

tens	ones
4	4
+3	5
7	**9**

tens	ones
2	4
+3	2
5	**6**

tens	ones
6	5
+1	1
7	**6**

tens	ones
7	3
+1	4
8	**7**

tens	ones
7	3
+	6
7	**9**

Page 77

2-DIGIT ADDITION: Regrouping

Name_____

Add ones first.
6 + 6 = 12
REGROUP
12 = 1 ten and 2 ones

tens	ones
1	
7	6
+	6
	2

tens	ones
1	
7	6
+	6
8	**2**

Row 1:
- 24 + 7 = **31**
- 8 + 35 = **43**
- 9 + 43 = **52**
- 54 + 7 = **61**

Row 2:
- 63 + 8 = **71**
- 54 + 7 = **61**
- 5 + 49 = **54**
- 88 + 5 = **93**

Row 3:
- 72 + 8 = **80**
- 7 + 26 = **33**
- 54 + 7 = **61**
- 26 + 9 = **35**

Row 4:
- 9 + 44 = **53**
- 72 + 9 = **81**
- 65 + 6 = **71**
- 63 + 7 = **70**

Page 78

2-DIGIT ADDITION: Regrouping

Name_____

Add ones first.
8 + 5 = 13
REGROUP
13 = 1 ten and 3 ones
Then, add tens.

tens	ones
1	
3	8
+2	5
	3

tens	ones
1	
3	8
+2	5
6	**3**

Row 1:
- 29 + 34 = **63**
- 55 + 28 = **83**
- 25 + 46 = **71**
- 45 + 25 = **70**

Row 2:
- 67 + 13 = **80**
- 74 + 18 = **92**
- 32 + 48 = **80**
- 37 + 16 = **53**

Row 3:
- 34 + 29 = **63**
- 51 + 29 = **80**
- 62 + 29 = **91**
- 66 + 25 = **91**

Row 4:
- 53 + 27 = **80**
- 46 + 25 = **71**
- 28 + 17 = **45**
- 73 + 19 = **92**

Page 79

2-DIGIT ADDITION: Regrouping

Name_____

T	N	O	I	G	A	E	L	H	S
61	53	92	44	65	31	76	84	52	80

Why did the turtle cross the road?

- 45 + 16 = 61 → **T**
- 48 + 44 = 92 → **O**
- 28 + 37 = 65 → **G**
- 57 + 19 = 76 → **E**
- 38 + 23 = 61 → **T**

- 59 + 2 = 61 → **T**
- 59 + 33 = 92 → **O**
- 24 + 37 = 61 → **T**
- 36 + 16 = 52 → **H**
- 49 + 27 = 76 → **E**

- 51 + 29 = 80 → **S**
- 29 + 23 = 52 → **H**
- 38 + 38 = 76 → **E**
- 29 + 55 = 84 → **L**
- 38 + 46 = 84 → **L**

- 36 + 44 = 80 → **S**
- 36 + 25 = 61 → **T**
- 22 + 9 = 31 → **A**
- 33 + 28 = 61 → **T**
- 18 + 26 = 44 → **I**
- 67 + 25 = 92 → **O**
- 19 + 34 = 53 → **N** !

Page 80

2-DIGIT SUBTRACTION

Name_____

Subtract ones first.
5 − 1 = 4
Then, subtract tens.
6 − 4 = 2

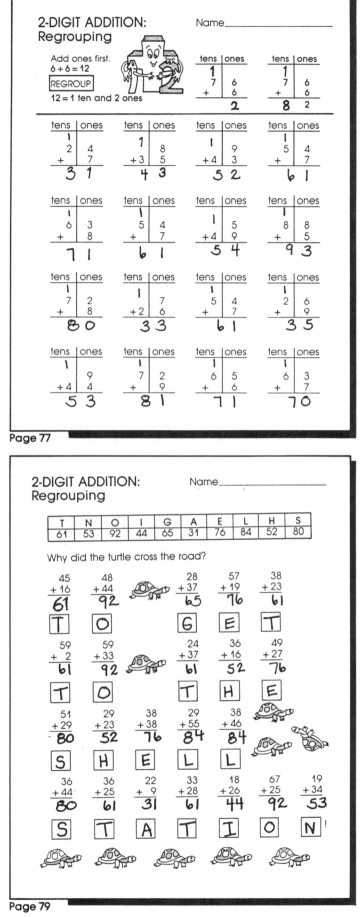

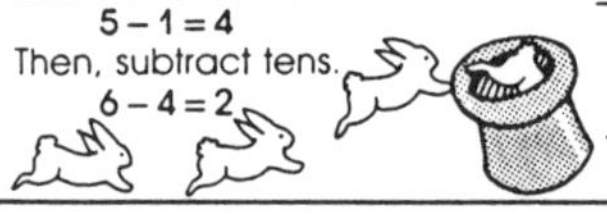

tens	ones
4	5
−2	1
	4

tens	ones
4	5
−2	1
2	**4**

Row 1:
- 72 − 51 = **21**
- 96 − 33 = **63**
- 88 − 57 = **31**
- 74 − 44 = **30**

Row 2:
- 69 − 28 = **41**
- 95 − 15 = **80**
- 58 − 35 = **23**
- 87 − 36 = **51**

Row 3:
- 27 − 15 = **12**
- 82 − 61 = **21**
- 77 − 56 = **21**
- 63 − 52 = **11**

Row 4:
- 86 − 32 = **54**
- 99 − 45 = **54**
- 46 − 23 = **23**
- 29 − 13 = **16**

Answer Key

Page 81

2-DIGIT SUBTRACTION

Name_____

Remember to subtract ones first. Then, subtract tens.

tens	ones
4	8
−2	3
2	**5**

tens	ones
6	2
−4	1
2	1

tens	ones
4	5
−3	5
1	0

tens	ones
2	9
−1	5
1	4

tens	ones
6	3
−4	2
2	1

tens	ones
8	7
−5	6
3	1

tens	ones
7	5
−3	4
4	1

tens	ones
5	8
−4	5
1	3

tens	ones
4	9
−1	3
3	6

tens	ones
3	9
−2	1
1	8

tens	ones
8	8
−1	8
7	0

tens	ones
6	5
−5	4
1	1

tens	ones
8	1
−6	0
2	1

tens	ones
7	6
−5	3
2	3

tens	ones
9	7
−8	3
1	4

tens	ones
5	8
−2	3
3	5

tens	ones
5	6
−4	5
1	1

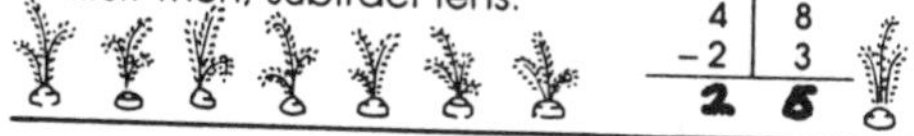

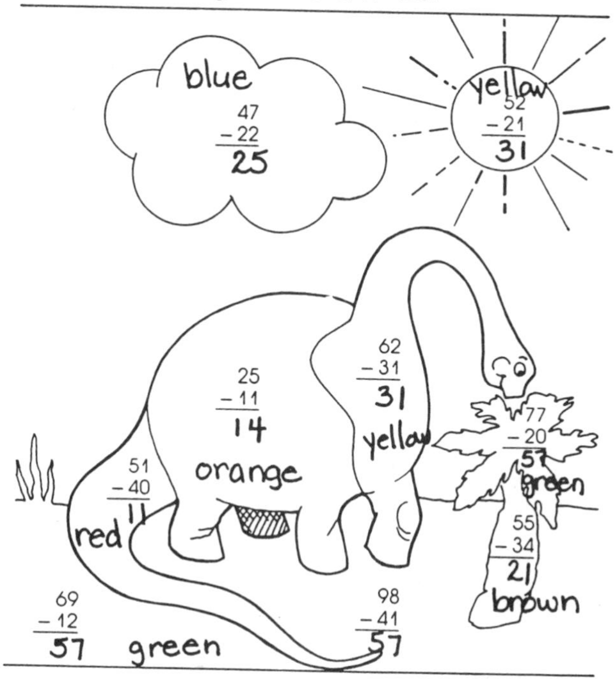

Page 82

2-DIGIT SUBTRACTION

Name_____

Work problems. Use color code. 25—blue, 31—yellow, 57—green, 14—orange, 21—brown, 11—red.

blue
47
− 22
25

yellow
52
− 21
31

25
− 11
14
orange

62
− 31
31
yellow

77
− 20
57
green

51
− 40
11
red

55
− 34
21
brown

69
− 12
57
green

98
− 41
57

Page 83

2-DIGIT SUBTRACTION: Regrouping

Name_____

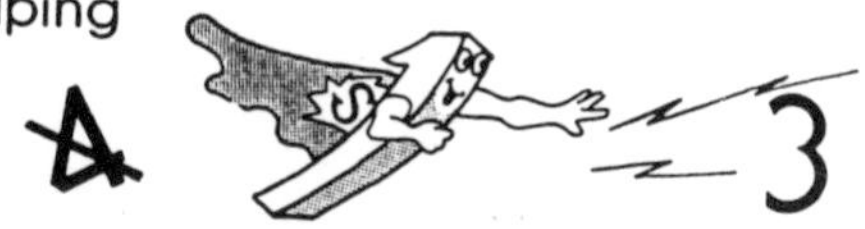

tens	ones
4	2
−	7

You cannot subtract 7 from 2.

REGROUP Take 1 ten from tens.

tens	ones
3 4	2
	8

Add 1 ten (10) to ones. (10 + 2 = 12)

tens	ones
3 4	12
−	2 7

Next, subtract ones. (12 − 7 = 5)

tens	ones
3 4	12 2
−	7
	5

Then, subtract tens. (3 − 0 = 3)

tens	ones
3 4	12
−	2 7
3	5

NOW, it's your turn!

tens	ones
3	4
−	6

You cannot subtract 6 from 4.

REGROUP Take 1 ten from tens.

tens	ones
2 3	4
−	6

Add 1 ten to ones. (10 + 4 = 14)

tens	ones
2 3	4 14
−	6

Next, subtract ones. 14 − 6 = 8 Then, subtract tens.

tens	ones
2 3	14 4
−	6
2	8

Page 84

2-DIGIT SUBTRACTION: Regrouping

Name_____

REGROUP

tens	ones
3 4	16 6
−1	9

Subtract ones. 16 − 9 = 7

tens	ones
3 4	16 6
−1	9
	7

Subtract tens.

tens	ones
3 4	16 6
−1	9
2	7

tens	ones
8	16 6
−4	8
4	8

tens	ones
4 5	13 3
−2	5
2	8

tens	ones
2 3	11 1
−1	5
1	6

tens	ones
5 6	14 4
−2	7
3	7

tens	ones
7 8	14 4
−5	5
2	9

tens	ones
6 7	12 2
−3	7
3	5

tens	ones
5 6	15 5
−1	7
4	8

tens	ones
3 4	18 8
−2	9
1	9

tens	ones
6 7	17 7
−2	9
4	8

tens	ones
7 8	11 1
−2	8
5	3

tens	ones
7 8	15 5
−5	8
1	7

tens	ones
2 3	12 2
−1	8
1	4

tens	ones
3 4	12 2
−1	3
2	9

tens	ones
4 5	16 6
−2	7
2	9

tens	ones
2 3	15 5
−1	9
1	6

tens	ones
7 8	15 5
−1	9
	6

Answer Key

Page 85

2-DIGIT SUBTRACTION: Regrouping

Name_____

Remember:
REGROUP
Subtract ones.
Subtract tens.

	tens	ones
	6	14
	7	4
−	2	8
	4	6

```
 4 17        7 16        8 18        6 15
 5 7         8 8         8 8         7 5
− 29        − 37        − 49        − 26
────        ────        ────        ────
  28          49          49          49

 5 16        3 11        2 12        3 15
 6 6         4 1         8 8         4 5
− 18        − 18        − 18        − 17
────        ────        ────        ────
  48          23          14          28

 8 12        7 12        5 15        6 13
 8 8         8 2         6 5         7 3
− 36        − 54        − 38        − 56
────        ────        ────        ────
  56          28          27          17

 4 17        3 16        5 13        6 15
 6 8         4 6         6 3         7 5
− 18        − 29        − 49        − 29
────        ────        ────        ────
  39          17          14          46
```

Page 86

2-DIGIT SUBTRACTION: Regrouping

Name_____

1. 2	5		2. 6	9	
9		3. 3| 7		5. 5| 7
	4. 4	6		5	7
	9		6. 2	3	
		8			

ACROSS

```
1.  50        2.  78        3.  62
  − 25          −  9          − 25
  ────          ────          ────
    25            69            37

4.  62        5.  85        6.  42
  − 16          − 28            19
  ────          ────          ────
    46            57            23
```

DOWN

```
1.  67        2.  94        3.  75
  − 38          − 27          − 39
  ────          ────          ────
    29            67            36

4.  78        5.  81        6.  76
  − 29          − 28          − 48
  ────          ────          ────
    49            53            28
```

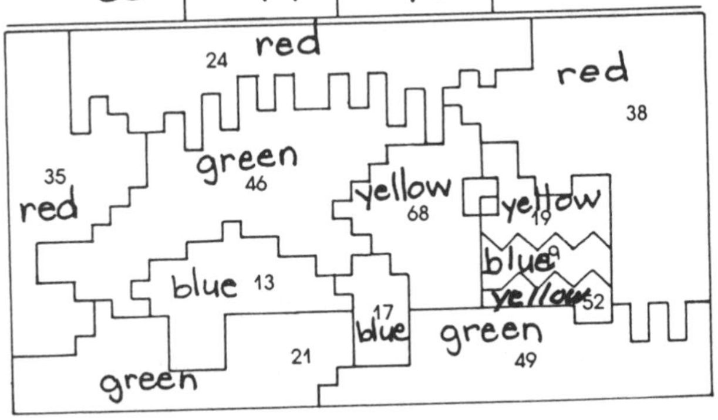

Page 87

2-DIGIT SUBTRACTION: Regrouping

Name_____

Work problems. Color picture by color chart.

Red	Blue	Yellow	Green
67 − 29 **38**	51 − 38 **13**	96 − 28 **68**	94 − 48 **46**
72 − 48 **24**	44 − 15 **29**	71 − 19 **52**	60 − 39 **21**
94 − 59 **35**	31 − 14 **17**	46 − 27 **19**	65 − 16 **49**

Page 88

2-DIGIT SUBTRACTION: Regrouping

Name_____

What happens when ducks fly upside down?

19	36	53	48	34	16	67	47	75	28
T	Q	C	H	U	K	E	P	A	Y

```
  47        62        95        76
− 28      − 14      − 28      − 48
────      ────      ────      ────
  19        48        67        28
 [T]       [H]       [E]       [Y]

  83        53        94        92        65
− 47      − 19      − 19      − 39      − 49
────      ────      ────      ────      ────
  36        34        75        53        16
 [Q]       [U]       [A]       [C]       [K]

  61        73
− 27      − 26
────      ────
  34        47
 [U]       [P]  !
```

Math IF8742

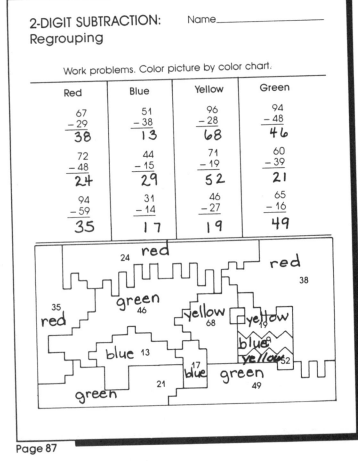

Answer Key

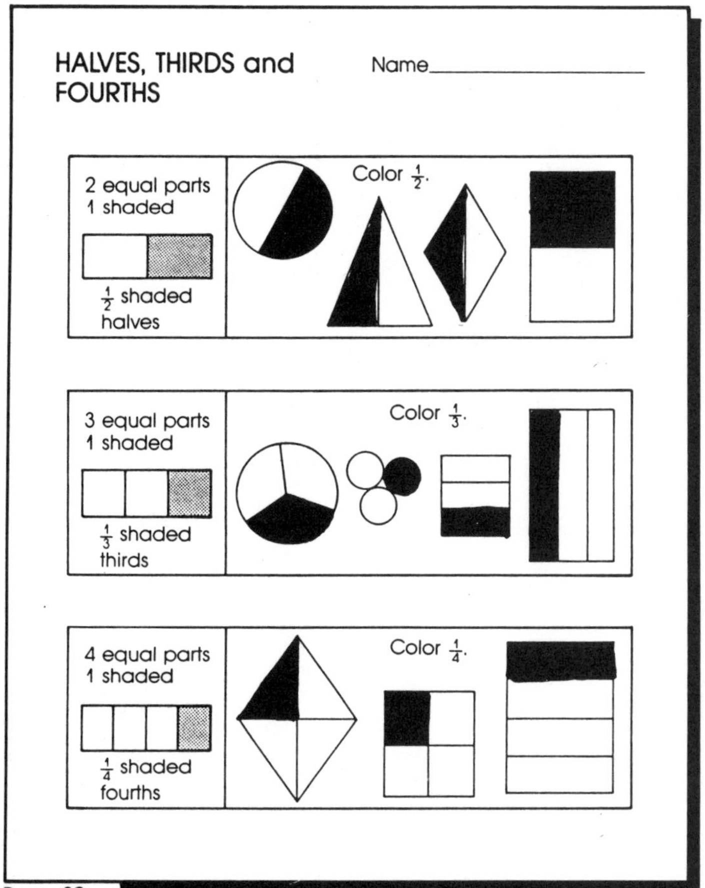

HALVES, THIRDS and FOURTHS

Name_____

**2 equal parts
1 shaded**

½ shaded
halves

Color ½.

**3 equal parts
1 shaded**

⅓ shaded
thirds

Color ⅓.

**4 equal parts
1 shaded**

¼ shaded
fourths

Color ¼.

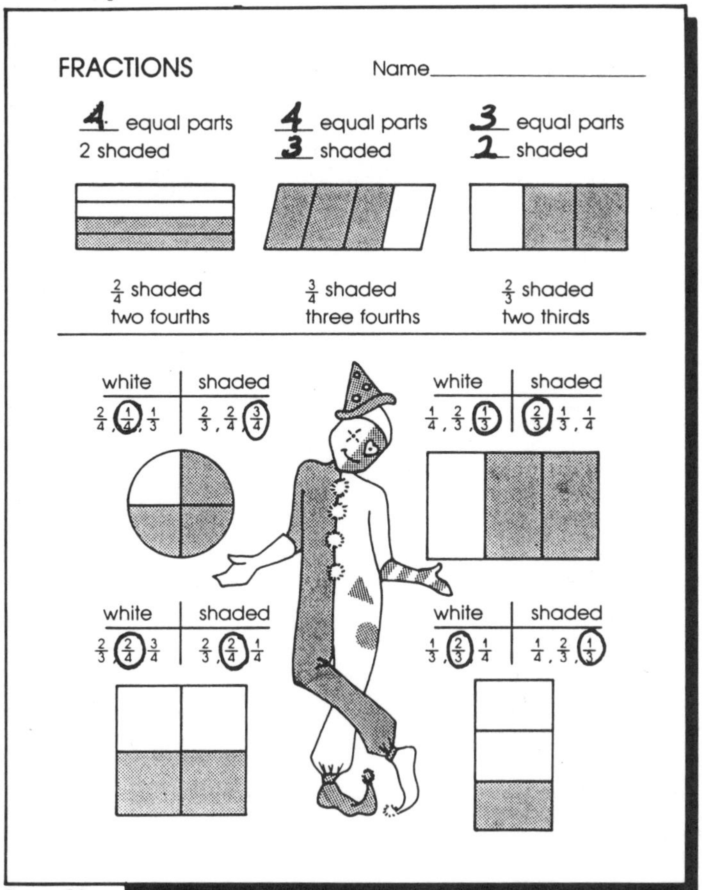

FRACTIONS

Name_____

4 equal parts
2 shaded

4 equal parts
3 shaded

3 equal parts
2 shaded

2/4 shaded
two fourths

3/4 shaded
three fourths

2/3 shaded
two thirds

| white | shaded |
| 2/4 ①/4, 1/3 | 2/3, 2/4 ③/4 |

| white | shaded |
| 1/4, 2/3 ①/3 | 2/3 1/3, 1/4 |

| white | shaded |
| 2/3 ②/4 3/4 | 2/3 ②/4 1/4 |

| white | shaded |
| 1/3, ②/3 1/4 | 1/4, 2/3 ①/3 |

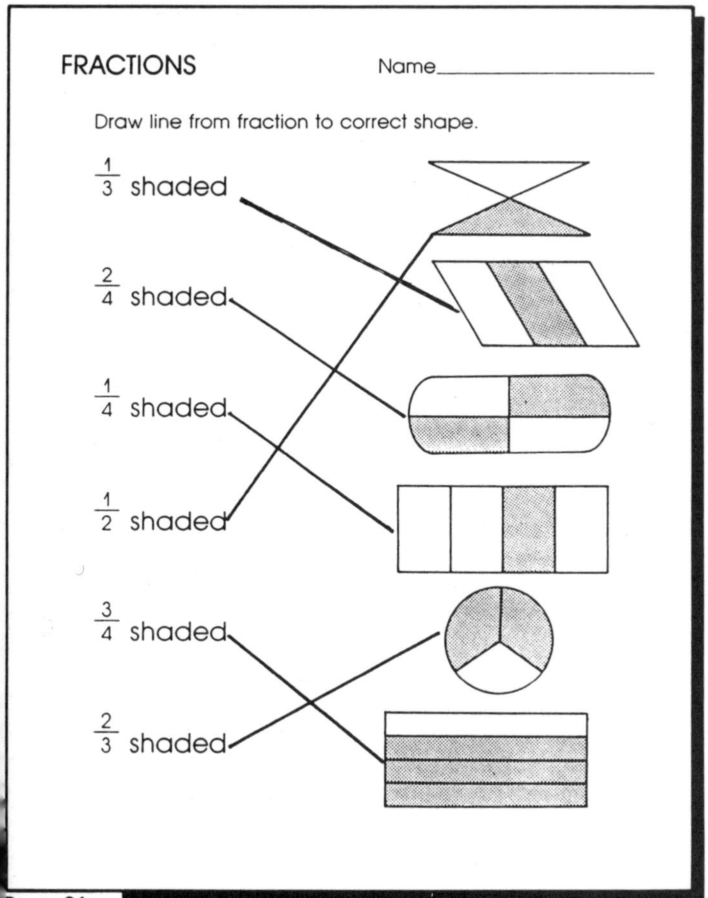

FRACTIONS

Name_____

Draw line from fraction to correct shape.

⅓ shaded

2/4 shaded

¼ shaded

½ shaded

¾ shaded

⅔ shaded

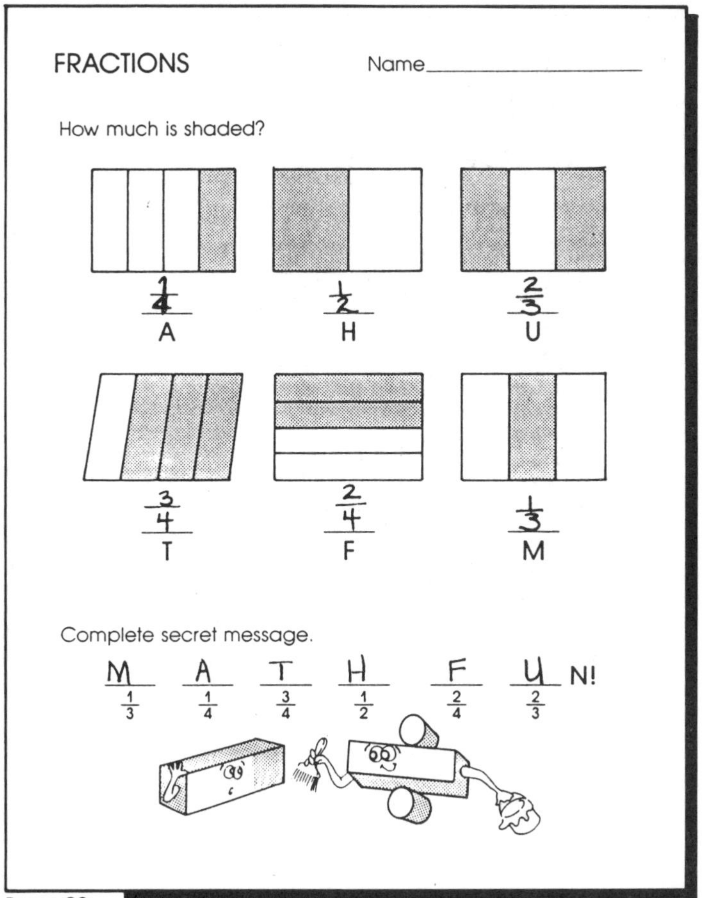

FRACTIONS

Name_____

How much is shaded?

¼
A

½
H

2/3
U

¾
T

2/4
F

⅓
M

Complete secret message.

M   A   T   H   F   U   N!
⅓ ¼ ¾ ½ 2/4 2/3

Math IF8742

125

© 1990 Instructional Fair, Inc.

Answer Key

FRACTIONS   Name_____

Color $\frac{1}{2}$

$\frac{1}{2}$

Color:

$\frac{3}{4}$ $\frac{1}{2}$

$\frac{1}{3}$ $\frac{2}{4}$

$\frac{2}{3}$ $\frac{1}{4}$

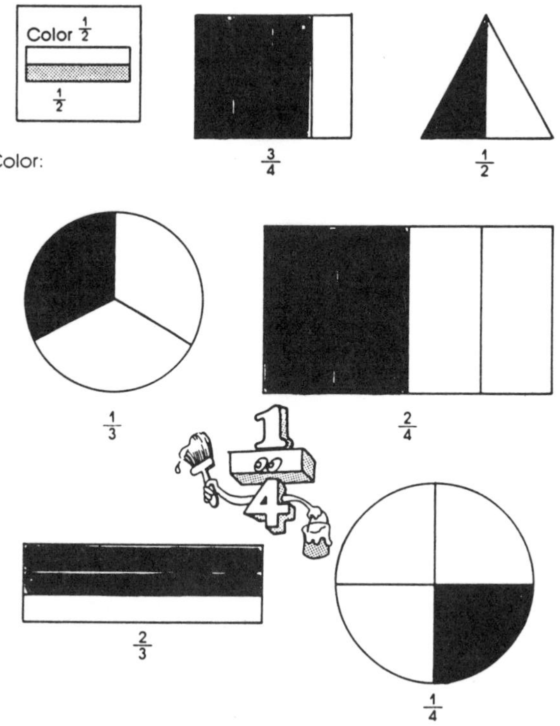

MATCHING FRACTIONS   Name_____

Put letter of drawing by matching white fractions. Do same for shaded fractions.

White		Shaded	
$\frac{1}{2}$	E	$\frac{1}{2}$	E
$\frac{1}{3}$	A	$\frac{1}{3}$	C
$\frac{2}{3}$	C	$\frac{2}{3}$	A
$\frac{1}{4}$	B	$\frac{1}{4}$	F
$\frac{2}{4}$	D	$\frac{2}{4}$	D
$\frac{3}{4}$	F	$\frac{3}{4}$	B

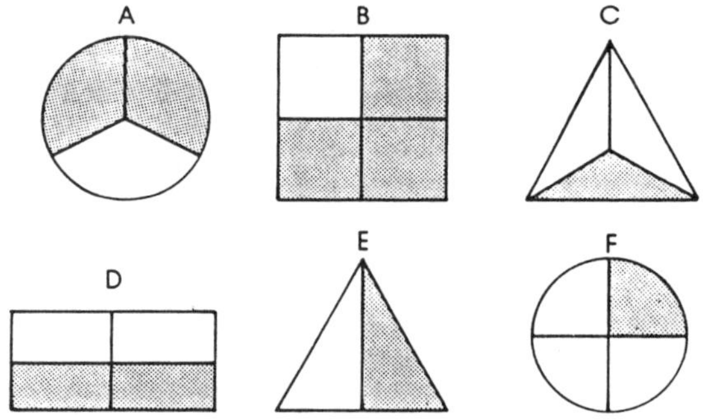

A   B   C

D   E   F

3-DIGIT ADDITION: Name_____
Regrouping

Work problems. Color balloons with matching answers.

880

green 940

863

green 683

yellow

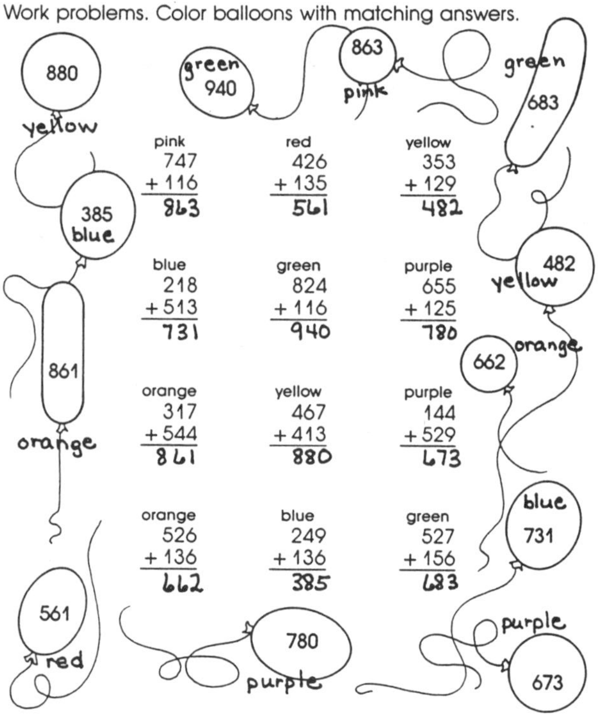

pink
747
+ 116
863

red
426
+ 135
561

yellow
353
+ 129
482

385
blue

blue
218
+ 513
731

green
824
+ 116
940

purple
655
+ 125
780

482
yellow

861

orange
317
+ 544
861

yellow
467
+ 413
880

purple
144
+ 529
673

662

orange

orange

orange
526
+ 136
662

blue
249
+ 136
385

green
527
+ 156
683

blue
731

561

red

780

purple

purple
673

3-DIGIT SUBTRACTION: Name_____
Regrouping

436's!

REGROUP Subtract ones.	Subtract tens.	Subtract hundreds.
6 12	6 12	6 12
5̶7̶2̶	5̶7̶2̶	5̶7̶2̶
− 136	− 136	− 136
6	36	436

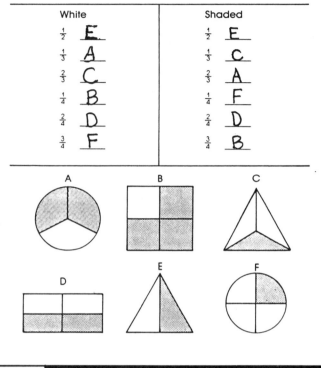

6 15
6̶7̶5̶
− 248
(427)

486
− 377
109

368
− 139
(229)

782
− 565
217

557
− 438
119

844
− 529
315

953
− 628
(325)

342
− 328
14

890
− 536
354

787
− 438
349

666
− 437
(229)

591
− 257
334

361
− 122
239

956
− 248
708

527
− 319
208

463
− 236
(227)

Circle answers with 2 in tens place.

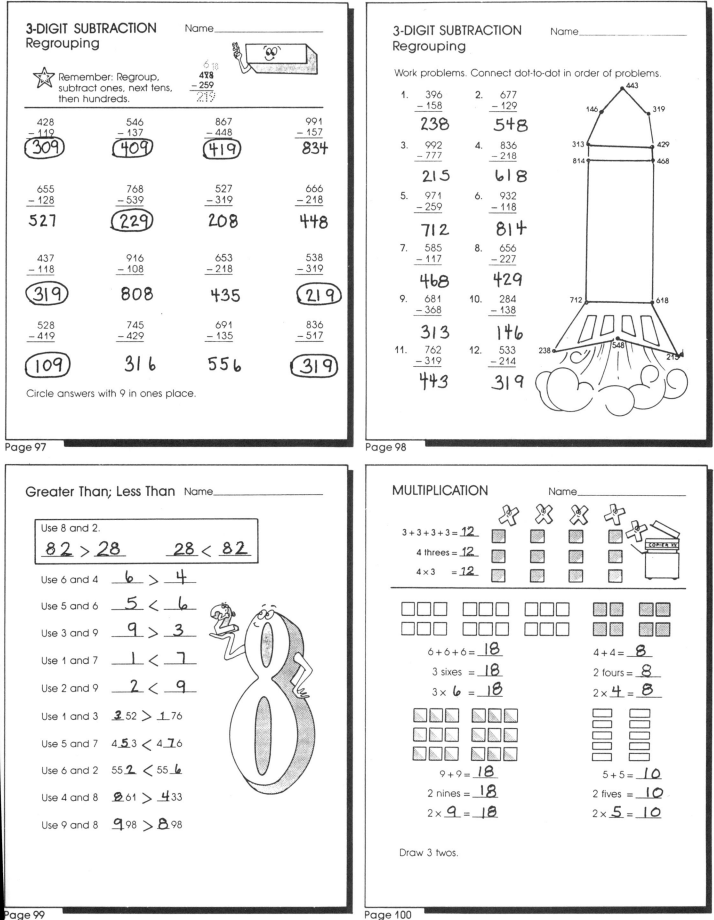

3-DIGIT SUBTRACTION
Regrouping
Name_____

⭐ Remember: Regroup, subtract ones, next tens, then hundreds.

$$\begin{array}{r} 6\ 18 \\ 4\cancel{7}\cancel{8} \\ -259 \\ \hline 219 \end{array}$$

428 −119 **(309)**	546 −137 **(409)**	867 −448 **(419)**	991 −157 **834**
655 −128 **527**	768 −539 **(229)**	527 −319 **208**	666 −218 **448**
437 −118 **(319)**	916 −108 **808**	653 −218 **435**	538 −319 **(219)**
528 −419 **(109)**	745 −429 **316**	691 −135 **556**	836 −517 **(319)**

Circle answers with 9 in ones place.

Page 97

3-DIGIT SUBTRACTION
Regrouping
Name_____

Work problems. Connect dot-to-dot in order of problems.

1. 396
−158
238
2. 677
−129
548
3. 992
−777
215
4. 836
−218
618
5. 971
−259
712
6. 932
−118
814
7. 585
−117
468
8. 656
−227
429
9. 681
−368
313
10. 284
−138
146
11. 762
−319
443
12. 533
−214
319

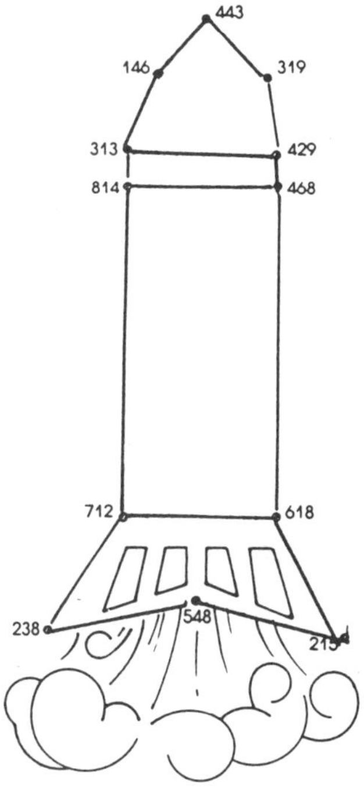

Page 98

Greater Than; Less Than
Name_____

Use 8 and 2.

$$\underline{8\ 2} > \underline{2\ 8} \qquad \underline{2\ 8} < \underline{8\ 2}$$

Use 6 and 4 $\underline{6} > \underline{4}$

Use 5 and 6 $\underline{5} < \underline{6}$

Use 3 and 9 $\underline{9} > \underline{3}$

Use 1 and 7 $\underline{1} < \underline{7}$

Use 2 and 9 $\underline{2} < \underline{9}$

Use 1 and 3 $\underline{3}52 > \underline{1}76$

Use 5 and 7 $4\underline{5}3 < 4\underline{7}6$

Use 6 and 2 $55\underline{2} < 55\underline{6}$

Use 4 and 8 $\underline{8}61 > \underline{4}33$

Use 9 and 8 $\underline{9}98 > \underline{8}98$

Page 99

MULTIPLICATION
Name_____

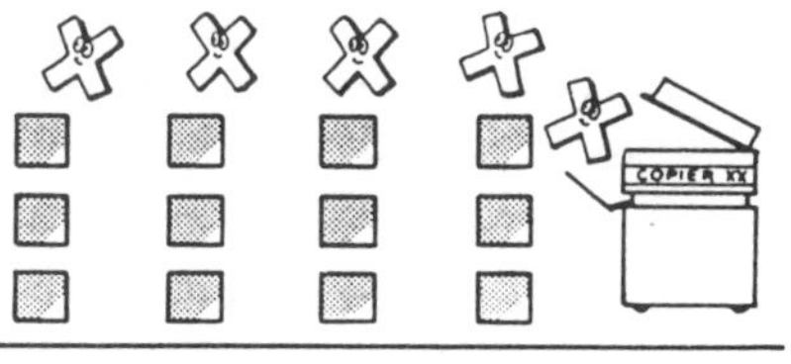

$3+3+3+3 = \underline{12}$
4 threes = $\underline{12}$
$4 \times 3 = \underline{12}$

$6+6+6 = \underline{18}$
3 sixes = $\underline{18}$
$3 \times 6 = \underline{18}$

$9+9 = \underline{18}$
2 nines = $\underline{18}$
$2 \times 9 = \underline{18}$

$4+4 = \underline{8}$
2 fours = $\underline{8}$
$2 \times 4 = \underline{8}$

$5+5 = \underline{10}$
2 fives = $\underline{10}$
$2 \times 5 = \underline{10}$

Draw 3 twos.

Page 100

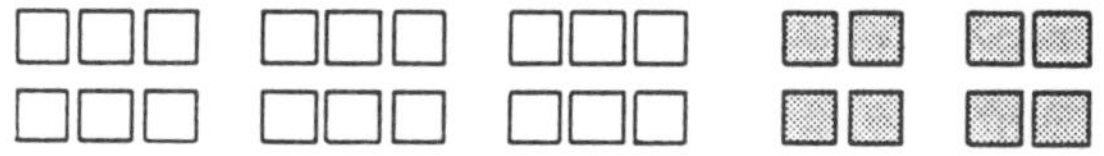

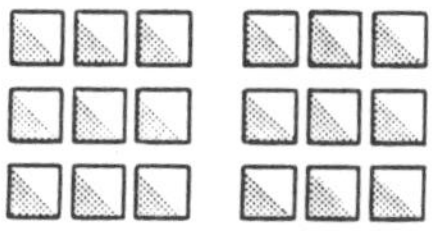

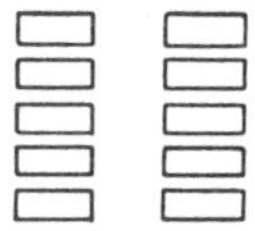

Answer Key

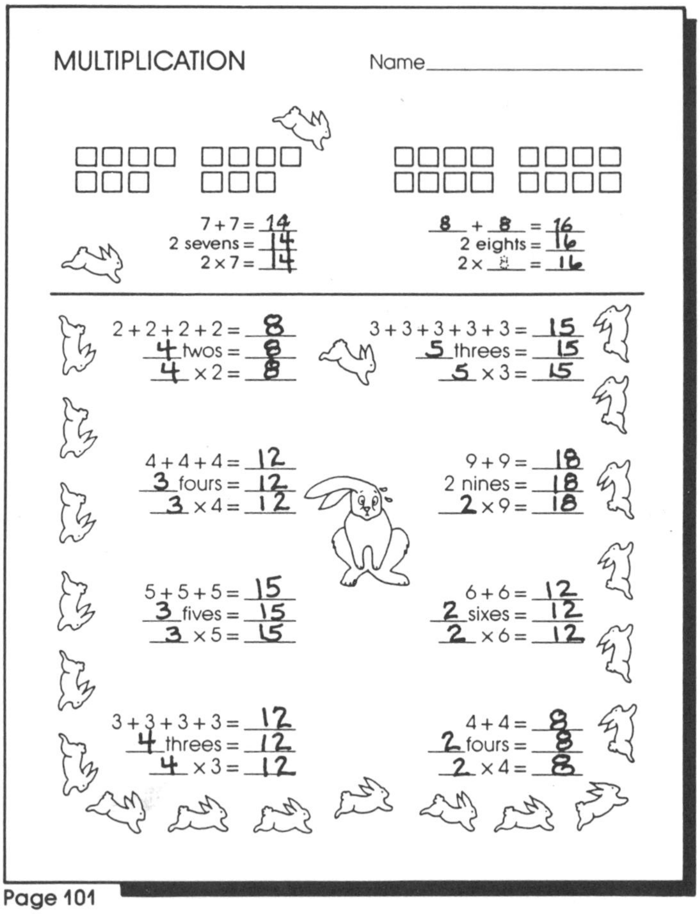
MULTIPLICATION Name
7 + 7 = 14
2 sevens = 14
2 × 7 = 14
8 + 8 = 16
2 eights = 16
2 × 8 = 16
2 + 2 + 2 + 2 = 8
4 twos = 8
4 × 2 = 8
3 + 3 + 3 + 3 + 3 = 15
5 threes = 15
5 × 3 = 15
4 + 4 + 4 = 12
3 fours = 12
3 × 4 = 12
9 + 9 = 18
2 nines = 18
2 × 9 = 18
5 + 5 + 5 = 15
3 fives = 15
3 × 5 = 15
6 + 6 = 12
2 sixes = 12
2 × 6 = 12
3 + 3 + 3 + 3 = 12
4 threes = 12
4 × 3 = 12
4 + 4 = 8
2 fours = 8
2 × 4 = 8

Page 101

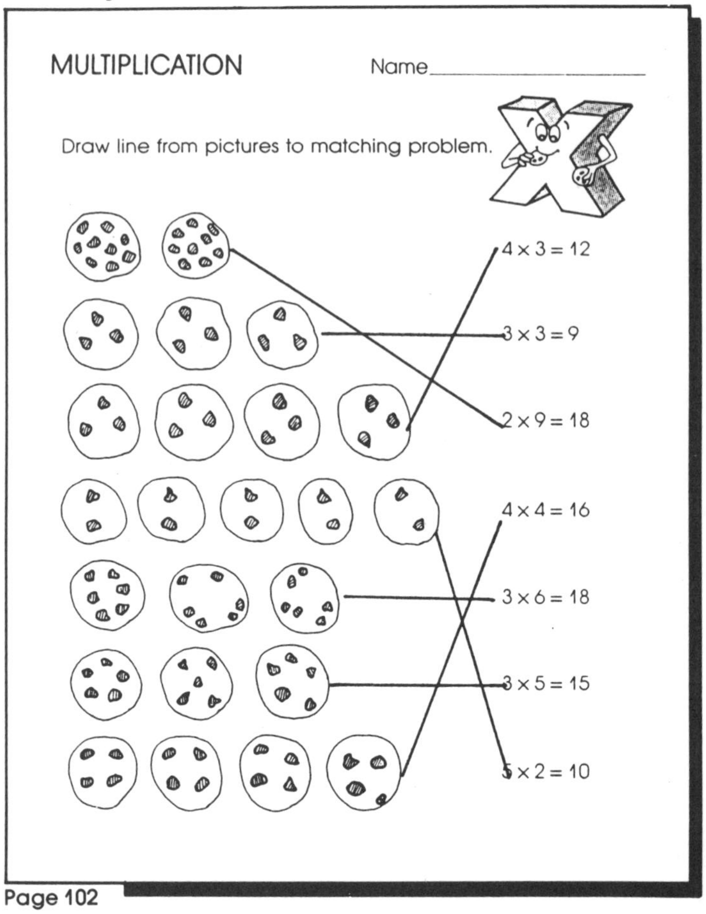
MULTIPLICATION Name
Draw line from pictures to matching problem.
4 × 3 = 12
3 × 3 = 9
2 × 9 = 18
4 × 4 = 16
3 × 6 = 18
3 × 5 = 15
5 × 2 = 10

Page 102

About the book . . .

This collection of activities concentrates on those very skills (basic facts, computation, place value, fractions, geometry, etc.) that the student needs extra drill and practice on to successfully master. A wide variety of approaches have been utilized whenever possible to stimulate interest and enhance motivation.

About the author . . .

Sandra Bryan not only holds an advanced degree in Elementary Education, but has practiced the skills of the profession in the classroom for more than a decade.

Author: Sandra Bryan
Editor: Lee Quackenbush
Asst. Editor: Mary Lynne Harris
Artists: Joyce Yarbrough / Ann Stein
Graphic Design: Julie Wiley
Production: Pat Geasler
Cover Photo: Frank Pieroni
Art Consultant: Jan Vonk

